KB101208

적중 100

영어 기출 문제집

중 **3**

능률 | 양현권

Best Collection

구성과 특징

교과서의 주요 학습 내용을 중심으로 학습 영역별 특성에 맞춰 단계별로 다양한 학습 기회를 제공하여
단원별 학습능력 평가는 물론 중간 및 기말고사 시험 등에 완벽하게 대비할 수 있도록 내용을 구성

Words & Expressions

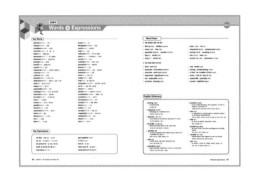

Step1	Key Words 단원별 핵심 단어 설명 및 풀이
	Key Expression 단원별 핵심 숙어 및 관용어 설명
	Word Power 반대 또는 비슷한 뜻 단어 배우기
	English Dictionary 영어로 배우는 영어 단어
Step2	실력평가 단원별 수시평가 대비 주관식, 객관식 문제풀이
Step3	서술형 대비 학업성취도 및 수행능력평가 대비 서술형 문제풀이

Conversation

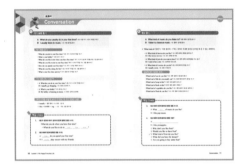

Step1	핵심 의사소통 소통에 필요한 주요 표현 방법 요약
	핵심 Check 기본적인 표현 방법 및 활용능력 확인
Step2	대화문 익히기 교과서 대화문 심층 분석 및 확인
Step3	교과서 확인학습 빈칸 채우기를 통한 문장 완성 능력 확인
Step4	기본평가 시험대비 기초 학습 능력 평가
Step5	실력평가 단원별 수시평가 대비 주관식, 객관식 문제풀이
Step6	서술형 대비 학업성취도 및 수행능력평가 대비 서술형 문제풀이

Grammar

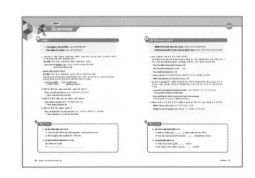

Step1	주요 문법 단원별 주요 문법 사항과 예문을 알기 쉽게 설명
	핵심 Check 기본 문법사항에 대한 이해 여부 확인
Step2	기본평가 시험대비 기초 학습 능력 평가
Step3	실력평가 단원별 수시평가 대비 주관식, 객관식 문제풀이
Step4	서술형 대비 학업성취도 및 수행능력평가 대비 서술형 문제풀이

Reading

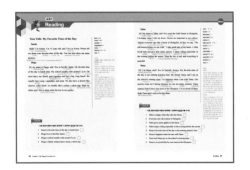

Step1	구문 분석 단원별로 제시된 문장에 대한 구문별 분석과 내용 설명
	확인문제 문장에 대한 기본적인 이해와 인지능력 확인
Step2	확인학습A 빈칸 채우기를 통한 문장 완성 능력 확인
Step3	확인학습B 제시된 우리말을 영어로 완성하여 작문 능력 키우기
Step4	실력평가 단원별 수시평가 대비 주관식, 객관식 문제풀이
Step5	서술형 대비 학업성취도 및 수행능력평가 대비 서술형 문제풀이
	교과서 구석구석 교과서에 나오는 기타 문장까지 완벽 학습

Composition

|영역별 핵심문제|

단어 및 어휘, 대화문, 문법, 독해 등 각 영역별 기출문제의 출제 유형을 분석하여 실전에 대비하고 연습할 수 있도록 문제를 배열

|단원별 예상문제|

기출문제를 분석한 후 새로운 시험 출제 경향을 더하여 새롭게 출제될 수 있는 문제를 포함하여 시험에 완벽하게 대비할 수 있도록 준비

|서술형 실전 및 창의사고력 문제|

학교 시험에서 점차 늘어나는 서술형 시험에 집중 대비하고 고득점을 취득하는데 만전을 기하기 위한 학습 코너

|단원별 모의고사|

영역별, 단계별 학습을 모두 마친 후 실전 연습을 위한 모의고사

INSIGHT on the textbook

교과서 파헤치기

- **단어Test1~3** 영어 단어 우리말 쓰기, 우리말을 영어 단어로 쓰기, 영영풀이에 해당하는 단어와 우리말 쓰기
- **대화문Test1~2** 대화문 빈칸 완성 및 전체 대화문 쓰기
- **본문Test1~5** 빈칸 완성, 우리말 쓰기, 문장 배열연습, 영어 작문하기 복습 등 단계별 반복 학습을 통해 교과서 지문에 대한 완벽한 습득
- **구석구석지문Test1~2** 지문 빈칸 완성 및 전문 영어로 쓰기

Lesson 1

How Are You Getting Along?

 의사소통 기능

- 의견 표현하기
  In my opinion, we should make more friends.
- 불평하기
  I'm not happy about it.

 언어 형식

- to부정사의 의미상 주어
  It was difficult for me to put up with her.
- 관계대명사 who의 계속적(비제한적) 용법
  I share a room with my sister, who is two years older than me.

교과서
Words & Expressions

Key Words

- **already** [ɔ:lrédi] 부 이미, 벌써
- **appreciate** [əprí:ʃièit] 동 진가를 알아보다, 고마워하다
- **around** [əráund] 부 대략, 약
- **bother** [báðər] 동 괴롭히다, 귀찮게 굴다
- **difficulty** [dífikʌlti] 명 어려움
- **fair** [fɛər] 형 공정한, 공평한
- **film** [film] 명 영화
- **golden** [góuldən] 형 금으로 만든, 멋진
- **grader** [gréidər] 명 (~학년) 학생
- **grandparent** [grǽndpɛərənt] 명 조부모
- **grow** [grou] 동 자라다, ~해지다, 증가하다
- **half** [hæf] 명 절반
- **interestingly** [íntərəstiŋli] 부 흥미롭게도
- **last** [læst] 동 지속되다
- **laughter** [lǽftər] 명 웃음
- **least** [li:st] 부 가장 적게
- **lonely** [lóunli] 형 외로운
- **loud** [laud] 형 시끄러운
- **lunar** [lú:nər] 형 음력의
- **meaning** [mí:niŋ] 명 의미
- **midnight** [mídnait] 명 자정
- **moment** [móumənt] 명 순간, 때
- **mood** [mu:d] 명 기분
- **often** [ɔ́:fən] 부 흔히, 종종
- **only** [óunli] 형 유일한, 단지

- **opinion** [əpínjən] 명 의견, 생각
- **order** [ɔ́:rdər] 동 주문하다 명 주문
- **passing** [pǽsiŋ] 명 (시간, 세월의) 경과, 흐름
- **permission** [pərmíʃən] 명 허락, 허가
- **pleased** [pli:zd] 형 기쁜
- **possibly** [pásəbli] 부 아마, 도저히
- **present** [préznt] 명 선물 형 현재의, 참석한
- **price** [prais] 명 가격, 물가
- **privacy** [práivəsi] 명 사생활
- **reader** [rí:dər] 명 독자
- **reply** [riplái] 명 대답 동 대답하다
- **scary** [skéəri] 형 무서운
- **serve** [sə:rv] 동 제공하다, 대접하다
- **some** [səm] 형 몇몇의, 일부의
- **sometimes** [sʌ́mtàimz] 부 때때로, 가끔
- **special** [spéʃəl] 형 특별한
- **stressful** [strésfəl] 형 스트레스가 많은, 걱정 등을 일으키는
- **support** [səpɔ́:rt] 동 지지하다
- **tear** [tiər] 명 눈물, 울음
- **teenager** [tí:nèidʒər] 명 십대
- **trade** [treid] 명 일, 직업, 업
- **turn** [tə:rn] 명 차례, 순번
- **view** [vju:] 명 생각, 의견
- **walk** [wɔ:k] 동 (개를) 산책시키다

Key Expressions

- **do without** ~ ~ 없이 지내다
- **don't have to** ~ ~할 필요가 없다
- **end up -ing** 결국 ~하게 되다
- **fall on** 날짜가 ~이다
- **get along with** ~ ~와 잘 지내다
- **get angry at** ~ ~에게 화를 내다
- **get better** 좋아지다
- **get on one's nerve** 신경을 건드리다
- **get together** (~와) 만나다
- **go out** 외출하다
- **have a hard time -ing** ~하는 데 어려움을 겪다

- **in my opinion** 내 생각에는
- **it could be** 그럴 수도 있지
- **lose one's temper** 화내다
- **over there** 저쪽, 저기
- **put up with** ~ ~을 견디다, 참다
- **seem to** ~ ~인 것 같다
- **stick by** ~ 의 곁을 지키다
- **take a second look** 다시 보다
- **wake up** 깨우다
- **You can say that again.** 네 말이 맞아.

Word Power

※ 서로 비슷한 뜻을 가진 어휘

- bother 귀찮게 굴다 – irritate 짜증나게 하다
- mood 기분 – emotion 감정
- present 선물 – gift 선물
- sometimes 때때로 – occasionally 가끔
- support 지지하다 – assist 지지하다
- appreciate 진가를 알아보다 – recognize 인정하다
- difficulty 어려움 – trouble 어려움

- film 영화 – movie 영화
- lonely 외로운 – isolated 고립된
- loud 시끄러운 – noisy 시끄러운
- often 흔히, 종종 – frequently 빈번하게
- opinion 의견, 생각 – view 의견
- reply 대답하다 – answer 대답하다
- trade 일, 직업, 업 – business 직업

※ 서로 반대의 뜻을 가진 어휘

- difficulty 어려움 ↔ ease 쉬움, 용이함
- support 지지하다 ↔ oppose 반대하다
- loud 시끄러운 ↔ silent 조용한
- pleased 기쁜 ↔ unpleased 기뻐하지 않는
- reply 대답하다 ↔ ask 묻다

- bother 귀찮게 굴다 ↔ please 즐겁게 하다
- fair 공정한, 공평한 ↔ unfair 불공평한
- permission 허락, 허가 ↔ prohibition 금지
- present 참석한 ↔ absent 결석한
- special 특별한 ↔ general 일반적인

English Dictionary

- **bother** 괴롭히다
  → to make someone feel slightly worried, upset, or concerned
  어떤 사람이 약간 걱정되거나 당황하거나 불편하게 느끼도록 만들다

- **difficulty** 어려움
  → a problem or something that causes trouble
  수고를 끼치는 문제나 어떤 것

- **fair** 공정한, 공평한
  → treating everyone in a way that is right or equal
  올바르거나 동등한 방식으로 대접하는

- **grandparent** 조부모
  → one of the parents of your mother or father
  아버지나 어머니의 부모 중 한 분

- **last** 지속되다
  → to continue for a particular length of time
  특정한 기간 동안 계속하다

- **laughter** 웃음
  → the sound of people laughing
  사람이 웃는 소리

- **lonely** 외로운
  → unhappy because you do not have anyone to talk to
  이야기할 사람이 없어 불행한

- **lunar** 음력의
  → relating to the Moon 달과 관련된

- **mood** 기분
  → the way you feel at a particular time
  특정한 때 느끼는 방식

- **privacy** 사생활
  → the state of being free from public attention
  대중의 관심에서 자유로운 상태

- **reader** 독자
  → a person who read a book, magazine, newspaper, etc.
  책, 잡지, 신문 등을 읽는 사람

- **reply** 대답하다
  → to answer someone by saying or writing something
  말을 하거나 글을 써서 어떤 사람에게 응답하다

- **support** 지지하다
  → to say that you agree with an idea
  어떤 생각에 동의한다고 말하다

01 다음 짝지어진 단어의 관계가 같도록 빈칸에 알맞은 단어를 고르시오.

> difficulty : _____ = noisy : silent

① lonely   ② midnight
③ ease   ④ present
⑤ scary

02 다음 문장에 들어가기에 적절한 말을 쓰시오. (주어진 철자로 시작할 것)

> I often ask myself whether I _____ _____ with my family members.

➡ g _____ a_____

03 다음 문장의 빈칸에 알맞은 것은?

> I can't put up _____ all this noise.

① with   ② for
③ on   ④ along
⑤ from

04 다음 대화의 빈칸에 들어갈 말로 적절한 것을 고르시오.

> G: Have you read this book?
> B: Yes, I have. The story is very scary.
> G: Is it? In my _____, it's a sad story.
> B: Well, it could be.

① trade   ② opinion
③ difficulty   ④ meaning
⑤ laughter

05 다음 문장의 빈칸에 들어가기에 적절한 단어를 주어진 철자로 시작하여 쓰시오.

> My sister comes into my room without my p_____ and shouts at me to wake up on Sunday mornings.

06 다음 중 〈보기〉에 있는 단어를 사용하여 자연스러운 문장을 만들 수 없는 것은?

> ┤ 보기 ├
> graders   replies   make   possibly

① In my opinion, we should _____ more friends.
② This cat may _____ be sick.
③ We are now third _____.
④ Here are some of their _____.
⑤ For one thing, they _____ me all the time.

07 다음 중 밑줄 친 부분의 뜻풀이가 바르지 않은 것은?

① My father is a wonderful cook. (요리하다)
② We have a different story. (다른)
③ The festival lasts for 15 days from the first day of the lunar year. (지속하다)
④ The meaning of a family can vary from person to person. (다르다)
⑤ Turn it down. It's too loud. (시끄러운)

01 다음 우리말에 맞게 빈칸에 알맞은 말을 쓰시오.

(1) 가족이 함께 모인다.
➡ Family members _____ together.

(2) 나는 언니와 방을 같이 쓴다.
➡ I _____ a room with my sister.

(3) 내가 화를 낼 때마다, 그녀는 나를 지지해 주려고 애쓴다.
➡ Whenever I _____ my _____, she tries to support me.

(4) 내가 그녀를 참는 것은 어려웠다.
➡ It was difficult for me to _____ _____ _____ her.

02 다음 영영풀이에 해당하는 단어를 쓰시오. (주어진 철자로 시작할 것)

the sound of people laughing

➡ l_____

03 다음 밑줄 친 부분과 의미가 가장 가까운 단어를 주어진 철자로 시작하여 쓰시오.

Our group <u>recommends</u> cooking dinner for your family.

➡ s_____

04 다음 주어진 단어를 이용해 빈칸을 완성하시오.

My older brother, who entered university this year, is the _____ child.

➡ _____ (gold)

05 다음 빈칸에 알맞은 단어나 숙어를 〈보기〉에서 골라 쓰시오.

보기
word   luck   stick by   wake up

(1) Red is a color of good _____ for the Chinese.

(2) The _____ *family* may have different meanings to different people.

(3) They _____ me now, and will continue to do so in the future.

(4) My sister shouts at me to _____ on Sunday mornings.

06 다음 대화의 빈칸에 〈보기〉의 단어를 알맞게 채워 넣으시오.

보기
only   privacy   out   big

Yujin: Did your family go (A)_____ to eat last weekend?

Seho: Yes, we did. The food was great, but my family is too (B)_____ and loud.

Yujin: Really? How big is it?

Seho: There are seven of us: my grandparents, my mom, my dad, two brothers, and me.

Yujin: That is a big family!

Seho: Well, I don't like it at all. There's no (C)_____.

Yujin: I get what you're saying, but to me, it's good to have a big family. I sometimes feel lonely because I'm an (D)_____ child.

Seho: Yeah ..., I see what you mean.

Conversation

① 의견 표현하기

> In my opinion, we should make more friends. 내 생각에 우리는 더 많은 친구를 사귀어야 해.

■ 자신의 의견을 표현할 때는 "내 생각에는" 또는 "내 의견으로는"이라는 의미로 "In my opinion"을 사용하고 "To me"라고 하기도 한다. 말하는 내용이 자신의 의견임을 표현하여 "I think ~", "I believe ~", "In my view, ~" 등을 사용할 수도 있다. 그 외에도 의견을 나타낼 때는 'It seems to me that ~. 내 생각에는 ~인 것 같다.' 등이 있다.

■ 의견을 물어볼 때는 "~는 어떠니?"의 의미로 "How do you like ~?" "~에 대한 네 생각은 뭐니? = What is your opinion about ~?" 등을 사용한다. "How do you feel about ~?" "What do you think about ~?" "What's your opinion about ~?" 등으로 의견을 묻기도 한다.

의견 표현하기

- In my opinion 내 생각에는 ~
- To me 나로서는
- I believe that ~. 나는 ~라고 믿는다.
- In my view 내 의견으로는 ~
- I think that ~. 나는 ~라고 생각한다.
- I feel that ~. 나는 ~라고 생각한다.
- It seems to me that ~. 내 생각에는 ~인 것 같다.

의견 묻기

- What do you think about ~? ~에 대하여 어떻게 생각하니?
- What's your opinion about ~? ~에 대한 너의 의견은 뭐니?
- How do you feel about ~? ~에 대하여 어떻게 생각하니?

핵심 Check

1. 다음 대화의 밑줄 친 부분 대신 쓰기에 <u>어색한</u> 것은?

> G: Have you read this book?
> B: Yes, I have. The story is very scary.
> G: Is it? <u>In my opinion, it's a sad story.</u>
> B: Well, it could be.

① I think it's a sad story.　② I wonder if it's a sad story.
③ To me, it's a sad story.　④ I feel that it's a sad story.
⑤ In my view, it's a sad story.

② 불평하기

I'm not happy about it. 나는 그것이 마음에 안 들어.

- 만족 또는 불만족을 나타낼 때는 happy, satisfied 등을 사용하여 "I am happy with ~." "I am satisfied with ~." 등이나 "It's good." "It's great." "It's nice." 등으로 나타내기도 한다. 불만족을 나타낼 때는 "I am not happy with ~." I am not satisfied with ~." 등으로 나타낸다.

- 만족이나 불만족에 대하여 물을 때는 "Are you satisfied with ~?" 또는 "Are you happy with ~?"를 사용하여 "~에 만족하니?"라고 물어보거나 "How do you like it? 그것이 마음에 드니?"라고 묻기도 한다. "Do you like ~? ~을 좋아하니?"와 "Is this the one that you want? 이것이 네가 원하는 것이니?" 같은 표현도 만족이나 불만족을 물어보는 표현이 된다.

- "How do you like ~?"에 대하여 대답할 때는 만족하는지 아닌지를 직접적으로 나타내어 "It is great." "It is nice." "It wasn't bad." 등으로 대답하거나 "It isn't interesting." 등으로 대답한다.

만족이나 불만족에 관해 묻기

- How do you like it? 그것이 마음에 드니?
- Are you satisfied with it? 그것이 만족스럽니? (= Are you happy with it?)
- Do you like it? 그것이 좋으니?
- Is this what you wanted? 이것이 네가 원한 것이니? (= Is this the one that you wanted?)

만족이나 불만족에 대한 대답

- It is great. = It is nice. 그것은 좋아.
- It wasn't bad. 그것은 나쁘지 않았어.

핵심 Check

2. 다음 대화의 밑줄 친 말 대신 쓰기에 <u>어색한</u> 것은?

> G: Did you hear that a new ice cream store opened last week?
> B: Sure. I have already been there.
> G: Have you? <u>How was it?</u>
> B: Thc ice cream was great.

① How did you like it? ② Were you satisfied with it?
③ Did you like it? ④ Were you happy with it?
⑤ How much was it?

Listen & Speak 1 A-1

G: Have you read this book?

B: Yes, I have. The story is very scary.

G: ❶Is it? In my opinion, it's a sad story.

B: Well, it could be.

소녀: 너 이 책 읽어봤니?
소년: 응, 읽어봤어. 이야기가 무척 무섭더라.
소녀: 그래? 내 생각에는 슬픈 이야기인데.
소년: 음, 그럴 수도 있지.

❶ "Is it?"은 "Is it very scary?"의 줄임말로 여기에서는 의외의 반응이라 놀랐다는 의미이다.

Check(√) True or False

(1) The girl and the boy had the same idea about the story.　　T ☐ F ☐

 Listen & Speak 1 A-2

B: ❶Have you seen this movie?

G: Yes, I have. It's one of the best movies I've ever seen.

B: ❷You seem to like it a lot. To me, it's just an old movie.

G: How can you possibly say that? In my view, it is just wonderful.

소년: 너 이 영화 봤니?
소녀: 응, 봤어. 내가 본 최고의 영화들 중 하나야.
소년: 그 영화 무척 좋아하는 것 같네. 나에겐 그건 그저 오래된 영화인데.
소녀: 어떻게 그런 말을 할 수 있어? 내 생각에, 그 영화는 정말 훌륭해.

❶ 현재완료의 용법 중에서 경험을 나타내는 용법이다.
❷ "You seem to ~."는 "너는 ~인 것 같다."의 의미로 상대에 대한 추측을 나타낸다.

Check(√) True or False

(2) The boy has a different idea from the girl about the movie.　　T ☐ F ☐

Conversation B

Yujin: Did your family ❶go out to eat last weekend?

Seho: Yes, we did. The food was great, but my family is too big and loud.

Yujin: Really? How big is it?

Seho: There are seven of us: my grandparents, my mom, my dad, two brothers, and me.

Yujin: That is a big family!

Seho: Well, I don't like it at all. There's no privacy.

Yujin: I get ❷what you're saying, but to me, it's good to have a big family. I sometimes feel lonely because I'm an only child.

Seho: Yeah ..., I see what you mean.

유진: 지난 주말에 가족들과 식사하러 외출했니?
세호: 응, 했어. 음식은 아주 괜찮았는데, 우리 가족이 너무 많고 시끄러워.
유진: 정말? 얼마나 많은데?
세호: 일곱 명이야. 할아버지, 할머니, 엄마, 아빠, 남동생 두 명, 그리고 나.
유진: 정말 대가족이구나!
세호: 그런데 난 그게 전혀 맘에 안 들어. 사생활이 없거든.
유진: 무슨 말인지 알겠지만, 나는 대가족이 있는 것이 좋아. 나는 외동아이라서 가끔 외롭거든.
세호: 그렇구나. 무슨 의미인지 알겠어.

❶ "go out to eat"은 "외식하다"의 의미로 "eat out"이라고 하기도 한다.
❷ what은 선행사를 포함한 관계대명사로 명사절을 유도한다.

Check(√) True or False

(3) Yujin doesn't have any brothers or sisters.　　T ☐ F ☐

(4) Seho sometimes feel lonely.　　T ☐ F ☐

Listen & Speak A-3

B: Isn't this painting strange?

G: Well, I think it's beautiful.

B: Hmm ..., after ❶taking a second look, there is something beautiful about the painting.

G: Hey, you ❷don't have to agree with me.

❶ take a second look = 다시 보다 ❷ don't have to ~ = ~할 필요가 없다

Listen & Speak 1 B

A: We are now third graders. This year is very important!

B: ❶You can say that again! What should we do to make this year special?

A: ❷In my opinion, we should make more friends.

B: You're right. I think it's also important to read a lot of books.

❶ "You can say that."은 동의한다는 의미로 "I agree." 또는 "That's right." 등으로 나타낼 수 있다.

❷ "In my opinion"은 "In my view"와 같이 "내 생각으로는"에 해당하고 "I think ~"라고 할 수 있다.

Listen & Speak 2 A-1

G: Did you hear that a new ice cream store opened last week?

B: Sure. ❶I have already been there.

G: ❷Have you? How was it?

B: The ice cream was great.

G: How was the price?

B: Well, it was very high. I was not happy about it.

❶ "have been"은 "~에 가본 적이 있다"는 의미로 현재완료의 경험에 해당한다.

❷ "Have you?"는 "Have you been there?"의 의미로 "벌써 다녀왔니?" "벌써 가본 적이 있니?"에 해당한다.

Listen & Speak 2 A-2

B: There are a lot of people here.

G: Yes, here are. ❶It's been 30 minutes since we ordered.

B: The service is so slow. I'm not happy about it.

G: Look at those people over there. ❷They are being served now.

B: Didn't we come in earlier?

G: Yes, we did. It's not fair.

❶ "It's been 30 minutes since we ordered."는 "It has been ~"을 줄여서 쓴 현재완료 문장이다. 현재완료의 문장에서 시간을 나타내는 접속사 since가 쓰여서 "~한 이래로"의 의미를 나타낸다.

❷ "They are being served now."는 현재진행시제의 수동태로 "그들이 지금 음식을 받고 있다."의 의미이다.

Real Life Task Step 1

W: People often say, "I'm not happy about my family." But we have a different story. We asked 2,000 people, ❶"With whom do you feel happiest?" More than half of them feel happiest when they are with their family. ❷The second-largest number of people are happiest with their friends. Interestingly, around 13% of the people we asked feel happiest ❸when alone.

❶ "With whom do you feel happiest? = Who(m) do you feel happiest with?"는 "누구와 같이 있을 때 가장 행복합니까?"이다.

❷ The second-largest number of people = 두 번째로 가장 많은 사람은

❸ when alone = when they are alone

Real Life Task Step 2

A: ❶It's important to have a happy family to live ❷a happy life.

B: I agree. What should family members do to have a happy family?

A: In my opinion, they should ❸try to help one another.

B: That's a good idea. I think they also have to be kind to one another. What else should they do?

❶ "It's important to have a happy family to live a happy life."는 가주어, 진주어의 구문이다.

❷ "a happy life"는 동사 live의 목적어이다. 이런 목적어를 동족목적어라고 한다.

❸ try to ~ = ~하려고 애쓰다

● 다음 우리말과 일치하도록 빈칸에 알맞은 말을 쓰시오.

Listen & Speak 1 A-1

G: _____ you _____ this book?

B: Yes, I have. The _____ is very _____.

G: Is it? In my _____, it's a _____ story.

B: Well, it _____ be.

소녀: 너 이 책 읽어봤니?
소년: 응, 읽어봤어. 이야기가 무척 무섭더라.
소녀: 그래? 내 생각에는 슬픈 이야기인데.
소년: 음, 그럴 수도 있지.

Listen & Speak 1 A-2

B: Have you _____ this _____?

G: Yes, I _____. It's one of the _____ movies I've ever seen.

B: You _____ to _____ it a lot. To me, it's just an old movie.

G: _____ can you _____ say that? In my _____, it is just _____.

소녀: 너 이 영화 봤니?
소년: 응, 봤어. 내가 본 최고의 영화들 중 하나야.
소녀: 그 영화 무척 좋아하는 것 같네. 나에겐 그건 그저 오래된 영화인데.
소년: 어떻게 그런 말을 할 수 있어? 내 생각에, 그 영화는 정말 훌륭해.

Listen & Speak 1 A-3

B: Isn't this _____ _____?

G: Well, I _____ it's beautiful.

B: Hmm ..., _____ _____ a second _____, there is something _____ about the painting.

G: Hey, you _____ have to _____ with me.

소년: 이 그림은 이상하지 않니?
소녀: 글쎄, 나는 아름답다고 생각하는데.
소년: 음, 다시 보니 그림에 뭔가 아름다운 것이 있군.
소녀: 이런, 내 의견에 동의하지 않아도 돼.

Listen & Speak 1 B

A: We are now _____ _____. This year is very _____!

B: You can _____ _____ again! _____ _____ we do to make this year special?

A: In my _____, we should _____ more _____.

B: You're _____. I think it's also _____ to read a lot of books.

A: 우리는 이제 3학년이야. 이번 해는 매우 중요해!
B: 정말 그래! 이번 해를 특별하게 보내기 위해 무엇을 해야 할까?
A: 내 생각에 우리는 더 많은 친구를 사귀어야 해.
B: 맞아. 많은 책을 읽는 것 또한 중요하다고 생각해.

Listen & Speak 2 A-1

G: Did you _____ that a new ice _____ store _____ last week?

B: _____. I have _____ been there.

G: _____ you? How _____ it?

B: The ice cream was _____.

G: _____ was the price?

B: Well, it was very _____. I was not _____ about it.

소녀: 지난주에 새 아이스크림 가게가 개업했다는 것 들었니?
소년: 물론이지. 나는 이미 거기 가봤어.
소녀: 그랬어? 어땠어?
소년: 아이스크림은 훌륭했어.
소녀: 가격은 어땠어?
소년: 음, 가격은 매우 비쌌어. 나는 그것이 마음에 들지 않았어.

Listen & Speak 2 A-2

B: _____ are a lot of people _____.

G: Yes, _____ are. It's been 30 minutes _____ we _____.

B: The _____ is so _____. I'm not _____ about it.

G: Look at _____ people _____ there. They are _____ _____ now.

B: _____ we come in _____?

G: Yes, we did. It's not _____.

Conversation B

Yujin: Did your family _____ _____ to _____ last weekend?

Seho: Yes, we did. The _____ was great, but my _____ is _____ big and loud.

Yujin: Really? _____ big is it?

Seho: There are _____ of us: my _____, my mom, my dad, two _____, and me.

Yujin: That is a big family!

Seho: Well, I _____ like it at all. There's no _____.

Yujin: I _____ _____ you're saying, but to me, it's _____ to _____ a big family. I sometimes feel _____ because I'm an _____ child.

Seho: Yeah ..., I see _____ you mean.

Real Life Task Step 1

W: People often say, "I'm not _____ about my family." But we have a _____ story. We _____ 2,000 people, "With _____ do you feel happiest?" _____ than half of them _____ happiest when they are _____ their family. The second-largest _____ of people are happiest _____ their _____. _____, around 13% of the people we _____ feel happiest when _____.

Real Life Task Step 2

A: It's _____ to have a happy _____ to live a happy _____.

B: I _____. What _____ family members _____ to _____ a happy family?

A: In my _____, they should _____ to help one _____.

B: That's a _____ idea. I think they also _____ to be _____ to one another. What _____ should they _____?

소년: 여기 사람들이 많다.
소녀: 응, 그러네. 우리가 주문한지 30 분이 지났어.
소년: 서비스가 너무 느려. 나는 그것이 마음에 안 들어.
소년: 저기 저 사람들 좀 봐. 저 사람들 은 지금 음식을 받는걸.
소년: 우리가 더 빨리 오지 않았니?
소녀: 응, 그랬지. 이건 공평하지 않아.

유진: 지난 주말에 가족들과 식사하러 외출했니?
세호: 응, 했어. 음식은 아주 괜찮았는 데, 우리 가족이 너무 많고 시끄러 워.
유진: 정말? 얼마나 많은데?
세호: 일곱 명이야. 할아버지, 할머니, 엄마, 아빠, 남동생 두 명, 그리고 나.
유진: 정말 대가족이구나!
세호: 그런데 난 그게 맘에 안 들어. 사 생활이 없거든.
유진: 무슨 말인지 알겠지만, 나는 대가 족이 있는 것이 좋아. 나는 외동이 라서 가끔 외롭거든.
세호: 그렇구나. 무슨 의미인지 알겠어.

W: 사람들은 종종 "난 내 가족이 마음에 안 들어."라고 말합니다. 그러나 우리 에게는 다른 이야기가 있습니다. 우 리는 2,000명의 사람들에게 "누구와 함께 있을 때 가장 행복하십니까?"라 고 물었습니다. 절반 이상의 사람들 이 가족과 함께 있을 때 가장 행복하 다고 느낍니다. 그다음으로 많은 사 람들이 그들의 친구와 함께 있을 때 가장 행복합니다. 흥미롭게도 우리가 조사한 사람들의 약 13퍼센트는 혼자 있을 때 가장 행복하다고 느낍니다.

A: 행복한 삶을 위해 행복한 가족을 갖는 것은 중요해.
B: 동의해. 행복한 가정생활을 위해 가족 구성원들이 무엇을 해야 할까?
A: 내 생각에 그들은 서로를 도우려고 노 력해야 해.
B: 좋은 생각이야. 나는 그들이 또한 서 로에게 친절해야 한다고 생각해. 그들 은 또 무엇을 해야 할까?

01 다음 대화의 빈칸에 들어갈 말로 적절한 것을 고르시오.

> G: Have you read this book?
> B: Yes, I have. The story is very scary.
> G: Is it? _____, it's a sad story.
> B: Well, it could be.

① So do I ② In my opinion ③ As a result
④ Instead of it ⑤ In other words

02 다음 대화의 순서가 바르게 배열된 것을 고르시오.

> G: Did you hear that a new ice cream store opened last week?
> B: Sure. I have already been there.
> G: Have you? How was it?
> (A) Well, it was very high. I was not happy about it.
> (B) How was the price?
> (C) The ice cream was great.

① (A) – (C) – (B) ② (B) – (A) – (C)
③ (B) – (C) – (A) ④ (C) – (A) – (B)
⑤ (C) – (B) – (A)

[03~04] 다음 대화를 읽고 물음에 답하시오.

> B: Isn't this painting strange?
> G: Well, I think it's beautiful.
> B: Hmm ..., 다시 보니 그림에 뭔가 아름다운 것이 있군. (after / a second / taking / look, / is / there / about the painting / something beautiful).
> G: Hey, you don't have to agree with me.

03 주어진 어구를 알맞게 배열하여 밑줄 친 우리말을 영어로 쓰시오.

➡ _____

04 위 대화의 내용과 일치하는 것은?

① 소년은 그림을 처음 보고 좋아했다.
② 소녀는 그림이 이상하다는 생각을 했다.
③ 소년은 그림에 대한 의견을 바꾸었다.
④ 소녀는 소년과 같은 의견이다.
⑤ 소년은 그림이 평범하다고 생각했다.

[01~02] 다음 대화를 읽고 물음에 답하시오.

B: Have you seen this movie?

G: Yes, I have. It's one of the best movies I've ever seen.

B: (A)_____ To me, it's just an old movie.

G: (B)어떻게 그런 말을 할 수 있니? (possibly) In my view, it is just wonderful.

01 빈칸 (A)에 들어가기에 적절한 것은?

① Didn't you see the movie?

② Why don't you see the movie?

③ Where did you see the movie?

④ You want to see the movie?

⑤ You seem to like it a lot.

02 밑줄 친 (B)의 우리말을 영어로 쓰시오. (주어진 단어 포함 / 6단어)

➡ _____

03 다음 대화의 빈칸에 들어가기에 어색한 것을 고르시오.

> B: Isn't this painting strange?
>
> G: Well, _____ it's beautiful.
>
> B: Hmm ..., after taking a second look, there is something beautiful about the painting.
>
> G: Hey, you don't have to agree with me.

① I think   ② I believe

③ In my opinion,   ④ I feel

⑤ To you,

[04~06] 다음 대화를 읽고 물음에 답하시오.

B: We are now third graders. This year is very important!

G: (A)You can say that again! What should we do to make this year special?

B: In my opinion, we should make more friends.

G: You're right. (B)책을 많이 읽는 것도 중요하다고 생각해. (think, also, important, it, lot)

04 밑줄 친 (A)와 바꾸어 쓰기에 적절한 것은?

① Do you think so?

② I think so, too.

③ What makes you think so?

④ How about?

⑤ Why is it so important?

서답형
05 밑줄 친 (B)의 우리말을 주어진 단어를 이용해 영어로 쓰시오. (11 words)

➡ _____

중요
06 위 대화의 내용과 일치하지 않는 것은?

① 소녀와 소년은 3학년이 되었다.

② 소녀와 소년은 둘 다 올해를 중요하다고 여긴다.

③ 소녀는 친구를 별로 사귀지 않을 것이다.

④ 소녀는 책을 많이 읽을 것이다.

⑤ 소녀는 소년의 생각에 동의한다.

서답형
07 다음 대화의 문맥상 또는 어법상 어색한 것을 찾아 고치시오.

> G: Have you read this book?
>
> B: Yes, I did. The story is very scary.
>
> G: Is it? In my opinion, it's a sad story.
>
> B: Well, it could be.

➡ _____

[08~09] 다음 대화를 읽고 물음에 답하시오.

> G: Did you hear that a new ice cream store opened last week?
> B: Sure. (A)_____
> G: Have you? How was it?
> B: The ice cream was great.
> G: How was the price?
> B: Well, it was very high. (B)_____

08 위 대화의 흐름으로 보아, 빈칸 (A)에 적절한 것은?

① Do you know where it is?
② Did you hear who opened it?
③ Have you bought anything there?
④ I haven't heard about it.
⑤ I have already been there.

09 빈칸 (B)에 들어가기에 적절한 것은?

① It's really worth visiting.
② It's what I wanted to introduce.
③ Are you satisfied with it?
④ I was not happy about it.
⑤ Why have you been there?

[10~12] 다음 대화를 읽고 물음에 답하시오.

> B: There are a lot of people here. (ⓐ)
> G: Yes, here are. (ⓑ) It's been 30 minutes since we ordered.
> B: (A)_____ I'm not happy about it.
> G: (ⓒ) They are being served now.
> B: Didn't we come in earlier? (ⓓ)
> G: Yes, we did. (ⓔ) It's not fair.

10 빈칸 (A)에 들어가기에 적절한 것은?

① The food looks very nice.
② The service is so slow.
③ They will serve us soon.
④ Are you satisfied with the food?
⑤ How was your food?

11 ⓐ~ⓔ 중에서 다음 문장이 들어가기에 적절한 곳은?

> Look at those people over there.

① ⓐ   ② ⓑ   ③ ⓒ   ④ ⓓ   ⑤ ⓔ

12 According to the dialogue, which one is NOT true?

① There are many people in the restaurant.
② They went to the restaurant about 30 minutes ago.
③ They were not happy with the taste of the food.
④ The service was not good there.
⑤ They were not satisfied with the service.

서답형
13 주어진 어구를 배열하여 다음 우리말을 영어로 쓰시오.

> A: It's important to have a happy family to live a happy life.
> B: I agree. <u>행복한 가정을 위하여 가족 구성원들은 무엇을 해야 하니?</u> (to, should, do, have, what, family members, a happy family)?

➡ _____

[01~03] 다음 대화를 읽고 물음에 답하시오.

Yujin: Did your family (A)go out to eat last weekend?

Seho: Yes, we did. The food was great, but my family is too big and loud.

Yujin: Really? How big is it?

Seho: There are seven of us: my grandparents, my mom, my dad, two brothers, and me.

Yujin: That is a big family!

Seho: Well, (B)I don't like it at all. There's no privacy.

Yujin: (C)네가 무슨 말을 하는지 알겠다. (get, what, saying), but to me, it's good to have a big family. I sometimes feel lonely because I'm an only child.

Seho: Yeah ..., I see what you mean.

01 밑줄 친 (A)와 같은 의미가 되도록 빈칸을 적절한 단어로 채우시오.

➡ go out to eat = _____ out

02 밑줄 친 (B)를 다음과 같이 바꿔 쓸 때 빈칸에 적절한 말을 쓰시오. (주어진 철자로 시작할 것)

➡ I am not s_____ with it at all.

03 밑줄 친 (C)의 우리말을 주어진 〈조건〉에 맞게 영작하시오.

┌─ 조건 ─┐
1. 주어진 단어를 포함할 것.
2. 현재진행시제가 포함되도록 할 것.
3. 줄임말 없이 6단어로 쓸 것.

➡ _____

04 다음 대화의 문맥상 또는 어법상 어색한 단어를 한 개 찾아 고치시오.

B: Isn't this painting strange?

G: Well, I think it's beautiful.

B: Hmm ..., after taking a second look, there is something boring about the painting.

G: Hey, you don't have to agree with me.

➡ _____

05 다음 대화의 흐름상 어색한 한 문장을 찾아 알맞게 고치시오.

A: What do you like most about your family?

B: My sister is one of my best friends.

A: Then, what do you like most about your family?

B: My mother wakes me up early every morning. I'm not happy about it.

➡ _____
_____

06 다음 대화의 내용으로 보아 빈칸에 들어가기에 적절한 한 단어를 쓰시오.

B: There are a lot of people here.

G: Yes, there are! This restaurant must be very popular.

B: Let's get started.

G: This pizza smells really great!

B: Yes, it does, but it's too _____. I'm not happy about its size.

➡ s_____

Grammar

1 to부정사의 의미상 주어

> **It** was difficult **for me to put up** with her. 나는 그녀를 견디는 것이 힘들었어.

- 형태: It is/was ~ for+목적격+to부정사
  의미: ~가 ~하는 것은 …하다

- to부정사구가 문장의 주어로 쓰일 경우에 주어 자리에 가주어 it을 쓰고 to부정사구를 뒤로 보내 「It+is/was+형용사+to부정사」로 나타낸다. 가주어 it은 의미가 없으므로 해석하지 않으며 to부정사구를 주어로 해석

  - **It** is interesting **to read a fantasy novel**. (판타지 소설을 읽는 것은 재미있다.)

- 부정사의 행위자를 '부정사의 의미상 주어'라고 하고 별도로 표시하는 것이 필요한 경우에는 'for+목적격' 형태로 to부정사 앞에 쓴다. It is 다음에는 difficult, easy, possible, impossible, dangerous, important 등의 형용사가 쓰인다.

  - **It** is impossible **for humans to live** without air. (의미상의 주어는 for humans이다.)
    (인간이 공기 없이 사는 것은 불가능하다.)

  - **It** is dangerous **for children to play** on the roof.
    (아이들이 지붕 위에서 노는 것은 위험하다.)

  - **It** was easy **for David to solve** the problem. (David이 그 문제를 푸는 것은 쉬웠다.)

- to부정사의 의미상의 주어가 사람의 성질이나 특징을 나타내는 형용사와 사용되면 주어를 'of+목적격'으로 쓴다. 주로 사용되는 형용사는 kind, nice, foolish, polite, wise, brave, thoughtful, careful 등이 있다.

  - **It** is kind **of you** to help me. (의미상의 주어는 of you이다.)
    (서를 도와주시다니 정말 친절하시군요.)

핵심 Check

1. 다음 우리말에 맞게 빈칸에 알맞은 말을 쓰시오.

   (1) 내가 새로운 친구를 사귀는 것은 쉽지 않아.

   ➡ It's not easy _____ _____ to make new friends.

   (2) 내가 파스타 만드는 것은 쉬워.

   ➡ It is easy _____ _____ to cook pasta.

   (3) 그가 그렇게 말하다니 어리석다.

   ➡ It is foolish _____ _____ to say so.

❷ 관계대명사 who의 계속적(비제한적) 용법

I share a room with my sister, **who** is two years older than me.
나는 언니와 방을 함께 쓰는데 그녀는 나보다 두 살 많다.

■ 형태: 선행사, who/which ~

■ 관계대명사절은 흔히 선행사를 직접 수식하는 제한적 용법(한정적 용법)으로 쓰인다.
  • He gave me a present **which** was very unique. (그가 나에게 굉장히 독특한 선물을 주었다.)

■ 선행사와 관계대명사 사이에 콤마를 쓰는, 계속적 용법(비제한적 용법)의 관계대명사절은 선행사가 가리키는 지시 대상에 대해 추가적인 정보를 제시하는 역할을 한다. 계속적(비제한적) 용법의 관계대명사는 쉼표로 표시하고, which는 앞에 나온 사물뿐만 아니라, 앞에 나온 구, 절 또는 앞 문장 전체를 선행사로 삼기도 한다. 관계대명사 that은 계속적 용법(비제한적 용법)으로 사용되지 않는다.

  • He gave me a present, **which** was very unique.
    (그가 나에게 선물을 주었는데, 그것은 굉장히 독특한 것이었다.)
    = He gave me a present, and it was very unique.

  • I have a girl friend, **who** runs a bakery.
    (나에게는 여자 친구가 있는데 그녀는 빵집을 운영한다.)
    = I have a girl friend, and she runs a bakery.

■ 관계대명사가 계속적 용법으로 쓰이면 선행사에 대한 추가적인 정보를 제시하며 「접속사+대명사」의 역할을 하고 해석은 앞에서 뒤로 보충 설명하듯이 해석한다. 제한적 용법의 관계대명사 목적격은 생략 가능하지만, 계속적 용법의 관계대명사 목적격은 생략할 수 없다.

  • She doesn't like her neighbors, **who** make loud noises at night.
    = She doesn't like her neighbors, **for they** make loud noises at night.
    (그녀는 이웃 사람들을 좋아하지 않는데, 그들은 밤에 큰 소란을 피운다.)
    – 관계대명사절이 her neighbors에 대한 추가적인 정보를 제공한다.

핵심 Check

2. 다음 우리말과 같도록 할 때, 두 문장의 의미가 같도록 빈칸을 채우시오.

  (1) 그녀는 김연아인데, 동계 올림픽에서 금메달을 땄어.
    She is Kim Yuna, who won a gold medal at the Winter Olympics.
    = She is Kim Yuna, and _____ won a gold medal at the Winter Olympics.

  (2) 저의 롤모델은 J. K. Rowling인데 그녀는 해리포터 시리즈를 썼습니다.
    My role model is J. K. Rowling, who wrote *Harry Potter* series.
    = My role model is J. K. Rowling, _____ she wrote *Harry Potter* series.

01 다음 중 밑줄 친 부분이 어법상 올바른 것은?

① It is very kind of you to say that.
② It is difficult of us move this chair.
③ It is not easy of me to speak English.
④ It was very nice for you to bring me home.
⑤ Is it okay for his to leave a little earlier today?

02 다음 우리말 의미와 같도록 괄호 안에 주어진 단어를 이용하여 영작하시오.

나는 오빠가 하나 있는데, 그는 의사이다.
(brother, who)

➡ _____

03 다음 중 빈칸에 들어갈 말이 나머지와 <u>다른</u> 것은?

① It is dangerous _____ the kids to go there.
② It is boring _____ me to watch action movies.
③ It was silly _____ her to believe your promise.
④ It is difficult _____ me to write letters in English.
⑤ It was not easy _____ him to get some exercise regularly.

04 다음 중 밑줄 친 부분이 어법상 올바른 것은?

① She has three sons, that all became doctors.
② This is my father, which is the nicest person in the world.
③ Paparazzi, that is the plural form of paparazzo, is now an everyday word around the world.
④ This is the book what my father bought me yesterday.
⑤ The word *sandwich*, which comes from the 4th Earl of Sandwich, is used in our lives.

01 다음 중 빈칸에 들어갈 말이 나머지와 다른 것은?

① It is hard _____ them to win the game.

② It is necessary _____ her to lose weight.

③ It is rude _____ him to ask such questions.

④ It's not safe _____ us to play outside at night.

⑤ Is it important _____ me to finish the work early?

02 다음 (A)~(E)의 빈칸에 들어갈 말이 바르게 짝지어진 것은?

> (A) It was hard _____ me to watch the boring game.
> (B) It was careless _____ me to take the wrong bus.
> (C) It's easy _____ me to remember phone numbers.
> (D) It might be difficult _____ Tom to share his toys with other kids.
> (E) _____ get up early is important.

	(A)	(B)	(C)	(D)	(E)
①	of	of	for	of	To
②	of	for	of	of	For
③	for	for	of	for	For
④	for	of	for	of	To
⑤	for	of	for	for	To

03 우리말에 어울리는 영어 문장을 쓸 때 빈칸에 적절한 말을 쓰시오.

> 그 사람이 이번 주에 그 일을 시작하는 것이 필요하다.
> ➡ It is necessary _____ _____ _____ start the work this week.

04 다음 중 어법상 어색한 문장은?

① I like the picture, that was taken last year.

② I'm proud of my grandfather, who is good at fishing.

③ Look at the trees that stand in the garden.

④ Do you know the boy who is standing over there?

⑤ He likes the bag that his father bought him.

05 다음 빈칸 (A), (B)에 들어갈 말이 바르게 짝지어진 것은?

> • I have an uncle, (A)_____ teaches chemistry at a high school.
> • It was kind (B)_____ him to come to help you.

	(A)	(B)
①	who	for
②	that	for
③	that	of
④	who	of
⑤	which	with

06 다음 빈칸에 들어갈 말이 바르게 짝지어진 것은?

> • This house has a bedroom, _____ faces south.
> • I had two sons, _____ became teachers.

① that – which   ② what – that

③ whom – that   ④ who – which

⑤ which – who

07 다음 중 밑줄 친 부분을 생략할 수 있는 문장은?

① The girl who is crying is my cousin.

② The man that I visited last night is my uncle.

③ This is the King Sejong, who invented Hangeul.

④ This is what my sister bought on my birthday.

⑤ This is the book which explains how to use the computer.

08 다음 〈보기〉에서 어법상 어색한 문장을 4개 고른 후, 기호를 쓰고 각각 올바른 문장으로 고쳐서 다시 쓰시오.

┌─── 보기 ├───

ⓐ I respect Mother Theresa, which devoted her life to others.

ⓑ We'll go to The Ken's Market, who sells fresh food.

ⓒ I'm proud of my uncle, who is good at cooking.

ⓓ Jessica sent the letter to Mike, that made him happy.

ⓔ I had a swimming lesson from Mr. Jackson, who got me to enjoy swimming.

ⓕ Yesterday, there was a car accident, which killed three and hurt many people.

ⓖ I don't know where my bag has gone, whom was put on the table a few hours ago.

└─────────────┘

       기호   고친 문장

(1) _____ → _____

    _____

(2) _____ → _____

    _____

(3) _____ → _____

    _____

(4) _____ → _____

    _____

09 다음 중 어법상 올바른 문장은?

① Show me the pictures which you took them in Busan.

② He said something, that made her feel happy.

③ I liked the bag my mom gave to me as a gift.

④ My nephew Tory, which is seven, is a smart boy.

⑤ Emma and Charlie, whom I met in Canada, is going to leave next month.

10 다음 중 짝지어진 두 문장의 의미가 같은 것은?

① I don't know the man, who lives next door.

   = I don't know the man, for he lives next door.

② I met Mr. Brown, who said nothing about it.

   = I met Mr. Brown, but he didn't say anything about it.

③ She had two sisters, who became doctors.

   = She had two sisters, and she became doctors.

④ I scolded the boy, who was lazy.

   = I scolded the boy, but he was lazy.

⑤ This is *the Mona Lisa*, which was painted by Leonardo da Vinci.

   = Leonardo da Vinci was painted by *the Mona Lisa*.

11 다음 주어진 문장을 〈조건〉에 맞게 바꿔 쓰시오.

> ┌ 조건 ┐
> • 관계대명사 계속적 용법을 사용할 것.
> • 주어와 동사를 포함한 완전한 문장으로 쓸 것.

(1) Here is some water, and it is fresh.

→ _____

(2) I know the girl, and Tom danced with her last night.

→ _____

_____

12 다음 중 빈칸에 들어갈 말이 나머지 넷과 <u>다른</u> 것은?

① It is important _____ us to be on time.

② It was easy _____ him to catch fish in the river.

③ It will be possible _____ Ted to win the contest.

④ It was very nice _____ you to drive us to the station.

⑤ It is necessary _____ students to wear school uniforms.

13 다음 두 문장을 한 문장으로 바꿔 쓸 때 빈칸에 알맞은 말을 쓰시오.

> He was very kind. He lent me his cell phone.
> ➡ It was very kind _____ _____ _____ _____ _____ his cell phone.

14 다음 중 밑줄 친 부분이 어법상 올바른 것은?

① Mrs. White has two sons, <u>that</u> all became actors.

② That is her father, <u>which</u> works at the bank.

③ She met the new teacher, <u>he</u> was very kind.

④ This is the phone <u>what</u> my father bought me yesterday.

⑤ I found the car, <u>which</u> he told me about.

15 다음 주어진 문장과 의미가 같은 것은?

> My brother, who is a writer, lives in New York.

① I have one brother, and he is a writer.

② My brother is a famous writer in New York.

③ My brother is a writer, and he lives in New York.

④ I have many brothers, and one of them is a writer.

⑤ I have many brothers, and one of them lives in New York.

16 다음 세 문장의 의미가 모두 포함되도록 관계대명사의 계속적 용법을 이용하여 한 문장으로 만드시오.

> • I have a brother.
> • He is a pilot.
> • He lives in Busan.

➡ _____

01 다음 두 문장을 한 문장으로 바꿀 때 빈칸에 알맞은 말을 쓰시오.

> • He helped me with my homework.
> • He was very kind.

➡ It was very kind _____
_____ .

02 다음 괄호 안에서 필요한 단어만 골라 우리말의 의미에 맞도록 영작하시오.

(1) 우리가 이 의자를 옮기는 것은 어렵지 않다.
➡ It isn't difficult _____ .
(move, for, to, this, chair, of, us)

(2) 네가 창문을 연 것은 조심성이 없었다.
➡ It was careless _____ .
(the, window, open, of, to, you)

03 다음 주어진 문장의 빈칸을 〈보기〉와 같이 완성하시오.

> ┌─── 보기 ───
> We go skating. It is so fun.
> → It is <u>so fun</u> for us <u>to go skating</u>.

I'm Karl. I can learn English easily.
➡ It is _____ for Karl _____ .

04 다음 문장을 관계대명사의 계속적 용법을 이용하여 한 문장으로 만드시오.

(1) I said nothing. It made Tom angry.
➡ _____

(2) Brian hates cold weather. He is from the South.
➡ _____

05 다음 글에서 어법상 <u>어색한</u> 곳을 찾아 바르게 고치시오.

> A few years ago, my village was hit by a huge tsunami, who killed many animals and destroyed the forest. So, my friends and I started to plant trees. We have planted thousands of trees. Now the forests are coming back very fast. I'm sure that we will have beautiful forests again soon.

(1) 어색한 부분 : _____
(2) 어법에 맞게 고쳐 쓰기 : _____

06 다음 우리말과 의미가 같도록 빈칸에 알맞은 말을 쓰시오.

> 내가 그 시를 이해하는 것은 어렵다.
> = It's hard _____ _____ to understand the poem.

07 다음 A, B에서 서로 관련된 표현을 각각 골라 관계대명사를 사용하여 한 문장으로 완성하시오.

A	• I took a swimming lesson from Mr. Jonson. • Everyone likes our kind and gentle teacher. • We'll go to The Hope Mart. • I read a story about Helen Keller.
B	• It sells fresh food. • She teaches English to us. • He made me enjoy swimming • She overcame her physical difficulties.

(1) _____

_____

(2) _____

_____

(3) _____

_____

(4) _____

_____

08 다음 문장에서 <u>잘못된</u> 부분을 바르게 고쳐 문장을 다시 쓰시오.

(1) It is important of the meeting to be a success.

➡ _____

(2) It is impossible for we to finish the job in time.

➡ _____

(3) *The Sherlock Holmes* stories were written by Arthur Conan Doyle, that was born in Edinburgh.

➡ _____

_____

(4) Samuel Johnson, that who died in 1784, is buried in Westminster Abbey.

➡ _____

_____

09 다음 우리말과 의미가 같도록 빈칸에 알맞은 말을 쓰시오.

(1) John에게 하루 종일 책읽기는 어렵다.

= It is difficult _____ John to read books all day long.

(2) 우리에게 스케이트 타러 가는 것은 재미있다.

= It is fun _____ _____ to go skating.

(3) 그녀에게 중국어 배우기는 쉽다.

= It is easy _____ _____ _____ _____ Chinese.

10 다음 주어진 두 문장을 관계대명사의 계속적 용법을 사용하여 한 문장으로 쓰시오.

(1) • This is my best friend, Rachel.

• She lives next door to me.

➡ _____

_____

(2) • David moved to his new apartment.

• It is very close to the park.

➡ _____

_____

Reading

Family: Love It, Hate It, and Can't Do Without It

(:)콜론 뒤에는 일반적으로 그 앞에 오는 말의 예나 설명이 옴

The word *family* may have different meanings to different people. We
추측의 조동사(~일지도 모른다)
asked our readers, "How are you doing with your family?" Here are
= We asked our readers how they were doing with their families.   some of their replies에 수의 일치
some of their replies.

I often ask myself whether I get along with my family members, and
명사절 접속사(~인지 아닌지)
more often than not, I'm not sure whether I really do. For one thing,
자주, 대개   get along with my family members   우선 한 가지 이유는
they bother me all the time. My sister comes into my room without my
항상
permission and shouts at me to wake up on Sunday mornings. Next,
comes와 병렬 관계   일어나다
Mom asks me to walk the dog, and then Dad tells me to clean my
to부정사를 목적격보어로 취하는 동사(tell, allow, force 등)
room. They keep getting on my nerves until I get angry at them. But
keep+Ving: 계속해서 V하다
I always end up loving them because they have been with me at my
end up Ving: 결국 V하다
worst, still stick by me now, and will continue to do so in the future.
내가 최악일 때   stick by me
Kamala, the U.S.A.

I share a room with my sister, who is two years older than me.
계속적 용법의 관계대명사(선행사 my sister에 대한 부연 설명)
When she became a teenager, her mood started changing every minute.
= started to change   매 순간마다
She would lose her temper over nothing one moment and happily read
과거의 습관을 나타냄(~하곤 했다)   아무것도 아닌 것에
a book or watch a film the next. It was difficult for me to put up with
to부정사의 의미상 주어(for+목적격)   진주어
her.

hate 미워하다
do without: ~ 없이 지내다
meaning: 의미
reader: 독자
some: 몇몇, 일부
reply: 대답; 대답하다
get along with: ~와 잘 지내다
bother: 귀찮게 하다
permission: 허락, 허가
walk: (개를) 산책시키다
get one's nerves: ~을 짜증나게 하다
~의 신경을 거스르다
end up ~ing: 결국 ~하다
stick by: ~의 곁을 지키다
mood: 기분
moment: 순간, 때
put up with: ~을 견디다, ~을 참다

 확인문제

● 다음 문장이 본문의 내용과 일치하면 T, 일치하지 <u>않으면</u> F를 쓰시오.

1 Kamala gets on her family member's nerves. ☐

2 Kamala's sister comes into Kamala's room without her approval. ☐

3 Kamala's mom and dad tell Kamala to do something. ☐

4 Rachel put up with her sister without difficulty. ☐

Now it's my turn to be a teenager. My sister is still one, but she is getting better. Whenever I lose my temper, she tries to support me.

I also understand her better than before because now I know what it feels like to be a teenager. As we get to know each other better, we feel greater love toward each other. Rachel, Australia

My older brother, who entered university this year, is the golden child. He is a perfect son at home and a perfect student at school. Needless to say, it is really stressful to have such a shining brother.

Well, in fact, he is not perfect and is poor at one thing that I am great at. He has no eye for fashion, and I always help him whenever he has a hard time choosing clothes for a date. I feel pleased when he thanks me for my help and appreciates my fashion sense. It is not always difficult for me to live with the perfect brother, and I believe in "every man for his own trade." Minsu, Korea

Kamala, Rachel, and Minsu all have their own difficulties in their family life. At the same time, they love their families and find special meanings in them. What story would you tell us about your family?

A FAMILY

A family

is made of love and tears,

laughter and years.

It grows stronger

with the passing of time

turn: 차례, 순번
lose one's temper: 화를 내다
whenever: ~할 때마다
support: 지지하다
get to V: ~하게 되다
each other: 서로
golden: 금으로 만든
golden child: 누구나 좋아하는 사람
stressful: 스트레스가 많은, 걱정 등을 일으키는
be poor at: ~에 서투르다
pleased: 기쁜
appreciate: 진가를 알아보다, 고마워하다
be great at: ~을 잘하다
trade: 일, 직업, 업
at the same time: 동시에

확인문제

● 다음 문장이 본문의 내용과 일치하면 T, 일치하지 <u>않으면</u> F를 쓰시오.

1 Rachel's sister is still a teenager. ☐

2 Rachel doesn't love her sister because she doesn't understand her. ☐

3 According to Minsu, no one likes his brother. ☐

4 Minsu helps his brother when he chooses clothes for a date. ☐

5 There is nothing Minsu is good at. ☐

● 우리말을 참고하여 빈칸에 알맞은 말을 쓰시오.

Family: Love It, Hate It, and Can't Do Without It

1 The word *family* _____ _____ _____ _____ to different people.

2 We asked our readers, "_____ are you _____ with your family?" Here are some of _____ _____.

3 I often _____ myself _____ I _____ _____ _____ my family members, and _____ _____ _____ _____, I'm not sure _____ I really do.

4 _____ _____ _____, they _____ me all the time.

5 My sister _____ _____ my room _____ my _____ and shouts at me _____ _____ _____ on Sunday mornings.

6 Next, Mom _____ me _____ _____ the dog, and then Dad _____ _____ _____ _____ my room.

7 They keep _____ _____ _____ _____ until I get angry at them.

8 But I always _____ _____ _____ them because they have been with me _____ _____ _____, still stick by me now, and will continue _____ _____ _____ in the future.
Kamala, U.S.A

9 I _____ a room with my sister, _____ _____ two years _____ than me.

10 _____ she became a teenager, _____ _____ started _____ every minute.

11 She _____ _____ her temper _____ _____ one moment and happily _____ a book or _____ a film the next.

12 It was _____ _____ _____ put up with her.

13 Now it's _____ _____ _____ _____ a teenager. My sister is still one, but she is _____ _____.

14 _____ I lose my temper, she _____ _____ _____ me.

가족: 사랑하고, 미워하고, 그런데 없어서는 안 되는 것

1 가족이라는 말은 사람들마다 다른 의미를 가질 수 있습니다.

2 우리는 독자들에게 '가족과 어떻게 지내나요?'라고 물었습니다. 여기 그 대답들 중 몇 가지가 있습니다.

3 나는 종종 가족들과 잘 지내는지 나 자신에게 물어보는데, 많은 경우에 잘 지내는지 확신하지 못한다.

4 한 예를 들자면, 가족들은 나를 항상 귀찮게 한다.

5 언니는 일요일 아침에 허락도 없이 내 방에 들어와서 일어나라고 소리친다.

6 그다음에는 엄마가 개를 산책시키라고 하시고, 그러고 나면 아빠가 방을 청소하라고 하신다.

7 가족들은 내가 화가 날 때까지 내 신경을 건드린다.

8 하지만 결국엔 항상 가족들을 사랑하게 되는데, 그들은 내가 가장 어려울 때 함께 있어 주었고, 지금도 내 곁을 지키며, 앞으로도 계속해서 그럴 것이기 때문이다.   카말라, 미국

9 나는 언니와 방을 함께 쓰는데, 언니는 나보다 두 살이 많다.

10 언니는 십대가 되었을 때, 기분이 매분마다 바뀌기 시작했다.

11 어느 순간 갑자기 아무것도 아닌 일에 화를 내다가 바로 다음 순간 즐겁게 책을 읽거나 영화를 보곤 했다.

12 나는 언니를 견디기가 힘들었다.

13 이젠 내가 십대가 될 차례이다. 언니도 아직 십대이지만 점점 나아지고 있다.

14 내가 화를 낼 때마다 언니는 나를 지지해 주려고 노력한다.

15 I also _____ her _____ _____ before _____ now I know _____ _____ _____ _____ to be a teenager.

16 As we _____ _____ _____ each other better, we _____ _____ _____ toward each other.

Rachel, Australia

17 My older brother, _____ _____ university this year, _____ _____ _____ _____ .

18 He is _____ _____ _____ at home and a perfect _____ _____ school.

19 _____ _____ _____ , it is really stressful to have _____ _____ _____ _____ .

20 Well, in fact, he is not perfect and is _____ _____ one thing _____ I _____ _____ _____ .

21 He has _____ _____ _____ fashion, and I always help him _____ he has a _____ _____ _____ clothes for a date.

22 I feel _____ when he _____ me _____ my help and _____ my fashion sense.

23 It is not always difficult _____ _____ _____ _____ _____ the perfect brother, and I _____ _____ "every man for his _____ _____ ."

Minsu, Korea

24 Kamala, Rachel, and Minsu all have _____ _____ in their family life.

25 At the same time, they love their families and _____ _____ _____ in them.

26 What story _____ you _____ us about your family?

27 A FAMILY

A family

_____ _____ _____ love and tears,

laughter and _____ .

It _____ stronger

with the _____ _____ _____ .

15 지금은 나도 십대라는 것이 어떤 느낌인지 알기 때문에 예전보다 언니를 더 잘 이해한다.

16 우리가 서로를 잘 알아 갈수록 우리는 서로에게 더 큰 사랑을 느낀다. 레이첼, 호주

17 우리 형은 올해 대학에 들어갔는데, 누구에게나 사랑받는 아들이다.

18 형은 집에서는 완벽한 아들이고 학교에서는 완벽한 학생이다.

19 말할 필요도 없이, 그렇게 눈부신 형이 있다는 것은 정말 골치 아픈 일이다.

20 하지만 사실 형도 완벽하지 않고, 내가 잘하는 일에는 형편없다.

21 형은 패션을 보는 눈이 없어서, 데이트에 입을 옷을 고르는 걸 어려워할 때마다 내가 항상 그를 도와준다.

22 형이 내 도움을 고마워하고 내 패션 감각을 알아줄 때 기분이 좋다.

23 완벽한 형과 함께 사는 것이 항상 어려운 일은 아니며, "굼벵이도 구르는 재주가 있다."는 것을 나는 믿는다. 민수, 한국

24 Kamala, Rachel, 그리고 민수 모두에게 가족생활의 어려움이 있습니다.

25 그와 동시에 그들은 자신들의 가족을 사랑하고 그 안에서 특별한 의미를 찾고 있습니다.

26 여러분은 여러분 가족에 대해 어떤 이야기를 할 건가요?

27 가족

가족은

사랑과 눈물

웃음과 세월로 만들어집니다.

가족은 시간의 흐름과 함께 점점 더 강해집니다.

● 우리말을 참고하여 본문을 영작하시오.

Family: Love It, Hate It, and Can't Do Without It

1 가족이라는 말은 사람들마다 다른 의미를 가질 수 있습니다.

➡ _____

2 우리는 독자들에게 '가족과 어떻게 지내나요?'라고 물었습니다. 여기 그 대답들 중 몇 가지가 있습니다.

➡ _____

3 나는 종종 가족들과 잘 지내는지 나 자신에게 물어보는데, 많은 경우에 잘 지내는지 확신하지 못한다.

➡ _____
_____

4 한 예를 들자면, 가족들은 나를 항상 귀찮게 한다.

➡ _____

5 언니는 일요일 아침에 허락도 없이 내 방에 들어와서 일어나라고 소리친다.

➡ _____

6 그다음에는 엄마가 개를 산책시키라고 하시고, 그러고 나면 아빠가 방을 청소하라고 하신다.

➡ _____

7 가족들은 내가 화가 날 때까지 내 신경을 건드린다.

➡ _____

8 하지만 결국엔 항상 가족들을 사랑하게 되는데, 그들은 내가 가장 어려울 때 함께 있어 주었고,
지금도 내 곁을 지키며, 앞으로도 계속해서 그럴 것이기 때문이다.

➡ _____
_____

Kamala, U.S.A.

9 나는 언니와 방을 함께 쓰는데, 언니는 나보다 두 살이 많다.

➡ _____

10 언니는 십대가 되었을 때, 기분이 매분마다 바뀌기 시작했다.

➡ _____

11 어느 순간 갑자기 아무것도 아닌 일에 화를 내다가 바로 다음 순간 즐겁게 책을 읽거나 영화를 보곤 했다.

➡ _____

12 나는 언니를 견디기 힘들었다.

➡ _____

13 이젠 내가 십대가 될 차례이다. 언니도 아직 십대이지만 점점 나아지고 있다.

➡ _____

14 내가 화를 낼 때마다 언니는 나를 지지해 주려고 노력한다.

➡ _____

15 지금은 나도 십대라는 것이 어떤 느낌인지 알기 때문에 예전보다 언니를 더 잘 이해한다.

➡ _____

16 우리가 서로를 잘 알아 갈수록 우리는 서로에게 더 큰 사랑을 느낀다.

➡ _____

Rachel, Australia

17 우리 형은 올해 대학에 들어갔는데, 누구에게나 사랑받는 아들이다.

➡ _____

18 형은 집에서는 완벽한 아들이고 학교에서는 완벽한 학생이다.

➡ _____

19 말할 필요도 없이, 그렇게 눈부신 형이 있다는 것은 정말 골치 아픈 일이다.

➡ _____

20 하지만 사실 형도 완벽하지 않고, 내가 잘하는 일에는 형편없다.

➡ _____

21 형은 패션을 보는 눈이 없어서, 데이트에 입을 옷을 고르는 걸 어려워할 때마다 내가 항상 그를 도와준다.

➡ _____

_____

22 형이 내 도움을 고마워하고 내 패션 감각을 알아줄 때 기분이 좋다.

➡ _____

23 완벽한 형과 함께 사는 것이 항상 어려운 일은 아니며, "굼벵이도 구르는 재주가 있다."는 것을 나는 믿는다.

➡ _____

Minsu, Korea

24 Kamala, Rachel, 그리고 민수 모두에게 가족생활의 어려움이 있습니다.

➡ _____

25 그와 동시에 그들은 자신들의 가족을 사랑하고 그 안에서 특별한 의미를 찾고 있습니다.

➡ _____

26 여러분은 여러분 가족에 대해 어떤 이야기를 할 건가요?

➡ _____

가족

27 가족은 / 사랑과 눈물 / 웃음과 세월로 만들어집니다. / 가족은 시간의 흐름과 함께 / 점점 더 강해집니다.

A FAMILY

➡ _____

[01~02] 다음 글을 읽고 물음에 답하시오.

The word *family* may have different meanings to different people. We asked our readers, "How are you doing with your family?" Here are some of their replies.

01 다음 중 위 글에 이어질 내용으로 가장 적절한 것은?

① many types of families
② people reading books all around the world
③ answers to the question about how students get along with their family
④ how to reply correctly
⑤ answers to the question about why there are different meanings of family

서답형
02 위 글의 내용에 맞게 빈칸에 알맞은 말을 쓰시오.

It is possible that the word *family* may have _____ _____ _____ _____ _____.

[03~06] 다음 글을 읽고 물음에 답하시오.

I often ask myself whether I get along with my family members, and more often than not, I'm not sure whether I really do. For one thing, they (A)_____ me all the time. My sister comes into my room without my permission and shouts at me to wake up on Sunday mornings. Next, Mom asks me to walk the dog, and then Dad tells me to clean my room. They keep getting on my nerves until I get angry at them. But I always end up loving them because they have been with me at my worst, still stick by me now, and will continue to do so in the future.

Kamala, the U.S.A.

03 위 글의 흐름상 빈칸 (A)에 들어갈 말로 가장 적절한 것은?

① surprise   ② bore   ③ excite
④ bother   ⑤ embarrass

04 다음 중 위 글의 내용과 일치하는 것은?

① Kamala is sure she gets along with her family very well.
② Kamala has a brother.
③ Kamala's dad cleans her room for her.
④ Kamala is asked to walk the dog by her dad.
⑤ Kamala becomes to love her family eventually.

서답형
05 다음과 같이 풀이되는 말을 위 글에서 찾아 쓰시오. (two words)

to be loyal to somebody and continue to support them in difficult times

➡ _____

서답형
06 According to the passage, what does Kamala's father tell her to do? Answer in English with a full sentence.

➡ _____

[07~10] 다음 글을 읽고 물음에 답하시오.

I share a room with my sister, who is two years older than me. (①) When she became a teenager, her mood started changing every minute. (②) She would lose her temper over nothing one moment and happily read a book or watch a film the next. (③) It was difficult for me to put up with her. (④) My sister is still one, but she is getting better. (A) <u>Whenever</u> I lose my temper, she tries to support me. (⑤) I also understand her better than before because now I know what it feels like to be a teenager. As we get to know each other better, we feel greater love toward each other.

Rachel, Australia

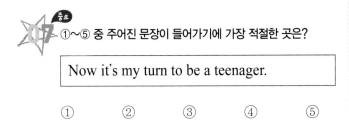

07 ①~⑤ 중 주어진 문장이 들어가기에 가장 적절한 곳은?

> Now it's my turn to be a teenager.

①   ②   ③   ④   ⑤

서답형
08 Write the reason why Rachel understands her sister better than before. Use the phrase 'It's because.'

➡ _____

_____

09 다음 중 밑줄 친 (A)를 대신하여 쓸 수 있는 것은?

① However   ② As soon as
③ Every time   ④ No matter what
⑤ More often than not

10 다음 중 위 글을 읽고 답할 수 <u>없는</u> 것은?

① How much older is Rachel's sister than Rachel?
② Where does Rachel come from?
③ With whom does Rachel share her room?
④ How old is Rachel?
⑤ How do they feel as they get to know each other better?

[11~13] 다음 글을 읽고 물음에 답하시오.

My older brother, who entered university this year, is the golden child. He is a perfect son at home and a perfect student at school. Needless to say, it is really stressful to have such a shining brother. Well, in fact, he is not perfect and is poor at one thing that I am great at. He has no eye for (A)_____, and I always help him whenever he has a hard time choosing clothes for a date. I feel pleased when he thanks me for my help and appreciates my (B)_____ sense. It is not always difficult for me to live with the perfect brother, and I believe in "every man for his own trade."

Minsu, Korea

11 위 글의 흐름상 (A)와 (B)에 공통으로 들어갈 말로 가장 적절한 것은?

① food   ② fashion   ③ machines
④ tool   ⑤ works of art

12 다음 중 위 글의 내용과 일치하는 것은?

① Minsu's brother entered university last year.
② Minsu thinks that he himself is the golden child.
③ Minsu's brother is perfect in every aspect.
④ Minsu helps his brother when he has difficulty choosing the place for a date.
⑤ Minsu has his own special ability, which his brother doesn't have.

서답형
13 How does Minsu feel when his brother thanks him for his help? Answer in English with three words.

➡ _____

[14~17] 다음 글을 읽고 물음에 답하시오.

The word *family* may have different meanings to different people. We asked our readers, "How are you doing with your family?" Here (A)[is / are] some of their replies.

I often ask myself (B)[that / whether] I get along with my family members, and more often than not, I'm not sure whether I really do. For one thing, they bother me all the time. My sister comes into my room without my permission and ①shouts at me to wake up on Sunday mornings. Next, Mom asks me to walk the dog, and then Dad tells me ②to clean my room. They keep ③ getting on my nerves until I ④smile at them. But I always end up (C)[loving / to love] them because they have been with me at my worst, still stick by me now, and will ⑤continue to do so in the future.   Kamala, the U.S.A.

14 (A)~(C) 중 어법상 옳은 것끼리 바르게 짝지은 것은?

① is – that – loving
② is – whether – to love
③ are – that – to love
④ are – whether – loving
⑤ are – that – loving

15 다음 중 위 글을 읽고 답할 수 있는 것은?

① What does Kamala's sister do every Saturday morning?
② What does Kamala's father do for a living?
③ How long has Kamala raised the dog?
④ Where does Kamala walk her dog?
⑤ What does Kamala's sister do without her permission?

서답형
16 다음은 Kamala 어머니의 영상 편지이다. 글의 내용에 맞게 빈칸에 알맞은 말을 쓰시오.

> Hi, Kamala. I'm sorry that I always ask you to _____ _____ _____.
> But remember that I love you and will always _____ _____ _____.

17 ①~⑤ 중 글의 흐름상 어색한 것은?

①   ②   ③   ④   ⑤

[18~21] 다음 글을 읽고 물음에 답하시오.

I share a room with my sister, who is two years older than me. When she became a teenager, her mood started changing every minute.

[A] It was difficult for me to put up with her. Now it's my turn to be a teenager. My sister is still one, but she is getting better. Whenever I lose my temper, she tries to support me.

[B] She would lose her temper over nothing one moment and happily read a book or watch a film the next.

[C] I also understand her better than before because now I know what it feels like to be a teenager. As we get to know each other better, we feel greater love toward each other.
          Rachel, Australia

18 자연스러운 글이 되도록 [A]~[C]를 바르게 배열한 것은?

① [A]–[C]–[B]   ② [B]–[A]–[C]
③ [B]–[C]–[A]   ④ [C]–[B]–[A]
⑤ [C]–[A]–[B]

19 다음 중 Rachel에 관한 사실이 <u>아닌</u> 것은?

① She has a sister.
② She is a teenager.
③ Her sister is two years older than her.
④ She gets to know her sister better.
⑤ Her sister is not a teenager any more.

서답형
20 Whenever Rachel loses her temper, what does her sister try to do? Answer in English with six words.

➡ _____

중요
21 According to the passage, what is the symptom of becoming a teenager?

① not sharing a room with one's sister
② having trouble with making friends
③ putting up with family members
④ the mood change in every minute
⑤ having difficulties with family members

[22~25] 다음 글을 읽고 물음에 답하시오.

My older brother, who entered university this year, is the golden child. He is a perfect son at home and a perfect student at school. (A)_____, it is really stressful to have such a shining brother. Well, in fact, he is not perfect and is poor at one thing that I am great (B)_____. He (C)has no eye for fashion, and I always help him whenever he has a hard time choosing clothes for a date. I feel pleased when he thanks me for my help and appreciates my fashion sense. It is not always difficult for me to live with the perfect brother, and I believe in "every man for his own trade."

Minsu, Korea

22 다음 중 빈칸 (A)에 들어갈 말로 가장 적절한 것은?

① Fortunately   ② Besides
③ Needless to say   ④ So to speak
⑤ To begin with

중요
23 다음 중 빈칸 (B)에 들어갈 말과 같은 말이 들어가는 것은?

① Did she really turn _____ your offer?
② Water consists _____ oxygen and hydrogen.
③ Jenny is responsible _____ taking care of these plants.
④ Mom was surprised _____ the news.
⑤ Tom used to think about you from time _____ time.

24 다음 중 밑줄 친 (C)와 바꿔 쓸 수 있는 것은?

① has a bad eye sight
② doesn't know how to buy clothes
③ is very interested in fashion
④ thinks he sees things very well
⑤ does not have good taste in clothes

서답형
25 According to the passage, when does Minsu help his brother? Answer in English with a full sentence.

➡ _____

_____

[01~02] 다음 글을 읽고 물음에 답하시오.

Kamala, Rachel, and Minsu all have their own difficulties in their family life. At the same time, they love their families and find special meanings in (A)them. What story would you tell us about your family?

A FAMILY

A family

is made of love and tears,

laughter and years.

It grows stronger

with the passing of time.

01 밑줄 친 (A)가 가리키는 것을 위 글에서 찾아 쓰시오.

➡ _____

02 According to the passage, what is a family made of? Answer in English with a full sentence.

➡ _____

[03~06] 다음 글을 읽고 물음에 답하시오.

The word *family* may have different meanings to different people. We asked our readers, "How are you doing with your family?" Here are some of their (A)_____.

I often ask myself whether I get along with my family members, and more often than not, I'm not sure whether I really (B)do. For one thing, they bother me all the time. My sister comes into my room without my permission and shouts at me to wake up on Sunday mornings. Next, Mom asks me to walk the dog, and then Dad tells me to clean my room. They keep getting on my nerves until I get angry at them. But I always end up loving them because they have been with me at my worst, still stick by me now, and will continue to do so in the future.

Kamala, the U.S.A.

03 다음은 빈칸 (A)에 해당하는 말의 풀이이다. 빈칸에 들어갈 말을 어법에 맞게 쓰시오.

> something that you say or write when you answer someone or answer a letter or a question

➡ _____

04 밑줄 친 (B)가 의미하는 것을 위 글에서 찾아 쓰시오.

➡ _____

05 What does Kamala ask herself? Answer in English using the word 'if.'

➡ _____

_____

06 According to the passage, who has been with Kamala at her worst? Answer in English with a full sentence.

➡ _____

[07~10] 다음 글을 읽고 물음에 답하시오.

I share a room with my sister, who is two years older than me. When she became a teenager, her mood started changing every minute. She would lose her temper over nothing one moment and happily read a book or watch a film the next. It was difficult for me to put up with her. Now it's my turn to be a teenager. My sister is still (A)one, but she is getting better. Whenever I lose my temper, she tries to support me. I also understand her better than before because now I know what it feels like to be a teenager. As we get to know each other better, we feel greater love toward each other.

Rachel, Australia

07 밑줄 친 (A)가 의미하는 것을 위 글에서 찾아 쓰시오.

➡ _____

08 When Rachel's sister became a teenager, what happened? Answer in English.

➡ _____

09 As Rachel and her sister get to know each other better, what do they feel? Answer in English with seven words.

➡ _____

10 다음은 Rachel의 언니가 Rachel에게 보낸 편지이다. 글의 내용에 맞게 빈칸에 알맞은 말을 쓰시오.

> Hello, Rachel. Now you _____ _____ _____ _____. When you _____ _____ _____, I will try to understand you.

[11~14] 다음 글을 읽고 물음에 답하시오.

My older brother, who entered university this year, is the golden child. He is a perfect son at home and a perfect student at school. Needless to say, it is really stressful to have such a shining brother. (A)Well, in fact, he is not perfect and is poor at one thing that I am great. He has no eye for fashion, and I always help him whenever he has a hard time choosing clothes for a date. I feel pleased when he thanks me for my help and appreciates my fashion sense. It is not always difficult for me to live with the perfect brother, and I believe in "every man for his own trade."

Minsu, Korea

11 Write the reason why Minsu thinks his brother is the golden child. Use the phrase 'It's because.'

➡ _____

_____

12 According to Minsu, what is really stressful? Answer in English with a full sentence.

➡ _____

13 글의 내용에 맞게 빈칸에 알맞은 말을 쓰시오.

> Unlike his brother, Minsu has _____ _____ _____ _____.

14 밑줄 친 (A)를 어법에 맞게 고쳐 쓰시오.

➡ _____

_____

Listen & Speak 2 B

A: What do you like most about your family?
　　동사 like의 목적어로 의문대명사 What이 적절하다.

B: My father is a wonderful cook.
　　　　　　　　cook은 명사일 때 "요리사"라는 의미이다.

A: Then, what do you like least about your family?
　　　　　　　　least는 최상급으로 "가장 적게"의 의미로 안 좋은 점을 나타낸다.

B: I have to share a room with my brother. I'm not happy about it.
　　=must

구문해설 · share a room with ~ ~와 방을 함께 쓰다

해석

A: 너희 가족에 대해 가장 좋은 점이 뭐니?

B: 우리 아빠는 요리를 아주 잘하셔.

A: 그러면, 너의 가족에 대해 가장 안 좋은 점은 뭐니?

B: 나는 형이랑 방을 같이 써야 해. 나는 그 점이 마음에 들지 않아.

Real-Life Task Step 3

Family is a very important part of our happy life, and there are many things
　　　　　　= ~의 매우 중요한 부분　　　　　　　"many things" 뒤에는 목적격 관계대명사 that이 생략되었다

family members should do. In our opinion, it is important for them to have a
　　　　　　　　　　　　　　　　　　　"it ~ for ... to ~"는 가주어, 의미상의 주어, 진주어의 구조이다.

lot of conversations. Next, ...

가족은 우리의 행복한 삶에서 매우 중요한 부분이고, 가족 구성원들이 해야 할 많은 것들이 있습니다. 우리의 의견으로는, 그들이 많은 대화를 하는 것이 중요합니다. 다음으로는…

Before I Read

What should I do?

Q: When Mom and Dad keep asking me about my school work, they get on
　　　　　　　　　　keep+Ving: 계속해서 V하다

　my nerves and I often lose my temper. I don't know why I get angry so
　　　　　　　　　　빈도부사(일반동사 앞, be동사나 조동사 뒤)　　　　　(the reason) why I get angry so easily

　easily. What should I do?

A: Many teenagers have the same problem. Try to just let it go and do your
　　　　　　　　　　　　　　　　　　　　　　　사역동사(let)+목적어+동사원형

　work. Then it will get better sooner or later.
　　　　　　　　　　(상황 따위가) 좋아지다, 호전되다

구문해설 · get on one's nerves: ~의 신경을 건드리다　· lose one's temper: 화를 내다
　　　　　　· sooner or later: 조만간, 머잖아

내가 무엇을 해야 할까요?

Q: 엄마와 아빠가 계속 학업에 대해 물으면, 그들은 제 신경을 건드려서 저는 종종 화를 냅니다. 제가 왜 그렇게 쉽게 화를 내는지 모르겠습니다. 어떻게 해야 하나요?

A: 많은 십대들이 같은 문제를 가지고 있습니다. 그냥 내버려두고 자신의 일을 하도록 하세요. 그러면 조만간 나아질 것입니다.

Words & Expressions

01 다음 중 밑줄 친 부분의 뜻풀이가 바르지 <u>않은</u> 것은?

① He has no <u>eye</u> for fashion. (안목)
② I'm sorry that I always ask you to <u>walk the dog</u>. (산책시키다)
③ I love you and will always <u>stick by</u> you. (~의 곁을 지키다)
④ Teenagers have <u>difficulties</u> in their family life. (어려움)
⑤ I don't know why I <u>get</u> angry so easily. (얻다)

02 다음 글의 밑줄 친 우리말에 해당하는 영어를 쓰시오. (괄호 안의 표현을 활용할 것)

> When my parents keep asking me about my friends, <u>그들은 내 신경을 건드린다.</u> (get/nerves) and I often lose my temper. I don't know why I get angry so easily.

➡ _____

03 다음 영영풀이에 해당하는 단어를 고르시오.

> unhappy because you are alone or do not have anyone to talk to

① lonely   ② only
③ lunar   ④ least
⑤ possibly

04 다음 대화의 빈칸에 들어가기에 적절한 것은?

> B: Have you seen this movie?
> G: Yes, I have. It's one of the best movies I've ever seen.

B: You seem to like it a lot. To me, it's just an old movie.
G: How can you possibly say that? In my view, it is just _____.

① wonderful   ② sad   ③ boring
④ worried   ⑤ long

Conversation

05 다음 대화의 순서가 바르게 배열된 것을 고르시오.

> G: Have you read this book?
> (A) Is it? In my opinion, it's a sad story.
> (B) Well, it could be.
> (C) Yes, I have. The story is very scary.

① (A) – (C) – (B)   ② (B) – (A) – (C)
③ (B) – (C) – (A)   ④ (C) – (A) – (B)
⑤ (C) – (B) – (A)

06 다음 대화의 빈칸에 들어가기에 <u>어색한</u> 것은?

> A: We are now third graders. This year is very important!
> B: _____ What should we do to make this year special?
> A: In my opinion, we should make more friends.
> B: You're right. I think it's also important to read a lot of books.

① You can say that again!
② That's right.
③ I think so, too.
④ I agree.
⑤ Why do you think so?

[07~08] 다음 대화를 읽고 물음에 답하시오.

> B: We are now third graders. This year is very important!
> G: You can say that again! What should we do to make this year special?
> B: In my _____, we should make more friends.
> G: You're right. I think it's also important to read a lot of books.

07 위 대화의 빈칸에 다음 영영풀이에 해당하는 단어를 쓰시오.

> your idea or belief about a particular subject

➡ _____

08 위 대화의 내용과 일치하는 것은?

① The boy and the girl are in the same class.
② The boy and the girl are in the same school.
③ The boy and the girl are in the same grade.
④ The boy and the girl live in the same village.
⑤ The boy and the girl have different ideas.

09 다음 대화에서 어법상 어색한 것을 찾아 고치시오.

> B: Have you seen this movie?
> G: Yes, I did. It's one of the best movies I've ever seen.
> B: You seem to like it a lot. To me, it's just an old movie.
> G: How can you possibly say that? In my view, it is just wonderful.

➡ _____

[10~12] 다음 대화를 읽고 물음에 답하시오.

> G: Did you hear that a new ice cream store opened last week?
> B: (ⓐ) Sure. (A)I have already been there. (ⓑ)
> G: Have you? (ⓒ)
> B: The ice cream was great. (ⓓ)
> G: How was the price?
> B: Well, it was very high. (ⓔ) I was not happy about it.

10 밑줄 친 (A)와 현재완료의 용법이 같은 것은?

① How often have you met him?
② She has done the work already.
③ He has lived in this house for five years.
④ She has lost her watch.
⑤ I have known him for a long time.

11 ⓐ~ⓔ 중에서 다음 문장이 들어가기에 적절한 곳은?

> How was it?

① ⓐ   ② ⓑ   ③ ⓒ   ④ ⓓ   ⑤ ⓔ

12 위 대화를 읽고 대답할 수 없는 것은?

① What are they talking about?
② Who has been to the new ice cream store?
③ How was the ice cream?
④ Is the boy satisfied with the price?
⑤ When does the new ice cream store open?

Grammar

13 다음 빈칸에 들어가기에 적절한 것은?

> 그 도시에서, 그는 Academy라고 불리는 학교를 세웠고, 그것은 그리스 세계 전역에 걸쳐 유명하게 되었다.
>
> ➡ At the city, he founded a school called the Academy, _____ became famous throughout the Greek world.

① who   ② whom   ③ which
④ that   ⑤ what

14 다음 중 빈칸에 들어갈 말이 나머지와 <u>다른</u> 것은?

① It's generous _____ you to say so.
② It was difficult _____ us to climb the tree.
③ Is it okay _____ me to use this computer?
④ It is impossible _____ him to move chairs.
⑤ It is important _____ him to listen to others.

15 다음 중 어법상 <u>어색한</u> 문장은?

① He called Dorothy, who didn't answer.
② Carl invented the machine, that made him rich.
③ They moved to China, where their baby was born.
④ I met my wife in 2000, when I was fifteen years old.
⑤ She likes this restaurant, which is popular for its spaghetti.

16 다음 문장의 빈칸에 들어갈 말이 바르게 짝지어진 것은?

> It is _____ dark _____ them to play soccer.

① so – of   ② so – for   ③ too – for
④ too – of   ⑤ very – for

17 다음 중 밑줄 친 부분을 생략할 수 있는 문장은?

① The car <u>which</u> is parked in front of the house looks nice.
② The man <u>who</u> is kicking the ball is the new coach.
③ This is the bag <u>that</u> his mother bought him.
④ Look at the star <u>which</u> shines in the night sky.
⑤ First read this book, <u>which</u> will tell you how to use the machine.

18 다음 우리말을 '가주어 It, 진주어, 의미상의 주어'를 이용하여 영작할 때 네 번째 오는 단어는?

> 그들이 영어 공부를 하는 것은 쉽다.
> (to study, easy, for them)

① it   ② is   ③ them
④ easy   ⑤ for

19 다음 빈칸에 들어갈 말로 알맞은 것은?

> Many students were late for class, _____ made the teacher angry.

① who   ② what   ③ that
④ where   ⑤ which

Reading

[20~23] 다음 글을 읽고 물음에 답하시오.

My older brother, who entered university this year, is @the golden child. He is a perfect son at home and a perfect student at school.

[A] I feel pleased when he thanks me for my help and appreciates my fashion sense. It is not always difficult for me to live with the perfect brother, and I believe in "every man for his own trade."

[B] He has no eye for fashion, and I always help him whenever he has a hard time choosing clothes for a date.

[C] Needless to say, it is really stressful to have such a shining brother. Well, in fact, he is not perfect and is poor at one thing that I am great at.

Minsu, Korea

20 자연스러운 글이 되도록 [A]~[C]를 바르게 배열한 것은?

① [A]-[C]-[B]　　② [B]-[A]-[C]
③ [B]-[C]-[A]　　④ [C]-[B]-[A]
⑤ [C]-[A]-[B]

21 민수가 형을 밑줄 친 @와 같이 표현하는 이유를 위 글에서 찾아 쓰시오.

➡ _____

_____

22 What is the one thing that Minsu's brother poor at? Use the word 'has.' (6 words)

➡ _____

23 다음 중 위 글의 내용과 일치하지 <u>않는</u> 것은?

① Minsu's brother is a university student.
② Minsu's brother is older than Minsu.
③ Minsu feels stressed to have a perfect brother.
④ Minsu always has a hard time choosing clothes for a date.
⑤ Minsu's brother appreciates Minsu's fashion sense.

[24~27] 다음 글을 읽고 물음에 답하시오.

I often ask myself (A)_____ I get along with my family members, and more often than not, I'm not sure (B)_____ I really do. For one thing, they bother me all the time. My sister comes into my room without my permission and shouts at me to wake up (C)_____ Sunday mornings. Next, Mom asks me to walk the dog, and then Dad tells me to clean my room. They keep getting (D)_____ my nerves until I get angry at them. But I always end up loving them because they have been with me at my worst, still stick by me now, and will continue to do so in the future.

Kamala, the U.S.A

24 빈칸 (A)와 (B)에 공통으로 들어갈 말로 가장 적절한 것은?

① while　　② although　　③ as
④ whether　　⑤ that

25 빈칸 (C)와 (D)에 들어갈 말이 바르게 짝지어진 것은?

① in – on
② at – in
③ on – on
④ in – in
⑤ at – at

26 다음 중 위 글에서 찾아볼 수 <u>없는</u> 것은?

① Kamala's mom asking her to walk the dog
② Kamala's sister shouting at Kamala to wake up
③ Kamala feeling bothered by her family members
④ Kamala's dad asking her to clean her room
⑤ Kamala allowing her sister to come into her room

27 How does Kamala's sister bother her? Answer in English with a full sentence.

➡ _____

_____

_____

[28~29] 다음 글을 읽고 물음에 답하시오.

> My Family in Twenty Years
>
> Kim Nara
>
> This is my family in twenty years.
> Here comes my husband,
> (A)_____ is very good at cooking.
> There go my three kids,
> who never stop talking.
> I love all of my family members,
> who always stick by one another.

28 빈칸 (A)에 알맞은 말을 쓰시오.

➡ _____

29 다음 중 위 시의 내용과 일치하지 <u>않는</u> 것은?

① Nara has three kids.
② Her husband is good at cooking.
③ The children keep talking.
④ Nara loves her family.
⑤ Nara has a small family of four.

✏ 출제율 90%

01 다음 빈칸에 들어갈 말로 적절한 것을 고르시오.

> When she became a teenager, her mood started changing every minute. She would lose her _____ over nothing one moment and happily read a book or watch a film the next.

① phone   ② hope   ③ attitude
④ temper   ⑤ chance

✏ 출제율 100%

02 다음 중 〈보기〉에 있는 단어를 사용하여 자연스러운 문장을 만들 수 없는 것은?

> ┌── 보기 ──
> without   share   made   get along with

① I often ask myself whether I _____ my family members.
② My sister comes into my room _____ my permission.
③ I _____ a room with my sister.
④ My older brother, who _____ university this year, is the golden child.
⑤ A family is _____ of love and tears.

✏ 출제율 90%

03 다음 영영풀이에 해당하는 단어를 고르시오.

> to make someone feel slightly worried, upset, or concerned

① last   ② bother   ③ reply
④ support   ⑤ appreciate

✏ 출제율 90%

04 다음 짝지어진 단어의 관계가 같도록 빈칸에 알맞은 단어를 고르시오.

> bother : irritate = _____ : trouble

① difficulty   ② present   ③ reply
④ order   ⑤ permission

✏ 출제율 90%

05 다음 대화의 빈칸 (A)에 들어갈 말을 고르시오.

> A: What do you like most about your family?
> B: My sister is one of my best friends.
> A: Then, what do you like least about your family?
> B: My mother wakes me up early every morning. (A) _____

① I'm not happy about it.
② I feel good about it.
③ I am always curious about it.
④ I have been worried about it.
⑤ I am satisfied with your idea.

✏ 출제율 95%

06 다음 대화의 순서가 바르게 배열된 것을 고르시오.

> Minsu: Have you seen the movie *Wonder Woman Returns*, Nara?
> Nara: Yes, I have. I think it's wonderful. Isn't it, Minsu?
> (A) You can say that again. What do you think, Namho?
> (B) How can you possibly say that, Namho?
> (C) Well, in my opinion, the story is too old and boring.

① (A) – (C) – (B)   ② (B) – (A) – (C)
③ (B) – (C) – (A)   ④ (C) – (A) – (B)
⑤ (C) – (B) – (A)

[07~09] 다음 대화를 읽고 물음에 답하시오.

> Yujin: Did your family go out to eat last weekend?
>
> Seho: Yes, we did. The food was great, but ⓐ my family is too big and loud.
>
> Yujin: Really? ⓑHow big is it?
>
> Seho: (A)_____ : my grandparents, my mom, my dad, two brothers, and me.
>
> Yujin: That is a big family!
>
> Seho: ⓒWell, I don't like it at all. There's no privacy.
>
> Yujin: I get what you're saying, but to me, it's good to have a big family. ⓓI sometimes feel lonely because I'm an only child.
>
> Seho: Yeah ..., ⓔI see that you mean.

출제율 90%

07 빈칸 (A)에 들어가기에 적절한 것은?

① I have a small family.
② There are seven of us
③ Do you like a big family?
④ What do you think about a big family?
⑤ Your family is really big!

출제율 95%

08 ⓐ~ⓔ 중에서 어법이 어색한 것은?

① ⓐ   ② ⓑ   ③ ⓒ   ④ ⓓ   ⑤ ⓔ

출제율 100%

09 위 대화를 읽고 대답할 수 없는 것은?

① Did Seho's family eat out last weekend?
② What restaurant did Seho's family visit?
③ How big is Seho's family?
④ Does Yujin understand what Seho says?
⑤ Does Yujin have a brother or sister?

[10~11] 다음 대화를 읽고 물음에 답하시오.

> G: Have you read this book?
>
> B: Yes, I have. The story is very scary.
>
> G: (A)_____ In my opinion, it's a sad story.
>
> B: (B) 음, 그럴 수도 있지. (could)

출제율 95%

10 빈칸 (A)에 들어가기에 어색한 것은?

① Do you think so?
② Is it?
③ I have a different idea.
④ Have you read the story?
⑤ I don't agree with you.

출제율 90%

11 (B)의 우리말에 해당하는 영어 문장을 4단어로 쓰시오.

➡ _____

출제율 100%

12 다음 중 어법상 올바른 문장은?

① I bought this book, what you need to read.
② Look at the actor, that is very handsome.
③ I heard the news, which surprised me.
④ She was English, who I knew from her accent.
⑤ I didn't call my mom which made her worried.

13 다음 빈칸에 들어갈 말로 알맞은 것은?

> There is a garden, _____.

① that has beautiful roses
② which is really beautiful
③ what he likes the most
④ what she liked the tree
⑤ which I grow vegetables

14 다음 중 빈칸에 들어갈 말이 나머지 넷과 <u>다른</u> 것은?

① It was difficult _____ them to finish the work on time.
② It is necessary _____ her to exercise every day.
③ It was kind _____ him to tell us the way to the park.
④ It is important _____ us to prepare for the exam.
⑤ It is hard _____ them to clean the room within an hour.

[15~18] 다음 글을 읽고 물음에 답하시오.

I share a room with my sister, who is two years older than me. When she became a teenager, her mood started (A)_____. She would lose her temper over nothing one moment and happily read a book or watch a film the next. It was difficult (B)_____ me to put up with her. Now it's my (C)turn to be a teenager. My sister is still one, but she is getting better. Whenever I lose my temper, she tries to support me. I also understand her better than before because now I know what it feels like to be a teenager. As we get to know each other better, we feel greater love toward each other.   Rachel, Australia

15 다음 중 빈칸 (A)에 들어갈 말로 가장 적절한 것은?

① to be very stable
② changing step by step
③ to be really good
④ to change every minute
⑤ being happy at all times

16 다음 중 빈칸 (B)에 들어갈 말과 <u>다른</u> 말이 들어가는 것은?

① It is safe _____ you to stay here.
② It is necessary _____ her to keep the rules.
③ It is important _____ them to be quiet.
④ It is unwise _____ him to behave like that.
⑤ It is impossible _____ us to do it on time.

17 With whom does Rachel share her room? Answer in English with a full sentence.

➡ _____

18 다음 중 밑줄 친 (C)와 쓰임이 같은 것은?

① It was a surprising turn of events.
② Give the handle a few turns.
③ Make a left turn into the West Street.
④ The leaves will turn brown.
⑤ Whose turn is it to cook?

[19~23] 다음 글을 읽고 물음에 답하시오.

I often ask myself whether I get along with my family members, and more often than not, I'm not sure whether I really do. For one thing, they bother me all the time. My sister comes into my room without my permission and shouts at me to wake ___(A)___ on Sunday mornings. Next, Mom asks me to walk the dog, and then Dad tells me to clean my room. They keep (B)_____ on my nerves until I get angry at them. But I always end ___(C)___ loving them because (D)they have been with me at my worst, still stick by me now, and will continue to do so in the future.

Kamala, the U.S.A.

19 위 글의 빈칸 (A)와 (C)에 공통으로 알맞은 것은?

① to   ② at
③ up   ④ with
⑤ from

20 동사 'get'을 어법에 맞게 빈칸 (B)에 쓰시오.

➡ _____

21 다음 중 밑줄 친 (D)의 의미에 가장 가까운 것은?

① they were with me when I was young
② they support me when I have much difficulty
③ they look down on me as always
④ they make me believe them
⑤ they support each other except me

22 What is Kamala not sure about? Answer in English with a full sentence.

➡ _____

_____

23 다음 중 위 글을 읽고 알 수 있는 것은?

① Kamala has a large family.
② Kamala wants to leave her family.
③ Kamala's dad doesn't like Kamala.
④ Kamala loves her family.
⑤ Kamala always gets up late on Sundays.

[01~02] 다음 대화를 읽고 물음에 답하시오.

B: There are a lot of people here.
G: Yes, here are. It's been 30 minutes since we ordered.
B: The service is so slow. I'm not happy about it.
G: Look at those people over there. They are being served now.
B: Didn't we come in later?
G: Yes, we did. It's not fair.

01 다음 대화의 문맥상 또는 어법상 <u>어색한</u> 것을 찾아 고치시오.

➡ _____

_____

02 Why wasn't the boy satisfied with the service?

➡ Because it was very _____.

03 다음 주어진 단어를 이용해 빈칸을 완성하시오.

She would lose her temper over nothing one moment and _____ read a book or watch a film the next.

➡ _____ (happy)

04 다음 우리말에 맞게 빈칸에 알맞은 말을 쓰시오. (주어진 철자로 시작할 것)

(1) 나는 언제나 결국 그들을 사랑하게 된다.
➡ I always e_____ _____
_____ them.

(2) 가족은 세월의 흐름과 함께 더 강해진다.
➡ A family grows stronger with the p_____ of time.

(3) 그가 나의 패션 감각의 진가를 인정할 때 나는 기분이 좋아진다.
➡ I feel pleased when he a_____ my fashion sense.

05 다음 두 문장을 〈보기〉와 같이 한 문장으로 바꾸어 쓰시오.

┌─ 보기 ┐
Mary had to make a presentation. That made her nervous.
➡ Mary had to make a presentation, which made her nervous.
└─────────┘

(1) I can't find my phone. That happens all the time.
➡ _____

(2) Tom got up late this morning. That made him miss the bus.
➡ _____
_____

06 다음 〈조건〉에 맞게 우리말과 같은 뜻이 되도록 문장을 완성하시오.

┌─ 조건 ┐
1. 주어진 단어를 반드시 이용하되, 필요한 경우 형태를 변화시킬 것. (a / such / strange / to / be / silly)
2. 10단어로 쓸 것.
└─────────┘

그가 그러한 이상한 소문을 믿는 것은 어리석었다.
➡ It _____.

[07~09] 다음 글을 읽고 물음에 답하시오.

What should I do?

Amie: When Mom and Dad keep asking me about my school work, they get on my nerves and I often (A)lose my temper. I don't know why I get angry so easily. What should I do?

Ms. Know-It-All: Many teenagers have the same problem. Try to just let it go and do your work. Then it will get better sooner or later.

07 밑줄 친 (A)의 의미를 위 글에서 찾아 쓰시오.

➡ _____

08 Write the reason why Amie says her mom and dad get on her nerves. Use the phrase 'It's because.'

➡ _____

_____

09 What does Ms. Know-It-All advise Amie to do? Answer in English with a full sentence.

➡ _____

[10~12] 다음 글을 읽고 물음에 답하시오.

I share a room with my sister, who is two years older than me. When she became a teenager, (A)her mood started changing every minute. She would lose her temper over nothing one moment and happily read a book or watch a film the next. (B)나는 언니를 견디기 힘들었다. Now it's my turn to be a teenager. My sister is still one, but she is getting better. Whenever I lose my temper, she tries to support me. I also understand her better than before because now I know what it feels like to be a teenager. As we get to know each other better, we feel greater love toward each other.

Rachel, Australia

10 밑줄 친 (A)를 구체적으로 설명하는 말을 위 글에서 찾아 쓰시오.

➡ _____

_____

_____

11 주어진 단어를 포함하여 총 10개의 단어로 밑줄 친 우리말 (B)를 영어로 쓰시오.

(it / put / difficult / to)

➡ _____

12 When does Rachel's sister try to support her? Answer in English with a full sentence.

➡ _____

_____

01 다음 대화의 빈칸에 주어진 (A)와 (B)의 어구를 이용하여 질문에 적절한 대답을 완성하시오.

(A)	(B)
• develop	• responsibility
• learn	• confidence
• build	• about a new culture

A: I ran a race last year.
B: How did you like it?
A: I liked it a lot. It helped me _____ .

02 다음 빈칸에 관계대명사를 이용하여 우리말과 같도록 영어로 쓰시오.

Q : Who do you want to thank for what?
A: I want to thank Ms. Kim Hana, my English teacher, _____ .
　(저는 저의 영어 선생님 김하나 선생님께 감사드리고 싶은데요,)

(1) _____ (선생님께서는 항상 제게 영어를 가르치시려고 열심히 노력하셨어요.)
(2) _____ (선생님께서는 흥미로운 이야기를 종종 해주셔요.)
(3) _____ (선생님께서는 저를 깨우기 위해 가끔 농담을 하십니다.)

03 다음 대화를 참고하여 민호의 시를 완성하시오.

Q : What is your wife like?
A : She has a warm and loving heart.
Q : How many kids do you have? What are they like?
A : I have two kids. They are healthy and smart.
Q : What are your family members like?
A : They are the funniest people in the world.

　My Family in Twenty Years

Kim Minho

This is my family in twenty years.
Here comes my _____, who _____ .
There go my _____, who _____ .
I love all of my family members, who _____ .

단원별 모의고사

01 빈칸에 알맞은 단어를 〈보기〉에서 골라 쓰시오.

┌─ 보기 ─┐
angry walk get together at my worst
└─────┘

(1) Next, Mom asks me to _____ the dog, and then Dad tells me to clean my room.

(2) They keep getting on my nerves until I get _____ at them.

(3) They have been with me _____.

(4) Family members living in different cities and states _____ to enjoy turkey and vegetables for dinner.

02 다음 빈칸에 들어갈 말로 적절한 것을 고르시오.

> Well, in fact, my older brother is not perfect and is poor at one thing that I am great at. He _____ fashion.

① has no eye for
② has a nose at
③ gives hands to
④ has ears for
⑤ has an emotion of

03 다음 주어진 단어를 이용해 빈칸을 완성하시오.

> My older brother is a perfect son at home and a perfect student at school. Needless to say, it is really _____ to have such a shining brother.

➡ _____ (stress)

[04~06] 다음 대화를 읽고 물음에 답하시오.

B: There are a lot of people here.
G: Yes, here are. It's been 30 minutes before we ordered.
B: The service is so slow. I'm not happy about it.
G: Look at those people over there. They are being served now.
B: Didn't we come in earlier?
G: Yes, we did. _____

04 위 대화의 문맥상 또는 어법상 어색한 문장을 찾아 알맞게 고치시오.

➡ _____

_____

05 위 대화의 빈칸에 들어가기에 적절한 것은?

① It looks very good.
② How delicious it looks!
③ They are working very hard.
④ What do you want to have?
⑤ It's not fair.

06 위 대화를 읽고 대답할 수 없는 것은?

① Where are they at the moment?
② What are they doing now?
③ Why aren't they happy now?
④ What have they ordered?
⑤ How long have they been waiting?

07 다음 설문 조사의 내용과 일치하는 것은?

W: People often say, "I'm not happy about my family." But we have a different story. We asked 2,000 people, "With whom do you feel happiest?" More than half of them feel happiest when they are with their family. The second-largest number of people are happiest with their friends. Interestingly, around 13% of the people we asked feel happiest when alone.

① More than 2,000 people answered the question.
② More than 1,000 people feel happiest when they are with their family.
③ About 1,000 people are happiest when they are with their friends.
④ About 130 people feel happiest when alone.
⑤ The question was "Are you happy with your family?"

[08~09] 다음 대화를 읽고 물음에 답하시오.

G: Did you hear that a new ice cream store opened last week?
B: Sure. I have already been there.
G: Have you? How was it?
B: The ice cream was great.
G: How was the price?
B: Well, it was very cheap. I was not happy about it.

08 위 대화에서 문맥상 어색한 단어를 하나 찾아 고치시오.

➡ _____

09 Which one is true about the dialogue?

① The girl has been to the ice cream store.
② The boy didn't know about the ice cream store.
③ The girl is satisfied with the ice cream store.
④ The boy wasn't satisfied with the price of the ice cream.
⑤ The girl wants to buy a big size of ice cream.

[10~12] 다음 대화를 읽고 물음에 답하시오.

Minsu: Have you seen the movie *Wonder Woman Returns*, Nara? (ⓐ)
Nara: Yes, I have. (ⓑ) I think it's wonderful. (ⓒ)
Minsu: (A)You can say that again. (ⓓ) What do you think, Namho?
Namho: Well, in my opinion, the story is too old and boring. (ⓔ)
Nara: How can you possibly say that, Namho?

10 밑줄 친 (A) 대신 쓸 수 있는 것은?

① I think it's old and boring.
② So am I.
③ Me, neither.
④ I agree with you.
⑤ How about you?

11 ⓐ~ⓔ 중에서 다음 문장이 들어가기에 적절한 곳은?

Isn't it, Minsu?

① ⓐ　　② ⓑ　　③ ⓒ　　④ ⓓ　　⑤ ⓔ

12 위 대화의 내용과 일치하지 <u>않는</u> 것은?

① Minsu has ever seen the movie.
② Minsu thinks the movie is good.
③ Namho agrees with Minsu about the movie.
④ Nara isn't satisfied with Namho's thought.
⑤ Nara thinks the movie is wonderful.

13 다음 문장의 밑줄 친 It과 쓰임이 같은 것은?

> It is difficult for him to repair the car.

① It will be very hot today.
② It takes three hours to get there.
③ It's his brother's new phone.
④ It's important to save energy.
⑤ It's ten miles from here to the station.

14 다음 빈칸에 들어갈 말이 나머지와 <u>다른</u> 것은?

① I met Ms. Nam, _____ taught me science last year.
② He showed me a T-shirt, _____ was the same as mine.
③ My favorite book is *Martian*, _____ was written by Andy Weir.
④ She is wearing Kimono, _____ is a traditional Japanese dress.
⑤ The new theater, _____ can hold 300 people, will be opened soon.

15 다음 두 문장이 같은 뜻이 되도록 빈칸을 완성하시오.

> I went to the Seoul National Science Museum. But it was closed.
> = I went to the Seoul National Science Museum, _____ _____ closed.

16 다음 〈보기〉에서 어법상 올바른 문장을 <u>모두</u> 고른 것은?

> ─── 보기 ───
> ⓐ She likes snakes, that surprises me.
> ⓑ Mr. Kim has a son who live in New York.
> ⓒ Eric finished his project, and it made him happy.
> ⓓ She came to class early today, which was very unusual.

① ⓐ
② ⓑ, ⓒ
③ ⓒ, ⓓ
④ ⓐ, ⓒ, ⓓ
⑤ ⓑ, ⓒ, ⓓ

17 다음 우리말을 주어와 동사가 포함된 완전한 문장으로 영작하시오. (단, 괄호 안에 주어진 단어를 사용하여 12단어로 영작하고 필요시 변형할 것)

> 내가 그 일을 끝내도록 네가 도와주다니 너는 사려 깊구나. (considerate, to finish)

➡ _____

[18~21] 다음 글을 읽고 물음에 답하시오.

I share a room with my sister, (A)<u>and she is</u> two years older than me. When she became a teenager, her mood started changing every minute. She would lose her temper over nothing one moment and happily read a book or watch a film the next. It was difficult for me to put up with her. (B)<u>Now it's my turn to be a teenager.</u> My sister is still one, but she is getting better. Whenever I lose my temper, she tries to support me. I also understand her better than before because now I know what it feels like to be a teenager. As we get to know each other better, we feel greater love toward each other.   Rachel, Australia

18 밑줄 친 (A)를 하나의 단어로 표현하시오.

➡ _____

19 밑줄 친 (B)의 의미로 가장 적절한 것은?

① Now I will have my best time.
② Now I am free from her.
③ Now I will get back at her.
④ Now nobody can say anything.
⑤ Now I also have strange mood changes.

20 다음 중 위 글을 읽고 답할 수 있는 것은?

① How old is Rachel's sister?
② When did Rachel become a teenager?
③ What does Rachel's sister try to do whenever Rachel gets angry?
④ Why does Rachel share her room with her sister?
⑤ Who gets on Rachel's nerves?

21 How is Rachel's sister now? Answer in English with four words.

➡ _____

[22~25] 다음 글을 읽고 물음에 답하시오.

My older brother, who entered university this year, is the golden child. ① He is a perfect son at home and a perfect student at school. ② Needless to say, it is really stressful to have such a shining brother. ③ Well, in fact, he is not perfect and is poor at one thing that I am great at. ④ I feel pleased when he thanks me for my help and appreciates my fashion sense. ⑤ It is not always difficult for me to live with the perfect brother, and I believe in "(A)_____."

Minsu, Korea

22 빈칸 (A)에 들어갈 말로 가장 적절한 것은?

① birds of a feather flock together
② there is no place like home
③ look before you leap
④ every man for his own trade
⑤ like father like son

23 ①~⑤ 중 주어진 문장이 들어가기에 가장 적절한 곳은?

He has no eye for fashion, and I always help him whenever he has a hard time choosing clothes for a date.

①　　②　　③　　④　　⑤

24 다음은 민수의 형이 민수에게 보낸 편지의 일부이다. 글의 내용에 맞게 빈칸에 알맞은 말을 쓰시오.

Dear brother,
I'm happy that you have _____ _____ _____ _____ _____.
Thank you for helping me when I _____ _____ _____ _____ choosing clothes.

25 다음 중 위 글의 내용과 일치하는 것은?

① Minsu is a college student.
② Minsu has a poor taste in fahsion.
③ Minsu's brother is loved by everyone.
④ Minsu's brother thinks it is easy to choose clothes.
⑤ Minsu wants not to live with his brother.

Lesson 2

Foods from Around the World

 의사소통 기능

- 만족하는지 묻기
  How do you like it?
- 칭찬에 답하기
  I'm glad you like it.

 언어 형식

- It ~ that 강조 구문
  It was in Central America that corn was originally grown.

- '주어+동사+목적어+목적격보어' 구문
  They thought popcorn a symbol of good health and goodwill.

교과서
Words & Expressions

Key Words

- **ancient** [éinʃənt] 형 고대의
- **ash** [æʃ] 명 재
- **base** [beis] 명 기초, 기본 (재료)
- **bloom** [blu:m] 동 꽃이 피다
- **bowl** [boul] 명 (우묵한) 그릇, 사발
- **cave** [keiv] 명 동굴
- **decoration** [dèkəréiʃən] 명 장식
- **delicious** [dilíʃəs] 형 맛있는
- **dynasty** [dáinəsti] 명 왕조
- **electric** [iléktik] 형 전기의
- **emperor** [émpərə] 명 황제
- **empire** [émpaiər] 명 제국
- **finally** [fáinəli] 부 마침내, 결국
- **flowery** [fláuəri] 형 꽃무늬의
- **freshly** [fréʃli] 부 갓 ~한, 새롭게
- **get** [get] 동 받다, 얻다
- **goodwill** [gùdwíl] 명 친선, 호의
- **grow** [grow] 동 재배하다 (**grow–grew–grown**)
- **historian** [histɔ́:riən] 명 역사가, 사학자
- **imagine** [imǽdʒin] 동 상상하다
- **inventor** [invéntər] 명 발명가
- **look** [luk] 동 ~하게 보이다, ~처럼 보이다
- **marriage** [mǽridʒ] 명 결혼, 결혼 생활
- **Native Americans** 아메리카 원주민
- **noodle** [nú:dl] 명 국수

- **once** [wʌns] 부 (과거의) 이전에, 한때
- **origin** [ɔ́:rədʒin] 명 기원
- **originally** [ərídʒənli] 부 원래, 최초에
- **pan** [pæn] 명 냄비
- **pleased** [pli:zd] 형 기쁜, 만족해하는
- **pop** [pɑp] 동 펑하고 터뜨리다, 불쑥 나타나다
- **popcorn popper** 팝콘을 튀기는 기계[사람]
- **popper** [pɑ́pər] 명 뻥뻥 소리를 내는 것, 팝콘을 만드는 사람
- **popular** [pɑ́pjulər] 형 인기 있는, 유명한
- **pot-shaped** 형 항아리 모양의
- **protect** [prətékt] 동 보호하다
- **seed** [si:d] 명 씨앗
- **serve** [sə:rv] 동 (음식을) 제공하다, 시중들다
- **share** [ʃɛər] 동 공유하다, 함께 나누다
- **slice** [slais] 명 조각
- **snack** [snæk] 명 간식
- **sneakers** [sní:kərz] 명 밑창이 고무로 된 운동화
- **sour** [sauər] 형 신 맛이 나는
- **spicy** [spáisi] 형 매운, 향신료를 넣은
- **spirit** [spírit] 명 영혼, 정령
- **statue** [stǽtʃu:] 명 조각상
- **stir** [stə:r] 동 젓다, 섞다
- **tasty** [téisti] 형 맛있는
- **throw** [θrou] 동 던지다 (**throw–threw–thrown**)

Key Expressions

- **as well as** ~에 더하여
- **be good at** ~을 잘하다, ~에 능숙하다
- **be interested in** ~에 관심이 있다
- **be made from** ~로 만들어지다
- **be mixed with** ~와 섞이다
- **be served with** ~와 함께 제공되다
- **before long** 오래지 않아, 얼마 후
- **believe it or not** 믿기 힘들겠지만
- **better still** 더 좋게는
- **by oneself** 혼자서
- **by the way** 그런데
- **come up with** ~을 생각해 내다

- **for ages** 오랫동안
- **Here you go.** 여기 있습니다.
- **in addition to** ~ 이외에도
- **in high demand** 수요가 많은
- **in the old days** 옛날에
- **long before** ~하기 오래전에
- **look forward to** ~을 기대하다, ~을 고대하다
- **not ~ at all** 전혀 ~ 아닌
- **not only ~ but also** ~뿐만 아니라 …도
- **pick out** 집어내다
- **tell fortunes for** ~에 대하여 점을 치다

Word Power

※ 서로 비슷한 뜻을 가진 어휘

- □ **believe** 믿다 – **trust** 신뢰하다
- □ **cool** 멋진 – **marvelous** 놀라운
- □ **decoration** 장식 – **ornament** 장식
- □ **freshly** 갓 ~한, 새롭게 – **newly** 새롭게
- □ **surprising** 놀라운 – **amazing** 놀라운
- □ **base** 기초 – **foundation** 기초

- □ **bloom** 꽃이 피다 – **blossom** 꽃피다
- □ **country** 국가 – **nation** 국가
- □ **delicious** 맛있는 – **tasty** 맛있는
- □ **finally** 마침내, 결국 – **eventually** 결국
- □ **origin** 기원 – **root** 근원

※ 서로 반대의 뜻을 가진 어휘

- □ **ancient** 고대의 ↔ **modern** 현대의
- □ **glad** 기쁜 ↔ **sad** 슬픈
- □ **pleased** 기쁜 ↔ **unpleased** 기쁘지 않은

- □ **arrive** 도착하다 ↔ **depart** 떠나다
- □ **goodwill** 친선, 호의 ↔ **hostility** 적개심
- □ **protect** 보호하다 ↔ **harm** 해를 주다

※ 동사 – 명사

- □ **decorate** 장식하다 – **decoration** 장식
- □ **invent** 발명하다 – **invention** 발명
- □ **arrive** 도착하다 – **arrival** 도착
- □ **originate** 유래하다 – **origin** 기원

- □ **imagine** 상상하다 – **imagination** 상상
- □ **protect** 보호하다 – **protection** 보호
- □ **believe** 믿다 – **belief** 믿음
- □ **marry** 결혼하다 – **marriage** 결혼

※ 동사 – 형용사

- □ **imagine** 상상하다 – **imaginative** 상상력이 풍부한
- □ **protect** 보호하다 – **protective** 방어적인

- □ **invent** 발명하다 – **inventive** 창의적인

English Dictionary

□ **ancient** 고대의
→ of or from a long ago 오래전의

□ **arrive** 도착하다
→ to get to the place you are going to 가려는 장소에 다다르다

□ **ash** 재
→ the soft grey powder that remains after burning
연소 후에 남은 부드러운 회색 가루

□ **bowl** (우묵한) 그릇, 사발
→ a wide round container that is open at the top
위가 열린 넓고 둥근 그릇

□ **cave** 동굴
→ a large natural hole in the side of a cliff
절벽 측면에 나 있는 자연적인 큰 구멍

□ **dynasty** 왕조
→ a period of time when a particular family ruled a country 한 가문이 한 나라를 지배한 시기

□ **goodwill** 친선, 호의
→ kind feelings towards or between people
사람들에 대한 친절한 감정

□ **noodle** 국수 (한 가락)
→ a long thin piece of food made from a mixture of flour, water, and eggs
밀가루, 물, 달걀의 반죽으로 만들어진 음식의 긴 가락

□ **origin** 기원
→ the place or situation in which something begins to exist 무엇이 존재하기 시작한 장소나 상황

□ **pan** 냄비
→ a round metal container that you use for cooking
요리를 위해 사용하는 둥근 금속 용기

□ **pop** 불쑥 나타나다
→ to come suddenly or unexpectedly out
갑자기 또는 예상치 못하게 나타나다

□ **sneakers** 운동화
→ a type of light soft shoe with a rubber sole
고무바닥을 가진 가볍고 부드러운 신발

□ **statue** 조각상
→ an image of a person or animal that is made in solid material
단단한 재료로 만든 사람이나 동물의 형상

01 다음 짝지어진 단어의 관계가 같도록 빈칸에 알맞은 단어를 고르시오.

finally : eventually - _____ : foundation

① slice   ② base   ③ seed
④ spirit   ⑤ cave

02 다음 빈칸에 들어갈 말로 적절한 것을 고르시오.

_____ Native Americans, many other people around the world enjoyed this tasty snack.

① In addition to   ② Owing to
③ As a result   ④ Because of
⑤ For example

03 다음 중 〈보기〉에 있는 단어를 사용하여 자연스러운 문장을 만들 수 없는 것은?

┌─ 보기 ─┐
goodwill   popular
flowery   long before
└────────┘

① It is one of the most _____ snacks around the world.
② _____ it or not, poppers were in high demand.
③ The game was to catch and enjoy the _____ snacks.
④ They thought popcorn a symbol of good health and _____.
⑤ The Chinese made popcorn _____ Columbus arrived in the West Indies.

04 다음 주어진 문장의 (A)와 (B)에 들어가기에 적절한 것으로 짝지어진 것은?

• Cake is made (A)_____ flour, milk and eggs.
• I'm trying to come up (B)_____ some ideas.

　(A)　(B)　　　　(A)　(B)
① from – with　　② with – of
③ for – from　　④ by – for
⑤ with – from

서답형
05 다음 영영풀이에 해당하는 단어를 쓰시오.

• to get to the place you are going to

➡ _____

06 다음 중 밑줄 친 부분의 뜻풀이가 바르지 않은 것은?

① This snack is often <u>served</u> with green tea. (제공된다)
② The <u>base</u> of this sweet cake is egg. (지하실)
③ Corn was <u>originally</u> grown in Central America. (원래)
④ They popped and <u>bloomed</u> into white flowers. (피어났다)
⑤ They were protected by popping <u>spirits</u>. (정령)

07 다음 중 밑줄 친 부분의 쓰임이 어색한 것은?

① My uncle is an art <u>historian</u>.
② This rule applies to parents <u>as long as</u> children.
③ <u>By the way</u>, are you free for dinner tomorrow evening?
④ You should not drive a car <u>by yourself</u>.
⑤ I don't like it <u>at all</u>.

01 다음 주어진 단어를 이용해 빈칸을 완성하시오.

• Thomas Edison had an _____ mind.

➡ _____(invent)

02 다음 짝지어진 단어의 관계가 같도록 빈칸에 알맞은 말을 쓰시오.

ancient : modern = _____ : depart

03 빈칸에 알맞은 단어를 〈보기〉에서 골라 쓰시오.

┌── 보기 ──────────────────┐
as well   freshly   forward to   seeds
└────────────────────────┘

(1) Don't you love the smell of _____ made popcorn?
(2) Corn _____ were thrown on hot stones over a fire.
(3) Native Americans used popcorn for decoration _____.
(4) I'm looking _____ the New Year's Eve party.

04 다음 밑줄 친 단어와 의미가 같은 단어를 쓰시오. (주어진 철자로 시작할 것)

• Fruits in season are tasty and good for your health.

➡ d_____

05 다음 영영풀이에 해당하는 말을 주어진 철자로 시작하여 쓰고, 알맞은 것을 골라 문장을 완성하시오. (문장에 쓸 때는, 필요하면 적절한 형태로 바꾸어 쓰시오.)

• s_____ : an image of a person or animal that is made in solid material
• n_____ : a long thin piece of food made from a mixture of flour, water, and eggs
• o_____ : the place or situation in which something begins to exist

(1) She wants to tell you the _____ of chocolate.
(2) I'm interested in Chinese _____.
(3) We make corn decorations for the _____ of the god of rain.

06 다음 빈칸에 공통으로 들어가기에 적절한 단어를 쓰시오.

A: What is Nara _____ at?
B: She is _____ at making hot chocolate.

07 다음 우리말에 맞게 빈칸에 알맞은 말을 쓰시오.

(1) 그는 건강할 뿐만 아니라 부유하다.
➡ He is _____ _____ healthy but also wealthy.
(2) 믿건 말건 그건 사실이에요.
➡ Believe _____ _____ _____ , it is true.
(3) 그 자동차들은 자동차 업계에서 수요가 높다.
➡ The cars are in high _____ in the car industry.
(4) 고대에는, 사람들이 나무와 바위에도 정령이 있다고 믿었다.
➡ In _____ times, people believed that even trees and rocks had spirits.

Conversation

1 만족하는지 묻기

How do you like it? 그거 어떠니?

- "How do you like it?"은 어떤 대상에 대한 느낌, 평가, 의견 등을 묻는 표현이다. 그에 대한 긍정적인 응답으로는 "I like it a lot.", "I just love it.", "I love it.", "It is great.", "It is nice.", "It's good.", "It wasn't bad." 등이 있고, 부정적인 응답으로는 "Well, I don't like it.", "Well, I think it's not good enough.", "It isn't interesting." 등이 있다.

- "How do you like ~?"는 '~는 어떠니?'라는 뜻으로 어떤 것에 대한 의견을 물을 때 쓰며, "Are you satisfied with ~?"로 만족 여부를 물을 수도 있다. "How do you like ~?"는 '(음식 등을) 어떻게 해드릴까요?'의 의미를 나타내기도 한다. "Are you satisfied[happy] with ~?"로 물으면 "Yes, I am. / No, I'm not."으로 대답할 수 있다.

만족이나 불만족에 관해 묻기

- How do you like it? 그것이 마음에 드니? / • Do you like it? 너는 그것을 좋아하니?
- Are you satisfied[happy] with it? 그것이 만족스럽니?
- What do you think of ~? / What is your opinion of[on] ~? ~을 어떻게 생각하니?

만족할 때와 만족하지 않을 때의 대답

〈만족할 때의 대답〉
- I like[love] it. 나는 그것을 좋아한다. / • I recommend it. 나는 그것을 추천한다.
- It's terrific[wonderful / excellent / great / impressive]. 굉장히 좋아.

〈만족하지 않을 때의 대답〉
- It wasn't bad. 나쁘지는 않았어.
- I don't like[love] it (that much). 나는 그것을 그리 좋아하지 않아.
- It's not for me. / It was terrible. 그것은 나에게는 어울리지 않아. / 그것은 끔찍했어.

핵심 Check

1. 다음 대화의 밑줄 친 부분 대신 쓸 수 있는 것은?

> B: I got these sneakers as a birthday present!
> G: How cool they look! <u>How do you like them?</u>
> B: I just love them.

① Are you satisfied with them? ② Are you worried about them?
③ Are you sure about them? ④ Would they like you?
⑤ Are they happy with you?

② 칭찬에 답하기

I'm glad you like it. 네가 좋아하니 기뻐.

■ 상대방이 만족하거나 칭찬을 할 때는 "I'm glad you like it."이라고 말한다. 자신이 한 일이나 제공한 물건에 대해 상대방이 칭찬을 하는 경우 그에 대해 응답하는 표현이다. 비슷한 뜻을 가진 표현으로는 "I'm happy you like it.", "I'm pleased you love it." 등이 있다.

칭찬하기

다음과 같은 표현들로 상대방을 칭찬할 수 있다
- (Very) Good! / Good for you! / Great! / Excellent! / Perfect!
- (You did a) Good job! / Well done!

칭찬에 답하기

칭찬을 해준 사람에게 고맙다고 말하는 표현으로 아래와 같은 것들이 있다.
- I'm glad you like it. 네가 좋아한다니 기뻐.
- I appreciate the compliment. 칭찬해 주어서 고마워.
- It's nice of you to say so. 그렇게 말해주니 친절하구나.

기쁜 감정을 나타내는 형용사

glad (기쁜), happy (행복한), pleased (기쁜), delighted (아주 기뻐하는), excited (신나는), joyful (아주 기뻐하는), satisfied (만족스러운)

핵심 Check

2. 다음 밑줄 친 말 대신 쓸 수 있는 것은?

> A: How do you like my pizza?
> B: I love it. How yummy!
> A: Thanks. <u>I'm very glad you love it.</u>

① It's nice of you to say so.
② I'm pleased with the pizza.
③ Would you try some?
④ How are you pleased with it?
⑤ I think it's good enough.

Listen & Speak 1 A-1

G: ❶You've got a new phone, haven't you?

B: Yes, I have.

G: ❷How do you like it?

B: I don't like it at all.

| |
소녀: 너 새 전화기 생겼구나. 그렇지 않니?
소년: 응, 그래.
소녀: 그거 어때?
소년: 전혀 마음에 들지 않아.

❶ have got은 have와 같은 의미로 "가지다"는 뜻을 나타낸다. haven't you?는 앞의 문장이 긍정의 평서문이므로 부정의 부가의문문으로 사용되었다.

❷ How do you like ~?는 만족이나 불만족에 대해 물어보는 표현으로 What do you think of ~? / What is your opinion of[on] ~? 등의 표현을 사용할 수 있다.

Check(√) True or False

(1) The boy asked the girl whether she liked the new phone.　　T ☐ F ☐

(2) The boy doesn't like his new phone.　　T ☐ F ☐

 Conversation

Nara: ❶Would you like some hot chocolate, Junha?

Junha: Sure, ❷I haven't had it for ages! ... Mmm.

Nara: How do you like it?

Junha: I like it a lot. ❸You are very good at making hot chocolate.

Nara: Thanks. I'm glad you like it. ❹By the way, did you know that chocolate was once called the "drink of the gods"?

Junha: Was it really?

Nara: Yes, chocolate was first enjoyed by the emperor of the Aztec Empire, and it was once called xoco-latl, "drink of the gods".

Junha: That's surprising! Well, thanks for the gods' drink, Nara.

Nara: You are welcome!

나라: 핫 초콜릿 좀 먹을래, 준하야?
준하: 물론이지, 오랫동안 먹지 못했어! … 음.
나라: 어떠니?
준하: 정말 좋아. 너 핫 초콜릿을 만드는 재주가 정말 좋구나.
나라: 고마워. 네가 좋아한다니 기뻐. 그런데, 너 초콜릿이 한때 "신들의 음료"라고 불렸던 것을 아니?
준하: 정말 그랬니?
나라: 응. 초콜릿은 처음에 아즈텍 제국의 황제에 의해 즐겨졌고, 한때 xoco-latl, 즉 "신들의 음료"라고 불렸어.
준하: 그것 놀라운데! 어쨌든, 신들의 음료에 대해 고마워, 나라야.
나라: 천만에!

❶ 상대방에게 음식을 권유할 때 'Would you like (some) 음식?'으로 표현한다.

❷ '계속'의 의미를 나타내는 현재완료시제로, 과거의 한 시점에서 말하는 시점까지 핫 초콜릿을 안 먹었음을 나타낸다.

❸ "be good at"은 '~을 잘하다, ~에 능숙하다'라는 의미이며, 전치사 at 뒤에는 명사구가 와야 하므로 동명사 형태인 making이 쓰였다.

❹ By the way(그런데)는 대화 중 화제를 바꿀 때 쓰인다.

Check(√) True or False

(3) Junha likes the hot chocolate Nara made.　　T ☐ F ☐

(4) Nara told Junha the origin of chocolate.　　T ☐ F ☐

Listen & Speak 1 A-2

B: I got these sneakers ❶as a birthday present!

G: ❷How cool they look! How do you like them?

B: I just love them.

❶ as는 전치사로 "~로"의 뜻이다.
❷ How로 시작하는 감탄문으로 "How+형용사/부사+주어+동사!"의 어순이다.

 Listen & Speak 2 A-1

B: ❶Would you like some soup?

G: Yes, I'd love some.

B: ❷ Here you go. ... How do you like it?

G: It's hot and sweet. I just love it.

B: I'm glad you like it.

❶ 음식을 권유하는 표현으로 '~ 좀 먹어 보실래요?'라는 뜻으로 'Would you like to try+음식?'으로도 쓸 수 있다.
❷ 상대방에게 물건을 건네주면서 "여기 있다."라고 할 때는 쓰는 말이다.

 Listen & Speak 2 A-2

G: ❶Did you make this bowl by yourself?

B: Yes, I did.

G: It looks just wonderful.

B: Thanks. ❷I'm happy you like it.

❶ "by oneself"는 "혼자서"라는 뜻이다.
❷ "I'm glad you like it."과 같은 의미로 칭찬에 대답하는 말이다.

 Listen & Speak 2 A-3

G: How do you like this face painting?

B: I just love it. Thanks.

G: ❶ I'm very pleased you love it.

❶ 상대방의 칭찬이나 감사에 대한 대답으로 "I'm glad you love it." 또는 "I'm happy you love it."과 같은 뜻이다.

 Real Life Task Step 1

W: How do you like the school lunch? ❶What would you like to have for your lunch? We'd like to have your cool ideas on the school

lunch menu. ❷Why don't you visit www.mslunch.ms.kr and answer the questions about your school lunch? ❸We're looking forward to getting your answers.

❶ 상대방의 의향을 물을 때는 What would you like to ~? / What do you want to ~? / What are you going to ~? 등의 표현을 사용한다.
❷ 상대방에게 권유하는 표현으로 제안이나 권유를 나타낼 때는 "Why don't you+동사원형 ~?"으로 나타낸다.
❸ look forward to는 '~을 기대하다, 학수고대하다'라는 의미이다. to는 전치사이므로 명사, 동명사를 목적어로 한다.

 Real Life Task Step 2

A: What do you have ❶on your Monday snack menu?

B: I have ice cream and apple juice. How do you like my menu?

A: That sounds great. ❷I like it a lot.

B: I'm glad you like it.

❶ menu 앞에 전치사 on을 쓴다.
❷ 상대방이 마음에 드는지 묻는 말에 만족을 나타낼 때 쓴다.

 Check My Progress 1

G: You've got a new backpack, Minsu?

B: Yes, I have. This is my birthday present from my mother.

G: ❶How nice of her! How do you like it?

B: ❷I like it a lot. I like the color.

G: Your favorite color is blue, isn't it?

B: Yes, it is.

❶ How로 시작하는 감탄문이다.
❷ 상대방이 만족하는지를 묻는 말에 대하여 만족감을 나타내는 표현이다.

 Check My Progress 2

G: Did you bake all of these ❶by yourself?

B: Yes, I did.

G: They look just wonderful.

B: Thanks. ❷Would you like to try some cake?

G: Sure.

B: How do you like it?

G: I just love this.

B: Thanks. I'm so happy you like it.

❶ "by oneself"는 "혼자서"의 의미이다.
❷ "Would you like to try some ~?"은 음식을 권하는 표현이다.

교과서 확인학습

● 다음 우리말과 일치하도록 빈칸에 알맞은 말을 쓰시오.

Listen & Speak 1 A-1

G: You've _____ a new _____, haven't you?

B: Yes, I _____.

G: _____ do you _____ it?

B: I don't like it _____ _____.

Listen & Speak 1 A-2

B: I _____ these _____ as a birthday _____!

G: _____ cool they look! How do you _____ _____?

B: I _____ _____ them.

Listen & Speak 2 A-1

B: _____ you like _____ soup?

G: Yes, I'd love some.

B: _____ you go. ... How do you _____ it?

G: It's _____ and _____. I just love it.

B: I'm _____ you like _____.

Listen & Speak 2 A-2

G: Did you _____ this bowl _____ _____?

B: Yes, I did.

G: It _____ just _____.

B: Thanks. I'm _____ you _____ it.

Listen & Speak 2 A-3

G: _____ do you like this _____ painting?

B: I just love it. Thanks.

G: I'm very _____ you _____ it.

Conversation

Nara: _____ you _____ some hot _____, Junha?

Junha: _____, I haven't _____ it for _____! ... Mmm.

Nara: How do you like it?

Junha: I like it a _____. You are very _____ _____ making hot chocolate.

해석

소녀: 너 새 전화기 생겼구나, 그렇지 않니?
소년: 응, 그래.
소녀: 그거 어때?
소년: 전혀 마음에 들지 않아.

소년: 나 이 운동화를 생일 선물로 받았어.
소녀: 정말 멋져 보인다! 마음에 드니?
소년: 정말 마음에 들어.

소년: 수프 좀 드시겠어요?
소녀: 네, 좀 먹고 싶어요.
소년: 여기 있습니다. … 어때요?
소녀: 뜨겁고 달콤하네요. 정말 좋습니다.
소년: 좋아하시니 기뻐요.

소녀: 혼자서 이 그릇을 만들었어요?
소년: 응, 그랬어요.
소녀: 정말 멋져 보여요.
소년: 고마워요. 좋아해서 기뻐요.

소녀: 이 페이스 페인팅이 어때요?
소년: 정말 좋아요. 고맙습니다.
소녀: 좋아하셔서 정말 기쁘군요.

나라: 핫 초콜릿 좀 먹을래, 준하야?
준하: 물론이지, 오랫동안 먹지 못했어! … 음.
나라: 어떠니?
준하: 정말 좋아. 너 핫 초콜릿을 만드는 재주가 정말 좋구나.

해석

Nara: _____. I'm _____ you like it. _____ the _____, did you know that chocolate was _____ _____ the "drink of the gods"?

Junha: Was it _____?

Nara: Yes, chocolate was first _____ by the _____ of the Aztec Empire, and it was _____ called xoco-latl, "drink of _____ gods."

Junha: That's surprising! Well, _____ for the gods' drink, Nara.

Nara: You are welcome!

나라: 고마워. 네가 좋아한다니 기뻐. 그런데, 너 초콜릿이 한때 "신들의 음료"라고 불렸던 것을 아니?
준하: 정말 그랬니?
나라: 응, 초콜릿은 처음에 아즈텍 제국의 황제에 의해 즐겨졌고, 한때 xoco-latl, 즉 "신들의 음료"라고 불렸어.
준하: 그것 놀라운데! 어쨌든, 신들의 음료에 대해 고마워, 나라야.
나라: 천만에!

Real Life Task Step 1

W: _____ do you _____ the school lunch? _____ would you like to _____ for your lunch? We'd _____ to have your _____ ideas on the school lunch menu. _____ _____ you visit www.mslunch.ms.kr and _____ the questions about your school lunch? We're _____ _____ to _____ your answers.

여자: 학교 점심은 어떤가요? 점심으로 무엇을 원하나요? 학교 점심 메뉴에 대해 여러분의 좋은 의견을 원합니다. www.mslunch.ms.kr을 방문하여 학교 점심에 대한 질문에 답해 주시겠어요? 여러분의 응답을 고대합니다.

Real Life Task Step 2

A: _____ do you _____ on your Monday _____ menu?

B: I _____ ice cream and _____ juice. How do you _____ my menu?

A: That _____ great. I _____ it a lot.

B: I'm _____ you like it.

A: 월요일 간식 메뉴에 무엇이 있니?
B: 아이스크림과 사과 주스가 있어. 내 메뉴 어때?
A: 그거 멋지네. 정말 좋아.
B: 네가 좋아한다니 기뻐

Check My Progress 1

G: You've _____ a new _____, Minsu?

B: Yes, I have. This is my birthday _____ from my mother.

G: _____ _____ of her! How do you like it?

G: I like it a lot. I like the _____.

G: Your _____ color is blue, isn't it?

B: Yes, it is.

소녀: 민수야, 새 가방 생겼구나?
소년: 응, 그래. 이거 우리 엄마께서 주신 생일 선물이야.
소녀: 네 엄마 정말 친절하시구나! 가방이 어때?
소년: 정말 좋아. 나는 색상이 마음에 들어.
소녀: 네가 가장 좋아하는 색깔은 파란색이지, 그렇지 않니?
소년: 응, 맞아.

Check My Progress 2

G: Did you _____ all of _____ by _____?

B: Yes, I did.

G: They _____ just _____.

B: Thanks. Would you like to _____ some cake?

G: Sure.

B: How _____ you like it?

G: I just love this.

B: Thanks. I'm so _____ you like it.

소녀: 이거 네가 다 직접 구웠니?
소년: 응, 내가 했어.
소녀: 정말 맛있어 보인다.
소년: 고마워. 케이크 좀 먹어 볼래?
소녀: 좋아.
소년: 어때?
소녀: 이거 정말 맛있다.
소년: 고마워. 네가 좋아하니 정말 기뻐.

01 다음 대화의 빈칸에 들어갈 말로 적절하지 <u>않은</u> 것을 고르시오.

> G: You've got a new phone, haven't you?
> B: Yes, I have.
> G: _____
> B: I don't like it at all.

① Are you satisfied with it?

② How do you like it?

③ Are you happy with it?

④ Don't you think so?

⑤ Do you like it?

02 다음 대화의 순서가 바르게 배열된 것을 고르시오.

> (A) How cool they look! How do you like them?
> (B) I got these sneakers as a birthday present!
> (C) I just love them.

① (A) – (C) – (B)　　② (B) – (A) – (C)

③ (B) – (C) – (A)　　④ (C) – (A) – (B)

⑤ (C) – (B) – (A)

[03~04] 다음 대화를 읽고 물음에 답하시오.

> B: <u>수프 좀 드시겠어요?</u> (would, some)
> G: Yes, I'd love some.
> B: Here you go. ... How do you like it?
> G: It's hot and sweet. I just love it.
> B: I'm glad you like it.

03 주어진 단어를 포함하여 밑줄 친 우리말을 영어 쓰시오.

➡

04 위 대화의 내용으로 알 수 있는 것은?

① They are in the living room.

② The boy often has soup.

③ The girl is satisfied with the soup.

④ The boy is not satisfied with the soup.

⑤ The girl isn't good at making soup.

[01~03] 대화를 읽고 물음에 답하시오.

G: You've got a new backpack, Minsu?
B: Yes, I have. This is my birthday present from my mother.
G: How nice of her! (A)How do you like it?
B: I like it a lot. I like the color.
G: Your favorite color is blue, isn't it?
B: Yes, it is.

01 밑줄 친 (A)와 바꾸어 쓰기에 적절한 것은?

① How about you?
② Are you happy with it?
③ What about your mother?
④ Do you think so?
⑤ What makes you think so?

서답형

02 Why do you think the boy likes the backpack?

➡ _____

03 위 대화의 내용과 일치하지 <u>않는</u> 것은?

① 두 사람은 배낭에 대한 이야기를 하고 있다.
② 배낭은 소년의 어머니가 생일선물로 준 것이다.
③ 소녀는 소년이 그 선물에 만족하는지 묻는다.
④ 소녀는 소년이 좋아하는 색을 알고 있었다.
⑤ 소년은 처음에는 그 선물이 마음에 들지 않았다.

[04~06] 다음 대화를 읽고 물음에 답하시오.

G: Did you bake all of these by yourself?
B: Yes, I did.
G: They look just wonderful.
B: _____ . (A)Would you like to try some cake?
G: Sure.
B: How do you like it?
G: I just love this.
B: _____ . I'm so happy you like it.

04 위 대화의 빈칸에 공통으로 들어가기에 적절한 것은?

① Sure   ② Never
③ Sorry   ④ That's right
⑤ Thanks

05 밑줄 친 (A)와 같은 의미로 쓸 수 있는 것은?

① Would you bake some cake?
② How would you like the cake?
③ Are you satisfied with the cake?
④ Would you like some cake?
⑤ How do you like the cake?

06 According the dialogue, which one is TRUE?

① They are in the same school.
② The girl baked the cake by herself.
③ The girl is satisfied with the cake.
④ The girl asks whether the boy likes it.
⑤ The boy and the girl like baking cake.

[07~09] 다음 대화를 읽고 물음에 답하시오.

> **Nara:** Would you like some hot chocolate, Junha?
> **Junha:** Sure, I haven't had it for ages! ... Mmm.
> **Nara:** (A)How do you like it?
> **Junha:** I like it a lot. You are very good at making hot chocolate.
> **Nara:** Thanks. (B)_____ By the way, (C)did you know that chocolate was once called the "drink of the gods"?
> **Junha:** Was it really?

07 밑줄 친 (A) 대신 쓸 수 있는 것은?

① Do you think so?
② Are you happy with it?
③ Have you had it for long?
④ Are you good at making it?
⑤ Do you know what it is?

서답형

08 위 대화의 빈칸 (B)에 주어진 어구를 배열하여 영어로 쓰시오.

> you / I'm / like / it /glad

➡ _____

중요

09 밑줄 친 (C)에 나타난 나라의 의도는?

① She wants to enjoy hot chocolate.
② She wants to tell Junha the origin of chocolate.
③ She wants to ask Junha about the taste of the gods' drink.
④ She wants to know about the Aztec Empire.
⑤ She wants to thank for the gods' drink.

[10~12] 다음 대화를 읽고 물음에 답하시오.

> **Minji:** Your cookies all look tasty.
> **Jinho:** Thanks. (ⓐ) (A)_____ some?
> **Minji:** Thanks, let me try one. (ⓑ)
> **Jinho:** Here you go. ... (ⓒ) How do you like it?
> **Minji:** It's so sweet. (ⓓ)
> **Jinho:** I'm glad you like it. (ⓔ)

10 위 대화의 내용으로 보아, 빈칸 (A)에 들어가기에 적절하지 않은 것은?

① Why don't you try
② Would you like to try
③ Why do you try
④ Would you like
⑤ How about trying

중요

11 ⓐ~ⓔ 중에서 다음 문장이 들어가기에 적절한 곳은?

> I just love it.

① ⓐ   ② ⓑ   ③ ⓒ   ④ ⓓ   ⑤ ⓔ

12 According to the dialogue, which one is NOT true?

① Jinho baked some cookies.
② Jinho asks Minji to try some.
③ Minji asks Jinho if he likes the cookies.
④ Jinho gives Minji a cookie that he has made.
⑤ Minji thinks the cookie is sweet.

[01~03] 다음 대화를 읽고 물음에 답하시오.

Nara: Would you like some hot chocolate, Junha?
Junha: Sure, I haven't had it for ages! ... Mmm.
Nara: How do you like it?
Junha: I like it a lot. (A)너 핫 초콜릿을 만드는 재주가 정말 좋구나. (very, good, making)
Nara: Thanks. I'm glad you like it. By the way, did you know that chocolate was once called the "drink of the gods"?
Junha: Was it really?
Nara: (B)Yes, chocolate was first enjoyed by the ordinary people of the Aztec Empire, and it was once called xoco-latl, "drink of the gods."
Junha: That's surprising! Well, thanks for the gods' drink, Nara.
Nara: You are welcome!

01 주어진 단어를 포함하여 밑줄 친 (A)에 해당하는 영어 문장을 완성하시오.

➡ _____

 밑줄 친 (B)에서 내용상 어색한 단어를 골라 적절한 것으로 바꾸어 쓰시오.

➡ _____

[03~04] 다음 대화를 읽고 물음에 답하시오.

G: You've got a new backpack, Minsu?
B: Yes, I have. This is my birthday present from my mother.
G: (A)네 엄마 정말 친절하시구나!(nice) How do you like it?

B: I like it a lot. I like the color.
G: Your favorite color is blue, (B)_____?
B: Yes, it is.

03 주어진 단어를 포함하여, 밑줄 친 (A)의 우리말에 해당하는 표현을 완성하시오. (4단어)

➡ _____

04 빈칸 (B)에 알맞은 말을 부가의문문으로 완성하시오.

➡ _____

05 What will the students do after listening to this announcement?

W: How do you like the school lunch? What would you like to have for your lunch? We'd like to have your cool ideas on the school lunch menu. Why don't you visit www.mslunch.ms.kr and answer the questions about your school lunch? We're looking forward to getting your answers.

➡ They will visit the Internet site and _____ _____ about school lunch.

06 밑줄 친 표현을 아래와 같이 바꾸어 쓸 때 주어진 철자로 시작하여 빈칸을 완성하시오.

G: You've got a new phone, haven't you?
B: Yes, I have.
G: How do you like it?
B: I don't like it at all.

➡ How do you like it?
= Are you s_____ with it?

Grammar

교과서

① It is[was] ~ that 강조 구문

> **It** was in Central America **that** corn was originally grown.
> 옥수수가 원래 재배된 것은 바로 중앙아메리카에서였다.

- 형태: It is[was] ~that …
  의미: …하는 것은 바로 ~이다.

- 문장의 한 가지 요소를 강조할 때는 "it is[was] ~ that"을 사용하여, 강조하려는 부분을 It is[was]와 that 사이에 두고 나머지 부분을 that 이하에 적어 "…하는 것은 바로 ~이다"라고 해석을 한다. 강조하는 요소에 따라서 that은 사람일 경우 who/whom, 사물이면 which로 바꿔 쓸 수 있다. It 뒤에 오는 be 동사는 문장 전체의 시제에 맞추어 현재시제이면 is, 과거시제이면 was를 쓴다.

  - **A:** Are you going on holiday in July? (너 7월에 휴가를 가니?)

    B: No, **it is** in August **that** I'm going on holiday. (아니, 내가 휴가를 떠나는 건 바로 8월이야.)
  - **A:** Is spring your favorite season? (봄이 네가 가장 좋아하는 계절이야?)

    B: No, **it's** fall **that** I like most. (아니, 내가 가장 좋아하는 것은 바로 가을이야.)

- It is[was] ~ that 강조 구문에서는 that 앞에 놓이는 요소에 초점이 주어진다. 초점이 되는 요소로는 주어, 목적어, 부사(구/절) 등이 있으며 동사는 강조의 요소가 될 수 없다. 의문사의 강조는 "의문사+is it that ~?"의 형태가 된다.

  - Tom will visit his grandmother tomorrow. (Tom은 내일 할머니를 방문할 것이다.)
    → **It** is Tom **that** will visit his grandmother tomorrow. (내일 그의 할머니를 방문하려는 것은 바로 Tom이다.)
    → **It** is his grandmother **that** Tom will visit tomorrow. (Tom이 내일 방문하려는 것은 바로 그의 할머니이다.)
    → **It** is tomorrow that **Tom** will visit his grandmother. (Tom이 할머니를 방문하려는 것은 바로 내일이다.)

핵심 Check

1. 다음 밑줄 친 부분을 강조하는 문장을 바꾸어 다시 쓰시오.

(1) <u>Mary</u> played the violin in the room.

➡ It _____ _____ _____ _____ the violin in the room.

(2) Jihun won <u>the first prize</u>.

➡ _____ _____ the first prize _____ Jihun won.

(3) I want to meet him <u>in the park</u>.

➡ It is _____ _____ _____ that I want to meet him.

② 「주어+동사+목적어+목적격보어」 구문

They thought popcorn a symbol of good health and goodwill.
그들은 팝콘을 좋은 건강과 호의의 상징으로 생각했다.

- 형태: 주어+동사+목적어+목적격보어(명사/형용사)
  의미: ~을 …라고 생각하다/여기다/믿다

- 어떤 사람이나 대상에 대한 평가, 의견, 느낌을 나타낼 때, "주어+동사+목적어+목적격보어" 구문을 사용한다. 이 구조에 사용되는 주요 동사로는 think, believe, find, name, call 등이 있다. 목적격보어로는 명사(구)가 쓰이기도 하고 형용사(구)가 쓰이기도 한다. 목적어와 목적격보어 사이에는 to be가 놓이기도 한다. "~을 …하게 만들다"의 의미일 때는 "make+목적어+목적격보어(형용사/명사)"의 구문이 된다.

  • I think him <u>a genius</u>. (나는 그가 천재라고 생각한다.)
  • I think his work very <u>original</u>. (나는 그의 작품이 매우 독창적이라고 생각한다.)
  • Abigail calls her boyfriend "<u>sweetheart.</u>" (Abigali은 그녀의 남자친구를 sweetheart라고 부른다.)
  • We believe her <u>to be a great artist</u>. (우리는 그녀가 훌륭한 예술가라고 믿는다.)

- ask, allow, advise, enable, expect, want, tell 등의 동사는 목적어 뒤에 목적격보어로 to부정사가 온다. 사역동사 let, make, have는 목적격보어로 동사원형을 취한다. 지각동사인 feel, hear, see, watch 등은 목적격보어로 동사원형이나 현재분사를 취한다.

  • I want you <u>to be</u> here on time. (나는 네가 이곳에 제시간에 오기를 원한다.)
  • He told me <u>to clean</u> the room. (그는 나에게 방을 청소하라고 말했다.)
  • Dad allowed me <u>to go</u> to the party. (아빠는 내가 파티에 가도록 허락하셨다.)
  • Tim let me <u>borrow</u> his pen. (Tim은 내가 그의 펜을 빌리게 해 주었다.)
  • I saw a bird <u>sitting</u> on the tree. (나는 새가 나무에 앉아 있는 것을 보았다.)

핵심 Check

2. 괄호 안에서 어법상 알맞은 것을 고르시오.

  (1) The children found the game (exciting / excitingly).
  (2) I thought him (kind / kindly).
  (3) Tom asked Jane (edit / to edit) her essay.

3. 우리말과 일치하도록 주어진 단어들을 바르게 배열하시오.

  사람들은 Newton을 천재라고 생각한다.
  (consider / a genius / people / Newton).

  ➡

Grammar 시험대비 기본평가

01 다음 빈칸에 들어갈 수 <u>없는</u> 것은?

> They think his painting _____.

① wonderful   ② nice   ③ great

④ well   ⑤ a masterpiece

02 다음 중 밑줄 친 부분의 쓰임이 나머지 넷과 <u>다른</u> 것은?

① It was Nara <u>that</u> I met yesterday.

② It is true <u>that</u> she is very kind.

③ It is David <u>that</u> speaks French very well.

④ It was yesterday <u>that</u> I met her

⑤ It was Jihun <u>that</u> broke the window.

03 다음 빈칸에 들어갈 말이 순서대로 바르게 짝지어진 것은?

> • We think him _____.
>
> • The book made Nara _____.

① kind – famous   ② happily – famous

③ kindly – fame   ④ exciting – sadly

⑤ happily – sad

04 다음 게시판을 보고 〈보기〉와 같이 대화를 완성하시오.

> NOTICE   Class 9
>
> • The Shy Boys will visit our school in May.
>
> • The school festival will start on May 20.

┌ 보기 ┐

> A: Will the Super Boys visit our school in May?
>
> B: No, it's the Shy Boys that will visit our school in May.

> A: Will the school festival start on May 22?
>
> B: No, _____.

01 다음 중 밑줄 친 부분의 쓰임이 옳은 것은?

① He thinks the house beautifully.
② I think him tired.
③ This movie made me sadly.
④ They believe him to be kindly.
⑤ The game made us exciting.

02 다음 중 주어진 문장의 밑줄 친 부분을 어법상 바르게 강조한 문장은? (2개)

Tom used my pen in the library yesterday.

① It was Tom that used my pen in the library yesterday.
② It was Tom when used my pen in the library yesterday.
③ It was Tom who used my pen in the library yesterday.
④ It was Tom which used my pen in the library yesterday.
⑤ It was Tom that using my pen in the library yesterday.

서답형
03 다음 문장에서 어법상 틀린 부분을 찾아 바르게 고치시오.

They think his work wonderfully.

➡ _____

04 다음 중 밑줄 친 that의 쓰임과 같은 것은?

It is the snake that I hate the most.

① Do you know that he made the machine?
② It is very easy to use that Internet service.
③ They said that it could make him a fortune.
④ It was at the wedding that I met Jack yesterday.
⑤ I'm looking for a cello class but it's not that easy.

05 다음 중 (A)~(C)의 빈칸에 들어갈 말로 바르게 짝지어진 것은?

(A) It was Tom _____ met Hana at the bus stop for the first time.
(B) It was Hana _____ Tom met at the bus stop for the first time.
(C) It was at the bus stop _____ Tom met Hana for the first time.

　　(A)　　(B)　　(C)
① that　– when　– that
② that　– where　– which
③ which – what　– that
④ who　– which – where
⑤ who　– that　– that

06 다음 중 밑줄 친 부분이 올바른 것은?

① Please keep clean the classroom.
② They think the city very quietly.
③ We found the beds quite comfortable.
④ My brother made angry my mother.
⑤ My dog always makes me happily.

서답형

07 아래 주어진 빈칸에 공통으로 들어갈 단어를 쓰시오.

> ⓐ It was Tom _____ used my pen in the library last Friday.
> ⓑ It was my pen _____ Tom used in the library last Friday.
> ⓒ It was in the library _____ Tom used my pen last Friday.
> ⓓ It was last Friday _____ Tom used my pen in the library.

➡ _____

중요

08 다음 중 우리말을 영작한 것이 어색한 것을 모두 고르면?

① 어제 그를 만난 사람은 바로 나였다.
　→ It was I that met him yesterday.
② 내가 작년 그를 만났던 곳은 바로 이 공원이었다.
　→ It was this park that I met him last year.
③ 어제 내게 그가 보낸 것은 바로 그 꽃이었다.
　→ It was the flowers that he sent me yesterday.
④ 우리가 그를 처음 만난 해는 2014년이었다.
　→ It was 2014 that we met for the first time.
⑤ 어제 창문을 깬 것은 Jack이었다.
　→ It was Jack that broke the window yesterday.

09 다음 중 문장 구조가 나머지와 다른 것은?

① They think this movie interesting.
② She made her son a doctor.
③ My mom made me the teddy bear.
④ He believes her to be honest.
⑤ Soccer games make people excited.

10 다음 중 밑줄 친 부분의 쓰임이 옳은 것은?

① I think the car very well.
② They think the show very exciting.
③ We believe this movie sadly.
④ The dog always makes my baby crying.
⑤ He found the book interested.

11 다음 중 밑줄 친 부분을 강조하는 문장으로 바르게 바꾼 것 두 개를 고르면?

> Hana saw Nara at the bus stop for the first time.

① It was Nara that Hana saw at the bus stop for the first time.
② It was Nara whom Hana saw at the bus stop for the first time.
③ It is Nara that Hana saw her at the bus stop for the first time.
④ It was Nara which Hana saw at the bus stop for the first time.
⑤ It was Nara whose Hana saw her at the bus stop for the first time.

12 다음 우리말을 영어로 적절하게 옮긴 것은?

> 사람들은 J.K.롤링을 훌륭한 작가로 생각한다.

① People think a great writer J. K. Rowling.
② People think J. K. Rowling a great writer.
③ J. K. Rowling thinks her a great writer.
④ J. K. Rowling thinks people a great writer.
⑤ People think writer J. K. Rowling great.

13 다음 우리말을 영어로 가장 적절하게 옮긴 것은?

> 나를 슬프게 한 것은 바로 시험 결과였다.

① The test result made me sad.
② I was sad because of the test result.
③ It was the test result that made me sad.
④ My test result was very bad, and I was sad.
⑤ The test result was so bad that I was very sad.

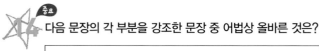

14 다음 문장의 각 부분을 강조한 문장 중 어법상 올바른 것은?

> Nara broke the window in my classroom yesterday.

① It was Nara who broke the window in my classroom yesterday.
② Nara does break the window in my classroom yesterday.
③ It was the window whom Nara broke in my classroom yesterday.
④ It was in my classroom when Nara broke the window yesterday.
⑤ It was yesterday where Nara broke the window.

15 Which one is grammatically NOT correct?

① We think Mozart a great musician.
② We think his work wonderful.
③ We think Monet a great painter.
④ We think his work brilliant.
⑤ They think Mike and Ken smartly.

16 다음 중 어법상 어색한 문장을 모두 고르면?

① It was Jack whom met yesterday.
② It was on Monday that we played soccer.
③ It was the song that he sang it on the stage.
④ It was a shooting star which you saw last evening.
⑤ It is her son who Amy is going to take to the hospital on Tuesday.

17 다음 빈칸 ⓐ, ⓑ에 들어갈 말로 바르게 연결된 것은?

> • We ⓐ_____ Picasso a great artist.
> • My father made me ⓑ_____ the dishes yesterday.

	ⓐ	ⓑ
①	say	washing
②	think	wash
③	consider	to wash
④	say	to wash
⑤	tell	wash

18 다음 중 밑줄 친 부분의 쓰임이 나머지 넷과 다른 것은?

① It is the window that John broke yesterday.
② It is the cat that always sits on the bookshelf.
③ I know that the movie was directed by Jane Smith.
④ It was at the store that Tony bought the pen.
⑤ It was Susie that I met at the park yesterday.

서답형
19 주어진 단어를 적절하게 배열하여 다음 우리말에 해당하는 영어 문장을 완성하시오.

> 사람들은 백남준을 세계적으로 유명한 비디오 아티스트라고 생각한다. (people, Nam June Paik, think, video artist, a world famous)

➡ _____

[01~02] 다음 주어진 문장에서 밑줄 친 부분을 어법에 맞게 고쳐 다시 쓰시오.

01 Kevin called <u>Angel me.</u>

➡ _____

02 I consider Paris <u>beautifully.</u>

➡ _____

03 우리말과 일치하도록 빈칸에 알맞은 말을 쓰시오.

> • 나는 그가 정직하기를 바란다. (honest)

➡ I want him _____ .

[04~05] 다음 우리말에 맞게 괄호 안의 단어들을 바르게 배열하여 문장을 완성하시오.

04
> They (of / popcorn / and / good health / thought / goodwill / a symbol).
> ➡ They _____
> _____ .
> (그들은 팝콘을 좋은 건강과 호의의 상징으로 생각했다.)

05
> (call / my friends / a couch potato / me).
> ➡ _____
> (내 친구들은 나를 '소파에 앉아 TV만 보는 사람'이라고 부른다.)

06 대화를 읽고 'it ~ that' 강조 구문을 이용하여 B의 대답을 밑줄 친 부분을 강조하는 문장으로 다시 쓰시오.

> A: <u>Where</u> did you lose your wallet?
> B: I lost my wallet in the park.
> ➡ _____

07 다음 게시판을 보고 물음에 답하시오. (단, 반드시 'it, that'을 포함하는 문장을 쓸 것)

> NOTICE   Class 3
> - The boy band will visit our school in May.
> - The third graders will take pictures in the park.
> - The midterm exams will start on April 30.

(1) **Q**: Will the girl band visit our school in May?
   A: No. It is _____
   _____ .

(2) **Q**: Will the third graders take pictures in the museum?
   A: No. It is _____
   _____ .

(3) **Q**: Will the midterm exams start on April 15?
   A: No. It is _____
   _____ .

08 다음 주어진 〈조건〉을 이용하여 문장을 다시 쓰시오.

> ┤ 조건 ├
> 1. 다음 문장의 밑줄 친 부분을 강조하여 문장을 다시 쓸 것
> 2. 주어, 동사를 포함한 완전한 문장으로 쓸 것

(1) <u>John</u> slept all day long.
   → _____

(2) Jane wrote <u>this novel</u> in 2015.
   → _____

09 다음 (A), (B)에 주어진 단어를 이용하여 다음 문장을 영어로 쓰시오. (단, 필요시 형태를 바꿀 것)

> (A) old movies, too much homework, math tests, baseball games
>
> (B) sad, tire, bore, happy, excite

(1) 나는 옛날 영화를 지겹다고 생각해.

→ _____

(2) 우리는 야구 경기를 신난다고 믿고 있어.

→ _____

10 다음 상황을 읽고 Eugene이 쓴 Thank-you note를 조건에 맞게 완성하시오.

> ┤ 조건 ├
> 1. 'It ~ that 강조 구문'을 사용할 것
> 2. make를 사용할 것

> When Eugene was feeling sad, John gave her beautiful flowers as a gift. She felt much better after receiving the gift.

> Thank-you note
> Dear John,
> Thank you for the beautiful flowers.
> It was _____ me feel much better when I was feeling sad.
> Love
> Eugene

11 다음 〈보기〉의 주어진 표현들을 한 번씩만 이용하여 문장을 완성하시오.

> ┤ 보기 ├
> a symbol of hope, think, too difficult, think, a rainbow, this work

(1) I _____.
(나는 이 일이 너무 어렵다고 생각한다.)

(2) People _____.
(사람들은 무지개를 희망의 상징이라고 생각한다.)

12 다음 괄호 안에 주어진 단어를 강조하여 질문에 알맞은 답을 완성하시오.

(1) Who broke the window?

➡ It _____.
(Robert)

(2) Where did you buy this sweater?

➡ It _____.
(at the Jay's shop)

13 다음 〈보기〉의 문장에서 밑줄 친 부분을 강조하여 〈조건〉에 맞게 다시 쓰시오.

> ┤ 조건 ├
> • 문장을 It으로 시작할 것
> • 〈보기〉의 문장과 의미가 변함없도록 할 것
> • 10단어의 영어 문장으로 쓸 것

> ┤ 보기 ├
> <u>The graduation ceremony</u> was held last Friday.

➡ _____

_____

Reading

A Bowl of Popcorn

Pop! Pop! Pop! Don't you love the smell of freshly made popcorn?

It is one of the most popular snacks around the world, and historians believe that people have enjoyed it for more than 5,000 years. It was in Central America that corn was originally grown, and it was in caves in New Mexico that the first popcorn was found.

Native Americans not only loved eating corn but also enjoyed the game of popping corn. Corn seeds were thrown on hot stones over a fire. Then they popped and bloomed into white flowers. The game was to catch and enjoy the flowery snacks.

Native Americans used popcorn for decoration as well. Their teenage girls used popped corn to decorate clothes. The Aztecs made corn decorations for the statues of the god of rain. They thought popcorn a symbol of good health and goodwill. They believed that they would be protected by popping spirits when they wore decorations made with popped corn.

In addition to Native Americans, many other people around the world enjoyed this tasty snack. The Chinese, as well as people in Sumatra and India, made popcorn long before Columbus arrived in the West Indies.

bowl: (우묵한) 그릇, 사발
freshly: 갓 ~한, 새롭게
historian: 역사가, 사학자
originally: 원래, 최초에
Native Americans: 아메리카 원주민
bloom: 꽃이 피다
decoration: 장식
statue: 조각상
goodwill: 친선, 호의
in addition to: ~ 이외에도
as well as: ~뿐만 아니라

 확인문제

● 다음 문장이 본문의 내용과 일치하면 T, 일치하지 않으면 F를 쓰시오.

1 Popcorn is popular mainly in America. ☐

2 Popcorn was originally grown in Central America. ☐

3 The first popcorn was found in the houses in New Mexico. ☐

4 Corn seeds turned into white flowers on hot stones over a fire. ☐

In ancient China, people popped corn to tell fortunes for the coming
_{to부정사의 부사적 용법 중 목적(~하기 위해서)}   현재분사
year and their daughters' future marriage. In the Song Dynasty,
Chinese people invented large pot-shaped popping machines to pop
_{to부정사의 부사적 용법 중 목적(~하기 위해서)}
corn, and these machines are still used by street poppers today.

It was Americans that tried interesting ways of popping corn during
_{It was ~ that 강조 구문(Americans 강조)}   동격   _{during+시간과 관련된 명사}
the nineteenth century. Some threw corn seeds onto hot ashes, stirred,
and then picked out the popped corn pieces. Others mixed corn
_{과거분사}
with fat or butter and cooked it in a pan. They thought popping corn
_{mixed와 병렬 연결}   _{think+목적어+목적격보어(목적어를 ~라고 생각하다)}
wonderful and exciting.

A more popular way was cooking popcorn over an open fire in a
_{동명사(보어)}
wire box with a long wooden handle. The fanciest popcorn popper
was invented by Charles Cretors in 1893, and before long many types
_{주어가 발명된 대상이므로 수동태}
of interesting poppers were seen in movie theaters and parks. Finally,
_{흥미를 유발하는 주체일 때 현재분사}
an electric popcorn popper for the home was invented in 1925.
_{주어가 발명된 대상이므로 수동태}
Believe it or not, poppers were in high demand and were even made
_{주어가 poppers이므로 수동태}
by middle school students in school clubs.

How do you like your popcorn? Sweet, hot, or spicy? Next time you
_{How do you like ~? (어떠한 방식을 선호하는지 묻는 의미)}   _{다음번에 ~할 때에는}
enjoy popcorn, imagine yourself as a Native American, an ancient
_{재귀대명사(주어와 목적어가 같을 때 사용)}
Chinese person, or an inventor. With a bowl of popcorn, you can
_{~으로 (도구)}
be a Native American and make pretty decorations or be an ancient
Chinese person and tell fortunes. Or better still, why don't you be an
_{이미 언급된 좋은 아이디어보다 더 낫다고 생각하는 새로운 아이디어를 추가할 때 사용}
inventor and come up with a new popper for your favorite popcorn?

확인문제

ancient: 고대의
dynasty: 왕조
marriage: 결혼, 결혼 생활
ash: 재
stir: 젓다, 섞다
before long: 오래지 않아
believe it or not: 믿기 힘들겠지만
in high demand: 수요가 많은
spicy: 매운, 향신료를 넣은
imagine: 상상하다
inventor: 발명가
come up with: ~을 생각해 내다, ~을 찾아내다

● 다음 문장이 본문의 내용과 일치하면 T, 일치하지 않으면 F를 쓰시오.

1 Modern Chinese people pop corn to tell fortunes. ☐

2 Interesting ways of popping corn were tried by Americans. ☐

3 It was in **1925** that Charles Cretors invented the fanciest popcorn popper. ☐

● 우리말을 참고하여 빈칸에 알맞은 말을 쓰시오.

1 Pop! Pop! Pop! _____ you _____ the smell of _____ made popcorn?

2 It is one of the _____ _____ _____ _____ the world, and historians believe _____ people _____ _____ _____ it for more than 5,000 years.

3 _____ _____ in Central America _____ corn was _____ _____, and it was in caves in New Mexico _____ the first popcorn was found.

4 Native Americans _____ _____ loved eating corn _____ _____ enjoyed the game of _____ _____.

5 Corn seeds _____ _____ _____ hot stones over a fire.

6 Then they _____ and _____ into white flowers.

7 The game was _____ _____ and _____ the _____ snacks.

8 Native Americans _____ popcorn _____ _____ as well.

9 Their teenage girls _____ popped corn _____ _____ clothes.

10 The Aztecs _____ corn _____ for the _____ of the god of rain.

11 They thought popcorn _____ _____ and goodwill.

12 They believed _____ they would _____ _____ by popping _____ when they wore _____ _____ _____ popped corn.

13 _____ _____ _____ Native Americans, many other people around the world _____ this _____ snack.

14 The Chinese, _____ _____ people in Sumatra and India, made popcorn _____ _____ Columbus _____ in the West Indies.

---

1 펑! 펑! 펑! 당신은 갓 만들어진 팝콘의 냄새를 좋아하지 않나요?

2 그것은 전 세계에서 가장 인기 있는 간식 중 하나이고, 역사가 들은 사람들이 5,000년 이상 그것을 즐겨 왔다고 믿고 있습니다.

3 옥수수가 본래 재배된 곳은 중앙 아메리카였고, 최초의 팝콘이 발견된 곳은 뉴멕시코의 동굴 안이었습니다.

4 아메리카 원주민들은 옥수수 먹는 것을 좋아했을 뿐만 아니라 옥수수를 튀기는 게임도 즐겼습니다.

5 옥수수 씨는 불 위의 뜨거운 돌들 위로 던져졌습니다.

6 그 다음 그것들은 펑 소리를 내며 튀겨졌고 하얀 꽃 모양으로 피어났습니다.

7 그 게임은 그 꽃 모양의 간식을 잡아서 즐기는 것이었습니다.

8 아메리카 원주민들은 팝콘을 장식을 위해서도 사용했습니다.

9 그들의 십 대 소녀들은 튀겨진 옥수수를 옷을 장식하는 데 사용했습니다.

10 아즈텍족 사람들은 비의 신 조각상을 위해 옥수수 장식품을 만들었습니다.

11 그들은 팝콘을 좋은 건강과 호의의 상징으로 생각했습니다.

12 그들은 튀겨진 옥수수로 만든 장식들을 달면 불쑥 나타나는 정령에 의해 보호받을 것이라고 믿었습니다.

13 아메리카 원주민 외에도, 전 세계의 많은 다른 사람들이 이 맛있는 간식을 즐겼습니다.

14 수마트라인과 인도인뿐 아니라 중국인들도 콜럼버스가 서인도 제도에 도착하기 훨씬 이전부터 팝콘을 만들었습니다.

15 In ancient China, people popped corn _____ _____ _____ for the _____ _____ and their daughters' future _____.

16 In the Song Dynasty, Chinese people _____ large pot-shaped popping _____ to pop corn, and these machines _____ still _____ by street poppers today.

17 _____ _____ Americans _____ tried _____ _____ _____ popping corn _____ the nineteenth century.

18 Some _____ corn seeds _____ hot ashes, stirred, and then _____ _____ the popped corn pieces.

19 Others _____ corn with fat or butter and _____ _____ in a pan.

20 They thought popping corn _____ and _____.

21 A more _____ way was _____ popcorn _____ an open fire in a wire box with a long _____ handle.

22 The fanciest popcorn popper _____ _____ _____ Charles Cretors in 1893, and before long _____ _____ of interesting poppers _____ _____ in movie theaters and parks.

23 _____, an electric popcorn popper for the home _____ _____ in 1925.

24 Believe it or not, poppers were _____ _____ _____ and were even _____ _____ middle school students in school clubs.

25 _____ do you _____ your popcorn? Sweet, hot, or spicy?

26 Next time you enjoy popcorn, _____ _____ as a _____ _____, an ancient Chinese person, or an inventor.

27 _____ a bowl of popcorn, you _____ _____ a Native American and make _____ _____ or be _____ _____ person and tell _____.

28 Or better still, _____ _____ _____ be an inventor and _____ _____ _____ a new popper for your favorite popcorn?

15 고대 중국에서, 사람들은 다음 해와 그들의 딸들의 장래의 혼사를 점치기 위해 옥수수를 펑 소리를 내며 튀겼습니다.

16 송나라 왕조에서, 중국 사람들은 옥수수를 튀기기 위해 커다란 항아리 모양의 팝콘 튀기는 기계를 발명하였고, 이 기계는 오늘날에도 길거리에서 팝콘 만드는 이들에 의해 사용되고 있습니다.

17 19세기 동안 옥수수를 튀기는 흥미로운 방법들을 시도해 본 것은 바로 미국인들이었습니다.

18 이들 중 일부는 뜨거운 잿더미 위로 옥수수 씨를 던지고, 뒤섞은 다음, 펑 터져 나온 옥수수 알갱이들을 집어냈습니다.

19 다른 이들은 옥수수를 기름이나 버터와 섞고 이를 납작한 냄비에 요리하였습니다.

20 그들은 옥수수를 튀기는 것을 멋지고 재미있다고 생각했습니다.

21 보다 인기 있는 방법은 팝콘을 긴 나무 손잡이가 있는 철사 상자 안에 넣어 덮개가 없는 불에서 요리하는 방법이었습니다.

22 가장 멋진 팝콘 튀기는 기계는 1893년 Charles Cretors에 의해 발명되었는데, 오래지 않아 많은 종류의 흥미로운 팝콘 만드는 기계들이 영화관이나 공원에서 보이게 되었습니다.

23 마침내 가정용 전기 팝콘 기계가 1925년에 발명되었습니다.

24 믿기 힘들겠지만, 팝콘 기계는 그 수요가 많았고, 심지어 학교 동아리에서 중학생들에 의해서도 제작되었습니다.

25 당신은 어떤 팝콘을 좋아하나요? 달콤한, 매운, 향신료를 친 팝콘?

26 다음 번에 팝콘을 즐길 때에는 당신이 아메리카 원주민, 고대 중국인, 혹은 발명가라고 상상해 보세요.

27 한 그릇의 팝콘으로, 당신은 아메리카 원주민이 되어 예쁜 장식을 만들 수도 있고, 또는 고대 중국인이 되어 운세를 점쳐 볼 수도 있습니다.

28 혹은 더 좋게는, 발명가가 되어 당신이 가장 좋아하는 팝콘을 위해 새로운 팝콘 기계를 생각해 내는 것은 어떤가요?

● 우리말을 참고하여 본문을 영작하시오.

1 ▶ 펑! 펑! 펑! 당신은 갓 만들어진 팝콘의 냄새를 좋아하지 않나요?
➡ _____

2 ▶ 그것은 전 세계에서 가장 인기 있는 간식 중 하나이고, 역사가들은 사람들이 5,000년 이상 그것을
즐겨 왔다고 믿고 있습니다.
➡ _____
_____

3 ▶ 옥수수가 본래 재배된 곳은 중앙아메리카였고, 최초의 팝콘이 발견된 곳은 뉴멕시코의 동굴 안이었습니다.
➡ _____

4 ▶ 아메리카 원주민들은 옥수수 먹는 것을 좋아했을 뿐만 아니라 옥수수를 튀기는 게임도 즐겼습니다.
➡ _____

5 ▶ 옥수수 씨는 불 위의 뜨거운 돌들 위로 던져졌습니다.
➡ _____

6 ▶ 그 다음 그것들은 펑 소리를 내며 튀겨졌고 하얀 꽃 모양으로 피어났습니다.
➡ _____

7 ▶ 그 게임은 그 꽃 모양의 간식을 잡아서 즐기는 것이었습니다.
➡ _____

8 ▶ 아메리카 원주민들은 팝콘을 장식을 위해서도 사용했습니다.
➡ _____

9 ▶ 그들의 십 대 소녀들은 튀겨진 옥수수를 옷을 장식하는 데 사용했습니다.
➡ _____

10 ▶ 아즈텍족 사람들은 비의 신 조각상을 위해 옥수수 장식품을 만들었습니다.
➡ _____

11 ▶ 그들은 팝콘을 좋은 건강과 호의의 상징으로 생각했습니다.
➡ _____

12 ▶ 그들은 튀겨진 옥수수로 만든 장식들을 달면 불쑥 나타나는 정령에 의해 보호받을 것이라고 믿었습니다.
➡ _____

13 ▶ 아메리카 원주민 외에도, 전 세계의 많은 다른 사람들이 이 맛있는 간식을 즐겼습니다.
➡ _____

14 ▶ 수마트라인과 인도인뿐 아니라 중국인들도 콜럼버스가 서인도 제도에 도착하기 훨씬 이전부터 팝콘을 만들었습니다.
➡ _____
_____

15 고대 중국에서, 사람들은 다음 해와 그들의 딸들의 장래의 혼사를 점치기 위해 옥수수를 펑 소리를 내며 튀겼습니다.

➡ _____

_____

16 송나라 왕조에서, 중국 사람들은 옥수수를 튀기기 위해 커다란 항아리 모양의 팝콘 튀기는 기계를 발명하였고, 이 기계는 오늘날에도 길거리에서 팝콘 만드는 이들에 의해 사용되고 있습니다.

➡ _____

_____

17 19세기 동안 옥수수를 튀기는 흥미로운 방법들을 시도해 본 것은 바로 미국인들이었습니다.

➡ _____

18 이들 중 일부는 뜨거운 잿더미 위로 옥수수 씨를 던지고, 뒤섞은 다음, 펑 터져 나온 옥수수 알갱이들을 집어냈습니다.

➡ _____

19 다른 이들은 옥수수를 기름이나 버터와 섞고 이를 납작한 냄비에 요리하였습니다.

➡ _____

20 그들은 옥수수를 튀기는 것을 멋지고 재미있다고 생각했습니다.

➡ _____

21 보다 인기 있는 방법은 팝콘을 긴 나무 손잡이가 있는 철사 상자 안에 넣어 덮개가 없는 불에서 요리하는 방법이었습니다.

➡ _____

22 가장 멋진 팝콘 튀기는 기계는 1893년 Charles Cretors에 의해 발명되었는데, 오래지 않아 많은 종류의 흥미로운 팝콘 만드는 기계들이 영화관이나 공원에서 보이게 되었습니다.

➡ _____

_____

23 마침내 가정용 전기 팝콘 기계가 1925년에 발명되었습니다.

➡ _____

24 믿기 힘들겠지만, 팝콘 기계는 그 수요가 많았고, 심지어 학교 동아리에서 중학생들에 의해서도 제작되었습니다.

➡ _____

_____

25 당신은 어떤 팝콘을 좋아하나요? 달콤한, 매운, 향신료를 친 팝콘?

➡ _____

26 다음 번에 팝콘을 즐길 때에는 당신이 아메리카 원주민, 고대 중국인, 혹은 발명가라고 상상해 보세요.

➡ _____

27 한 그릇의 팝콘으로, 당신은 아메리카 원주민이 되어 예쁜 장식을 만들 수도 있고, 또는 고대 중국인이 되어 운세를 점쳐 볼 수도 있습니다.

➡ _____

_____

28 혹은 더 좋게는, 발명가가 되어 당신이 가장 좋아하는 팝콘을 위해 새로운 팝콘 기계를 생각해 내는 것은 어떤가요?

➡ _____

[01~02] 다음 글을 읽고 물음에 답하시오.

Pop! Pop! Pop! Don't you love the smell of freshly made popcorn? It is one of the most popular snacks around the world, and historians believe that people have enjoyed (A)it for more than 5,000 years. It was in Central America that corn was originally grown, and it was in caves in New Mexico that the first popcorn was found.

서답형

01 밑줄 친 (A)it이 가리키는 것을 위 글에서 찾아 쓰시오.

➡ _____

중요

02 다음 중 위 글을 읽고 답할 수 <u>없는</u> 것은?

① What is one of the most popular snacks around the world?
② How long have people enjoyed the snack?
③ Where was corn originally grown?
④ When was the first popcorn found?
⑤ What was found in caves in New Mexico?

[03~06] 다음 글을 읽고 물음에 답하시오.

Native Americans not only loved eating corn but also enjoyed the game of popping corn. ① Corn seeds were thrown on hot stones over a fire. Then they popped and bloomed into white flowers. ② The game was to catch and enjoy the flowery snacks. ③ Their teenage girls used popped corn to decorate clothes. ④ The Aztecs made corn decorations for the statues of the god of rain. They thought popcorn a symbol of good health and

goodwill. ⑤ They believed that they would be protected by popping spirits when they wore decorations made with popped corn.

03 ①~⑤ 중 주어진 문장이 들어가기에 가장 적절한 곳은?

Native Americans used popcorn for decoration as well.

①   ②   ③   ④   ⑤

04 다음 중 위 글의 내용과 일치하는 것은?

① Native Americans loved only eating corns.
② Corn seeds popped and bloomed on cold stones.
③ Native American teenagers used popped corn when decorating clothes.
④ The Aztecs wore decorations made with popped corn.
⑤ The Aztecs protected popping spirits with popped corn.

서답형

05 According to the passage, for what did the Aztecs make corn decorations? Answer in English with a full sentence.

➡ _____
_____

서답형

06 다음과 같이 풀이되는 말을 위 글에서 찾아 쓰시오.

a large sculpture of a person or an animal, made of stone or metal

➡ _____

[07~09] 다음 글을 읽고 물음에 답하시오.

In addition to Native Americans, ①many other people around the world enjoyed (A) this tasty snack. The Chinese, ②as well as people in Sumatra and India, made popcorn long before Columbus ③arrived in the West Indies. In ancient China, people popped corn ④tell fortunes for the coming year and their daughters' future marriage. In the Song Dynasty, Chinese people ⑤invented large pot-shaped popping machines to pop corn, and these machines are still used by street poppers today.

서답형

07 밑줄 친 (A)this tasty snack이 의미하는 것을 위 글에서 찾아 쓰시오.

➡ _____

08 ①~⑤ 중 어법상 바르지 않은 것은?

①   ②   ③   ④   ⑤

서답형

09 When were popping machines invented in China? Answer in English with a full sentence.

➡ _____

[10~13] 다음 글을 읽고 물음에 답하시오.

It was Americans that tried (A)_____ during the nineteenth century. Some threw corn seeds onto hot ashes, stirred, and then picked out the popped corn pieces. Others mixed corn with fat or butter and cooked it in a pan. They thought popping corn wonderful and exciting.

A more popular way was cooking popcorn

over an open fire in a wire box with a long wooden handle. The fanciest popcorn popper (B)invent by Charles Cretors in 1893, and before long many types of interesting poppers were seen in movie theaters and parks. Finally, an electric popcorn popper for the home was invented in 1925. Believe it or not, poppers were in high demand and were even made by middle school students in school clubs.

중요

10 다음 중 빈칸 (A)에 들어갈 말로 가장 적절한 것은?

① to grow corn all around the world
② interesting ways of popping corn
③ not to pop corn in front of fire
④ many interesting ways of cooking corn
⑤ to invent a popping machine

서답형

11 밑줄 친 (B)의 올바른 형태를 쓰시오.

➡ _____

12 다음 중 위 글의 내용과 일치하는 것은?

① There were some people in America who threw corn seeds onto cold ashes.
② Most people cooked corn with fat in a kettle.
③ The wire box had a long handle made of wood.
④ Nobody invented popcorn poppers after Charles Cretors made one.
⑤ It was hard to see poppers in movie theaters.

서답형

13 Where did middle school students make poppers? Answer in English with six words.

➡ _____

[14~15] 다음 글을 읽고 물음에 답하시오.

How do you like your popcorn? Sweet, hot, or spicy? Next time you enjoy popcorn, imagine yourself as a Native American, an ancient Chinese person, or an inventor. With a bowl of popcorn, you can be a Native American and make pretty decorations or be an ancient Chinese person and tell fortunes. Or better still, why don't you be an inventor and come up (A)_____ a new popper for your favorite popcorn?

14 다음 중 빈칸 (A)에 들어갈 말과 같은 말이 들어가는 것은?

① Please pay attention _____ me.

② Sarah took care _____ her sister.

③ Do you listen _____ yourself?

④ She dealt _____ the problem by herself.

⑤ You need to work _____ regularly to be healthy.

서답형

15 If you can be a Native American, what can you do with a bowl of popcorn? Answer in English with five words.

➡ _____

[16~17] 다음 글을 읽고 물음에 답하시오.

Pop! Pop! Pop! Don't you love the smell of freshly made ①popcorn? ②It is ③one of the most popular snacks around the world, and historians believe that people have enjoyed ④it for more than 5,000 years. It was in Central America that corn was originally grown, and ⑤it was in caves in New Mexico that the first popcorn was found.

16 ①~⑤ 중 의미하는 바가 다른 하나는?

① ② ③ ④ ⑤

서답형

17 Where was the first popcorn found? Answer in English with a full sentence.

➡ _____

[18~20] 다음 글을 읽고 물음에 답하시오.

Native Americans not only loved eating corn but also enjoyed the game of popping corn.

[A] Their teenage girls used popped corn to decorate clothes. The Aztecs made corn decorations for the statues of the god of rain.

[B] The game was to catch and enjoy the flowery snacks. Native Americans used popcorn for decoration as well.

[C] Corn seeds were thrown on hot stones over a fire. Then they popped and bloomed into white flowers.

They thought popcorn a symbol of good health and goodwill. They believed that they would be protected by popping spirits when they wore decorations made with popped corn.

서답형

18 자연스러운 글이 되도록 [A]~[C]를 바르게 나열하시오.

➡ _____

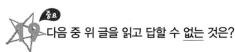

19 다음 중 위 글을 읽고 답할 수 없는 것은?

① What did Native Americans love doing with popcorn?

② What did Native American teenage girls do with popped corn?

③ Where were corn seeds thrown?

④ What was a symbol of good health and goodwill?

⑤ What did the Aztecs do for a living?

20 위 글의 내용에 맞게 빈칸에 알맞은 말을 쓰시오.

> Corn seeds thrown on hot stones over a fire turned into shapes of _____ .

[21~22] 다음 글을 읽고 물음에 답하시오.

In addition to Native Americans, many other people around the world enjoyed this tasty snack. The Chinese, as well as people in Sumatra and India, made popcorn long before Columbus arrived in the West Indies. In ancient China, people popped corn to tell fortunes for the coming year and their daughters' future marriage. In the Song Dynasty, Chinese people invented large pot-shaped popping machines to pop corn, and these machines are still used by street poppers today.

서답형
21 다음 중 위 글의 내용과 일치하는 것은?

① As soon as Columbus arrived in the West Indies, he taught people how to make popcorn.
② Only Native Americans made popcorn.
③ Chinese people don't enjoy popcorn any longer.
④ People in Sumatra didn't know how to cook corn before Columbus arrived in the West Indies.
⑤ The ancient Chinese people told fortunes by popping corn.

서답형
22 What did the popping machine made in the Song Dynasty look like? Answer in English with five words.

➡ _____

[23~25] 다음 글을 읽고 물음에 답하시오.

It was Americans that tried interesting ways of popping corn during the nineteenth century. Some threw corn seeds onto hot ashes, stirred, and then picked out the popped corn pieces. Others mixed corn with fat or butter and cooked it in a pan. They thought popping corn wonderful and exciting.

A more popular way was cooking popcorn over an open fire in a wire box with a long wooden handle. The fanciest popcorn popper was invented by Charles Cretors in 1893, and before long many types of interesting poppers were seen in movie theaters and parks. Finally, an electric popcorn popper for the home was invented in 1925. Believe it or not, poppers were (A)in high demand and were even made by middle school students in school clubs.

중요
23 다음 중 위 글을 읽고 답할 수 <u>없는</u> 것은?

① Who tried interesting ways of popping corn during the nineteenth century?
② With what did people mix corn?
③ What did people think of popping corn?
④ What was a more popular way of cooking popcorn?
⑤ When was Charles Cretors born?

서답형
24 다음 중 위 글의 내용과 일치하지 <u>않는</u> 것을 찾아 바르게 고쳐 쓰시오.

> People in America threw corn seeds on hot ashes, stirred them, and threw away the popped corn pieces.

➡ _____

25 다음 중 밑줄 친 (A)의 의미로 가장 적절한 것은?

① 요구 사항이 많은   ② 수요가 많은
③ 손이 많이 가는   ④ 관심이 많은
⑤ 매우 비싼

[01~03] 다음 글을 읽고 물음에 답하시오.

Pop! Pop! Pop! Don't you love the smell of (A)갓 만들어진 팝콘? It is one of the most popular snacks around the world, and historians believe that people have enjoyed it for more than 5,000 years. It was in Central America that corn was originally grown, and it was in caves in New Mexico that the first popcorn was found.

01 주어진 단어를 활용하여 밑줄 친 우리말 (A)를 영어로 쓰시오.

(fresh / make)

➡ _____

02 According to the passage, how long have people enjoyed popcorn? Answer in English with a full sentence.

➡ _____

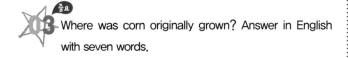 Where was corn originally grown? Answer in English with seven words.

➡ _____

[04~07] 다음 글을 읽고 물음에 답하시오.

Native Americans not only loved eating corn but also enjoyed the game of popping corn. Corn seeds were thrown on hot stones over a fire. Then they popped and bloomed into white flowers. The game was to catch and enjoy the flowery snacks. Native Americans used popcorn for decoration as well. Their teenage girls used popped corn to decorate clothes. The Aztecs made corn decorations for the statues of the god of rain. They thought popcorn a symbol of good health and goodwill. They believed that they would be protected by popping spirits when they wore decorations made with popped corn.

04 위 글의 내용에 맞게 빈칸에 알맞은 말을 쓰시오.

Native Americans enjoyed _____ _____ as well as loved _____ .

05 What happened to the corn seeds which were thrown on hot stones? Answer in English with seven words.

➡ _____

06 For what did the teenage girls use popped corn? Use the phrase 'in order to.'

➡ _____

 를 포함한 강조 구문을 활용하여 다음 물음에 답하시오.

Q: What did the Aztecs make for the statues of the god of rain?

➡ _____

_____

[08~09] 다음 글을 읽고 물음에 답하시오.

In addition to Native Americans, many other people around the world enjoyed this tasty snack. The Chinese, as well as people in Sumatra and India, made popcorn long before Columbus arrived in the West Indies. In ancient China, people popped corn to tell fortunes for the coming year and their daughters' future marriage. In the Song Dynasty, Chinese people invented large pot-shaped popping machines to pop corn, and these machines are still used by street poppers today.

08 Write the reason why ancient Chinese people popped corn. Answer in English with a full sentence.

➡ _____

_____

09 다음 중 글의 내용과 일치하지 <u>않는</u> 부분을 찾아 바르게 고쳐 쓰시오. (2군데)

> The Chinese made popcorn long after Columbus arrived in the West Indies. Large pot-shaped popping machines have been used since ancient times.

➡ _____

_____

[10~14] 다음 글을 읽고 물음에 답하시오.

It was Americans that tried interesting ways of popping corn during the nineteenth century. Some threw corn seeds onto hot ashes, stirred, and then picked out the popped corn pieces. Others mixed corn with fat or butter and cooked it in a pan. They thought popping corn wonderful and exciting.

A more popular way was cooking popcorn over an open fire in a wire box with a long wooden handle. The fanciest popcorn popper was invented by Charles Cretors in 1893, and before long many types of interesting poppers were seen in movie theaters and parks. Finally, an electric popcorn popper for the home was invented in 1925. Believe it or not, poppers were in high demand and were even made by middle school students in school clubs.

10 Who tried interesting ways of popping corn during the nineteenth century? Answer in English with eleven words.

➡ _____

_____

11 What did people do after throwing corn seeds onto hot ashes? Answer in English.

➡ _____

12 What did the wire box have?

➡ _____

13 Who invented the fanciest popcorn popper? Answer in English the phrase 'It ~ that.'

➡ _____

_____

14 위 글의 내용에 맞게 빈칸에 알맞은 말을 쓰시오.

> It was not until _____ that people could finally use an electric popcorn popper for the home.

Write & Speak 2 B

A: How do you like my hamburger?
"How do you like ～?"는 만족하는지 묻는 말이다.
B: I just love it. How tasty!
"How tasty it is!"에서 "주어+동사"가 생략되었다.
A: Thanks. I'm glad you like.
상대의 칭찬에 감사하는 표현이다.

구문해설 • tasty 맛있는

해석

A: 내 햄버거 어때?

B: 너무 좋아. 정말 맛있다!

A: 고마워. 네가 마음에 든다니 기쁘다.

Real-Life Task Step 3

On our Monday snack menu, we have ice cream and apple juice.
menu에는 전치사 on을 쓴다.
On the Tuesday menu, we have bananas and orange juice. On Wednesday, we

enjoy carrot cake and chocolate milk. On Thursday, we have potato chips and
즐기다
milk. And on Friday, we enjoy apple slices and mango juice.

구문해설 • carrot 당근 • potato chips 감자 칩 • slice 조각

우리의 월요일 간식 메뉴에는 아이스크림과 사과 주스가 있다. 화요일 메뉴에는 바나나와 오렌지 주스가 있다. 수요일에는 당근 케이크와 초콜릿 우유를 즐긴다. 목요일에는 감자 칩과 우유가 있다. 그리고 금요일에는 사과 조각과 망고 주스를 즐긴다.

Before I Read

1. Throw corn seeds onto hot ashes.
throw A onto B: A를 B에 던지다. 뿌리다
2. Mix corn with fat and cook it in a pan.
지방에 섞은 옥수수
3. Cook corn over an open fire in a wire box.
～ 위로
4. Pop corn in a popcorn popper.
튀기다(동사)

구문해설 • ash 재 • fat 지방 • open fire 덮개가 없는 불 • wire box 철사 상자
• popcorn popper 팝콘 튀기는 기계

1. 옥수수 씨를 뜨거운 재에 뿌린다.
2. 옥수수와 지방을 섞어서 팬에 요리한다.
3. 철사 상자 안에 넣어 덮개가 없는 불에서 옥수수를 요리한다.
4. 팝콘 튀기는 기계에서 옥수수를 튀긴다.

영역별 핵심문제

01 다음 영영풀이에 해당하는 단어를 고르시오.

> a period of time when a particular family ruled a country

① kingdom   ② ancient
③ dynasty   ④ decoration
⑤ tradition

02 다음 주어진 문장의 빈칸에 공통으로 들어갈 단어로 적절한 것은?

> • It is often mixed _____ ice and sweet fruit.
> • This snack is often served _____ green tea.

① from   ② with   ③ about
④ by   ⑤ after

03 다음 빈칸에 들어갈 말로 적절한 것은?

> Why don't you answer the questions above? We're _____ getting your answers.

① taking care of   ② looking up to
③ getting used to   ④ paying attention to
⑤ looking forward to

04 다음 밑줄 친 단어와 의미가 같은 단어를 쓰시오. (주어진 철자로 시작할 것)

> She wants to tell Junha the <u>origin</u> of chocolate.

➡ r_____

05 다음 대화의 빈칸에 들어갈 말로 알맞은 것은?

> A: Would you like some soup?
> B: Yes, I'd love some.
> A: Here you go. _____
> B: It's hot and sweet. I just love it.
> A: I'm glad you like it.

① What about you?
② Don't you think so?
③ How do you like it?
④ Why do you like it?
⑤ How about eating some soup?

[06~08] 다음 대화를 읽고 물음에 답하시오.

> G: _____ a new backpack, Minsu?
> B: Yes, I have. This is my birthday present from my mother.
> G: How nice of her! How do you like it?
> B: I like it a lot. I like the color.
> G: Your favorite color is blue, isn't it?
> B: Yes, it is.

06 빈칸 (A)에 들어가기에 적절한 것은?

① You've been   ② You had
③ You're weaving   ④ You have bought
⑤ You've got

07 How did the boy get the new backpack?

① He bought it for his birthday.
② His mother gave it to him.
③ The girl friend presented it to him.
④ He liked the color of the backpack.
⑤ Because the girl liked it.

08 위 글의 내용과 일치하는 것은?

① The girl liked the color of the backpack.

② The boy wanted another birthday present.

③ The backpack was the birthday present from his father.

④ The color of the backpack is blue.

⑤ They both think it is a very good present.

10 다음 〈보기〉에 주어진 표현을 포함하여 밑줄 친 (B)를 영어로 쓰시오.

┌─── 보기 ├──────
 that, by the way, know, once, chocolate, the "drink of the gods", called
└────────────────

➡ _____

_____

11 위 대화의 내용과 일치하도록 할 때, 빈칸에 알맞은 말로 짝지어진 것은??

• Nara is (A)_____ at making hot chocolate.

• They once called chocolate "drink of the (B)_____."

	(A)	(B)
①	better	kings
②	good	gods
③	poor	emperor
④	less	natives
⑤	little	Aztecs

[09~11] 다음 대화를 읽고 물음에 답하시오.

Nara: Would you like some hot chocolate, Junha?

Junha: Sure, I haven't had it for ages! ... Mmm.

Nara: How do you like it?

Junha: I like it a lot. You (A)_____ making hot chocolate.

Nara: Thanks. I'm glad you like it. (B)그런데, 너 초콜릿이 한때 "신들의 음료"라고 불렸던 것을 알고 있었니?

Junha: Was it really?

Nara: Yes, chocolate was first enjoyed by the emperor of the Aztec Empire, and it was once called xoco-latl, "drink of the gods."

09 글의 흐름으로 보아 빈칸 (A)에 들어가기에 적절한 것은?

① are very busy with

② are very tired of

③ are very satisfied with

④ are very worried with

⑤ are very good at

12 다음 주어진 말에 이어질 대화의 순서가 바르게 배열된 것을 고르시오.

G: What are you reading?

(A) It's just wonderful.

(B) A mystery novel.

(C) How do you like it?

① (A) – (C) – (B) 　② (B) – (A) – (C)

③ (B) – (C) – (A) 　④ (C) – (A) – (B)

⑤ (C) – (B) – (A)

Grammar

13 주어진 어구를 활용하여 다음 우리말을 영어로 쓰시오.

> • 우리는 장영실을 조선시대의 위대한 과학자라고 생각한다. (Jang Yeong-sil, during the Chosun Dynasty)

➡ _____

_____

14 다음 중 어법상 어색한 문장을 <u>모두</u> 고르면?

① It makes you healthier.
② I think the movie sadly.
③ They called him Lion King.
④ Do you really want to make she angry?
⑤ Do you consider him a good artist?

15 다음 중 'It ~ that'의 쓰임이 나머지 넷과 <u>다른</u> 것은?

① It was certain <u>that</u> he went to Seoul.
② It was yesterday <u>that</u> I went to the museum.
③ It was my brother <u>that</u> you saw at the park.
④ It was in the street <u>that</u> I saw my old friend.
⑤ It was cookies <u>that</u> Ted made on my birthday.

16 다음 중 주어진 문장을 밑줄 친 부분을 강조하는 문장으로 바르게 바꾼 것은?

> Tom met her <u>in December</u>.

① In December that Tom met her.
② When Tom met her is in December.
③ It was December that Tom met her.
④ It was in December that Tom met her.
⑤ It was in December which Tom met her.

17 다음 중 어법상 옳은 문장을 고르시오.

① I want him telling the truth.
② It was the window that broke.
③ Don't let him to use your phone.
④ I consider him the leader of this group.
⑤ I made him to clean the room.

18 다음 우리말을 영어로 옮긴 것이 <u>어색한</u> 것은?

① 나는 그가 천재라고 생각한다.
  = I think him a genius.
② 우리는 그녀가 훌륭한 예술가라고 믿는다.
  = We believe her a great artist.
③ 그녀는 그녀의 남자친구를 honey라고 부른다.
  = She calls her boyfriend "honey."
④ 우리는 그를 훌륭한 음악가라고 믿는다.
  = We believe him to be a great musician.
⑤ 나는 그가 일찍 오기를 바란다.
  = I want him come early.

19 다음 문장을 <보기>와 같이 바꾸어 쓰시오.

> ┤ 보기 ├
> I met him yesterday. (him을 강조)
> → It was him that I met yesterday.

Q: Hana speaks French very well. (Hana를 강조)

➡ _____

20 다음 문장의 밑줄 친 that의 쓰임과 같은 것을 <u>모두</u> 고르면? (정답 2개)

> It was in this way <u>that</u> I solved the problem.

① It was yesterday <u>that</u> I saw Yuna.
② It is true <u>that</u> he helped the man.
③ It is this book <u>that</u> I was looking for.
④ It is so cold <u>that</u> I don't want to go outside.
⑤ The fact is <u>that</u> the person needs some help.

Reading

[21~25] 다음 글을 읽고 물음에 답하시오.

Pop! Pop! Pop! Don't you love the smell of freshly made popcorn? It is one of the most popular snacks around the world, and historians believe that people have enjoyed it for more than 5,000 years. It was in Central America that corn was originally grown, and it was in caves in New Mexico that the first popcorn was found.

Native Americans not only loved eating corn but also enjoyed the game of popping corn. ① Corn seeds were thrown on hot stones over a fire. ② The game was to catch and enjoy the flowery snacks. ③ Native Americans used popcorn (A)_____ as well. ④ Their teenage girls used popped corn to decorate clothes. The Aztecs made corn decorations for the statues of the god of rain. ⑤ They thought popcorn a symbol of good health and goodwill. They believed that they would be protected by popping spirits when they wore decorations made with popped corn.

21 글의 흐름상 빈칸 (A)에 들어갈 말로 가장 적절한 것은?

① to express their feeling
② for fighting with their enemy
③ to feel satisfied
④ for decoration
⑤ to get married

22 ①~⑤ 중 주어진 문장이 들어가기에 가장 적절한 곳은?

Then they popped and bloomed into white flowers.

①　　②　　③　　④　　⑤

23 다음과 같이 풀이되는 말을 위 글에서 찾아 쓰시오.

features that are added to something in order to make it look more attractive

➡ _____

24 According to the passage, what did Native Americans throw on hot stones over a fire? Answer in English with a full sentence.

➡ _____
_____

25 다음 중 위 글을 읽고 답할 수 <u>없는</u> 것은?

① What do historians believe?
② What is the most popular snack in the world?
③ Where was the first popcorn found?
④ What did the Native American teenage girls use to decorate clothes?
⑤ What did the Aztecs do to be protected by popping spirits?

[26~27] 다음 글을 읽고 물음에 답하시오.

In addition to Native Americans, many other people around the world enjoyed this tasty snack. The Chinese, as well as people in Sumatra and India, made popcorn long before Columbus arrived in the West Indies.

In ancient China, people popped corn (A) to tell fortunes for the coming year and their daughters' future marriage. In the Song Dynasty, Chinese people invented large pot-shaped popping machines to pop corn, and these machines are still used by street poppers today.

26 다음 중 밑줄 친 (A)to tell과 쓰임이 같은 것은?

① It is my duty to know the truth.

② It was difficult to choose one thing.

③ They just wanted to relax.

④ Mike went out to meet her.

⑤ I am really happy to hear from her.

27 다음 중 위 글의 내용과 일치하는 것은?

① People in Sumatra and India didn't enjoy eating popcorn.

② People in India couldn't make popcorn before Columbus arrived in the West Indies.

③ There was no corn in ancient China.

④ People in ancient China used popped corn to tell fortunes.

⑤ Large pot-shaped popping machines which Chinese people invented aren't used nowadays.

[28~30] 다음 글을 읽고 물음에 답하시오.

It was Americans ①that tried interesting ways of popping corn during the nineteenth century. Some threw corn seeds onto hot ashes, stirred, and then ②picked out the popped corn pieces. Others mixed corn with fat or butter and cooked it in a pan. They thought popping corn wonderful and exciting.

A more popular way ③was cooking popcorn over an open fire in a wire box with a long ④wooden handle. The fanciest popcorn popper was invented by Charles Cretors in 1893, and before long many types of interesting poppers were seen in movie theaters and parks. Finally, an electric popcorn popper for the home ⑤invented in 1925. Believe it or not, poppers were in high demand and were even made by middle school students in school clubs.

28 ①~⑤ 중 어법상 바르지 않은 것은?

①   ②   ③   ④   ⑤

29 다음 중 위 글의 내용과 일치하지 않는 것은?

① Interesting ways of popping corn were tried by Americans.

② There were some people who threw corn seeds onto hot ashes.

③ Popcorn poppers started to become common shortly after 1893.

④ Many people wanted to have poppers.

⑤ Middle school students made poppers in their homes.

30 위 글의 내용에 맞게 빈칸에 알맞은 말을 쓰시오.

As soon as _____
_____, many types of interesting poppers were seen in movie theaters and parks.

01
출제율 90%

다음 짝지어진 단어의 관계가 같도록 빈칸에 알맞은 말을 쓰시오. (주어진 철자로 시작할 것)

freshly : newly - f_____ : eventually

02
출제율 85%

다음 주어진 문장의 (A)와 (B)에 들어가기에 적절한 것으로 짝지어진 것은?

(A) What food from other countries are you interested _____?

(B) Why don't you come up _____ a new popper for our favorite popcorn?

	(A)	(B)		(A)	(B)
①	from	– with	②	in	– from
③	with	– for	④	by	– of
⑤	in	– with			

03
출제율 90%

다음 빈칸에 들어갈 말로 적절한 것을 고르시오.

• 머지않아 날이 어두워질 것이다.
  = It will be dark _____.

① long before
② for a long time
③ before long
④ longer and longer
⑤ for a while

04
출제율 100%

다음 중 〈보기〉에 있는 단어를 사용하여 자연스러운 문장을 만들 수 없는 것은?

보기
good   arrive   long before   forward to

① I'm looking _____ the New Year's Eve party.
② The Chinese made popcorn _____ Columbus arrived in the West Indies.
③ He is _____ at solving difficult math problems.
④ Be sure you _____ at work on time every morning.
⑤ Chinese people _____ large pot-shaped popping machines to pop corn.

[05~07] 다음 대화를 읽고 물음에 답하시오.

G: (A)이거 네가 다 직접 구웠니?
B: Yes, I did.
G: They look just wonderful.
B: Thanks. (B)Would you like to try some cake?
G: Sure.
B: How do you like it?
G: I just love this.
B: Thanks. I'm so happy you like it.

05
출제율 90%

〈보기〉의 표현을 포함하여 (A)의 우리말에 해당하는 영어 문장을 완성하시오.

보기
by   bake   did   all of these

➡ _____

06 밑줄 친 (B)와 같은 의미로 쓰기에 적절한 것은?

① Why don't you buy some cake?
② How about baking some cake?
③ Are you satisfied with the cake?
④ What do you think about the cake?
⑤ Would you like some cake?

07 According to the dialogue, which one is TRUE?

① The boy wants to try some cake.
② The girl baked the cake by herself.
③ The girl is satisfied with the cake.
④ The boy thinks they look delicious.
⑤ The girl doesn't like the cake.

08 다음 주어진 문장에 자연스럽게 이어지도록 순서대로 배열한 것은?

> **Junha:** It's a snack from Japan, isn't it?
> (A) What is it made from?
> (B) It's made from mochi. It is often served with green tea.
> (C) Yes, it is.

① (A) – (C) – (B)   ② (B) – (A) – (C)
③ (B) – (C) – (A)   ④ (C) – (A) – (B)
⑤ (C) – (B) – (A)

09 다음 중 어법상 <u>어색한</u> 문장은?

① It was the boat that he proposed to Mary.
② It was last year that Chris wrote this novel.
③ It was James who broke the vase the other day.
④ It was in July that she saw fireworks at the park.
⑤ It is when people enjoy his show that he is happy.

10 다음 주어진 문장의 밑줄 친 'It ～ that'과 쓰임이 <u>다른</u> 것은?

> <u>It</u> is on Friday <u>that</u> I have a guitar lesson.

① <u>It</u> is so hot <u>that</u> I don't want to go outside.
② <u>It</u> was in 1995 <u>that</u> the accident took place.
③ <u>It</u> is you <u>that</u> should take care of the child.
④ <u>It</u> was Daniel <u>that</u> I dated with in the amusement park last Sunday.
⑤ <u>It</u> was at the station <u>that</u> I lost the hat.

11 다음 문장의 밑줄 친 부분을 강조하는 문장으로 바꿔 쓰시오.

> He worked <u>for 20 hours</u> without rest.
> (10단어)

➡ _____

12 다음 중 어법상 올바른 문장을 <u>모두</u> 고르면?

① I consider his work greatly.
② I thought the school trip exciting.
③ This painting makes me felt peaceful.
④ The woman thought him a famous singer.
⑤ I don't think the old movie sadly.

13 다음 빈칸 ⓐ, ⓑ에 들어갈 말로 바르게 연결된 것은?

> • My mother didn't consider him ⓐ_____.
> • My father thinks him ⓑ_____.

	ⓐ	ⓑ
①	kind	– a good teacher
②	kind	– teach well
③	kindly	– teach well
④	kindly	– a good teacher
⑤	kindness	– have taught

14 다음 우리말의 밑줄 친 부분을 강조하여 영어로 쓰시오. (단, 주어진 단어를 활용하고, 필요시 변형할 것)

> 내가 어제 만난 것은 바로 <u>Hana</u>이었다.

➡ It _____.
(meet / that / yesterday)

[15~16] 다음 글을 읽고 물음에 답하시오.

> Popcorn is a popular snack around the world. People have enjoyed ①it for more than 5,000 years. It was in New Mexico that ②<u>the snack</u> was first found, and ③it was Native Americans that tried interesting ways of enjoying ④it. In addition to Native Americans, many people around the world have enjoyed this tasty snack. Americans as well as people in China have enjoyed making ⑤it.

15 다음 중 위 글의 제목으로 가장 적절한 것은?

① History of Corn Seeds
② How to Cook Corn Seeds
③ History of Popcorn
④ Why People Like to Eat Popcorn
⑤ Interesting Ways of Eating Popcorn

16 ①~⑤ 중 지칭하는 것이 <u>다른</u> 하나는?

①　　　②　　　③　　　④　　　⑤

[17~20] 다음 글을 읽고 물음에 답하시오.

It was Americans that tried interesting ways of popping corn during the nineteenth century. Some threw corn seeds onto hot ashes, stirred, and then picked out the popped corn pieces. Others mixed corn with fat or butter and cooked it in a pan. They thought popping corn wonderful and exciting.

A more popular way was cooking popcorn over an open fire in a wire box with a long wooden handle. The fanciest popcorn popper was invented by Charles Cretors in 1893, and before long many types of interesting poppers were seen in movie theaters and parks. Finally, an electric popcorn popper for the home was invented in 1925. Believe it or not, poppers were (A)_____ high demand and were even made by middle school students in school clubs.

🖊 출제율 95%

17 다음 중 빈칸 (A)에 들어갈 말로 가장 적절한 것은?

① on   ② by   ③ in   ④ at   ⑤ to

🖊 출제율 90%

18 다음과 같이 풀이되는 말을 위 글에서 찾아 쓰시오.

> to move something around or mix it in a container using something such as a spoon

➡ _____

🖊 출제율 95%

19 What was a more popular way of cooking popcorn? Answer in English with a full sentence.

➡ _____

_____

🖊 출제율 100%

20 다음 중 위 글의 내용과 일치하지 <u>않는</u> 것은?

① Americans popped corn in interesting ways during the nineteenth century.
② There were people who mixed corn with butter or fat.
③ Americans thought that popping corn was wonderful.
④ There were many ways of cooking corn in the seventeenth century.
⑤ The fanciest popper was invented in 1893.

[21~22] 다음 글을 읽고 물음에 답하시오.

①How do you like your popcorn? Sweet, hot, or spicy? Next time you enjoy popcorn, imagine ②you as a Native American, an ancient Chinese person, or an inventor. With a bowl of popcorn, you can be a Native American and ③make pretty decorations or be an ancient Chinese person and tell fortunes. Or ④better still, why don't you ⑤be an inventor and come up with a new popper for your favorite popcorn?

🖊 출제율 95%

21 위 글의 밑줄 친 ①~⑤ 중 어법상 바르지 <u>않은</u> 것은?

①   ②   ③   ④   ⑤

🖊 출제율 90%

22 With what can we be an ancient Chinese person and tell fortunes?

➡ _____

_____

01 다음 문장의 빈칸에 들어가기에 적절한 단어를 주어진 철자로 시작하여 쓰시오.

> • 발명가가 되어 당신이 가장 좋아하는 팝콘을 위해 새로운 팝콘 기계를 생각해 내는 것은 어떤가요?
> = Why don't you be an inventor and c_____ u_____ w_____ a new popper for our favorite popcorn?

02 다음 짝지어진 단어의 관계가 같도록 빈칸에 알맞은 말을 쓰시오.

> invent : invention - marry : _____

[03~04] 다음 대화를 읽고 물음에 답하시오.

> A: What Korean street snacks do you want to share with people from other countries?
> B: I'd like to share *tteokbokki* and *chapssaltteok*. (A)내 생각이 어때?
> A: That sounds cool.
> B: Thanks. (B)I'm glad you like my idea.

03 보기의 단어들을 이용하여 밑줄 친 (A)에 해당하는 영어 문장을 완성하시오.

> ┤ 보기 ├
> idea   how   like

➡ _____

04 밑줄 친 (B)와 같은 의미의 문장이 되도록 빈칸에 적절한 단어를 주어진 철자로 시작하여 쓰시오.

➡ I'm glad you like my idea.
= I'm p_____ you love my idea.

05 다음 우리말에 해당하는 영어 문장을 완성하시오.

> • 우리는 Mozart를 위대한 음악가라고 여긴다. (consider, musician) (6 words)

➡ _____

06 다음 문장을 'It ~ that' 강조 구문을 이용하여 괄호 안의 조건에 맞게 완성하시오.

> Hana bought some food on her way home.

(1) (some food를 강조)
➡ _____
_____

(2) (on her way home을 강조)
➡ _____
_____

[07~09] 다음 글을 읽고 물음에 답하시오.

> Popcorn is a popular snack around the world. People have enjoyed it for more than 5,000 years. (A)It was New Mexico that the snack was first found, and it was Native Americans that tried interesting ways of enjoying it. In addition to Native Americans, many people around the world have enjoyed this tasty snack. Americans as well as people in China have enjoyed making it.

07 다음 물음에 조건에 맞게 답하시오.

> Q: What did Native Americans try?

조건
1. Answer in English with a full sentence.
2. Use the phrase 'It ~ that'.

➡ _____

_____

08 위 글의 내용에 맞게 빈칸에 알맞은 말을 쓰시오.

> Not only _____ but also _____ have enjoyed making popcorn.

09 밑줄 친 (A)를 어법에 맞게 바르게 고쳐 쓰시오.

➡ _____

[10~12] 다음 글을 읽고 물음에 답하시오.

It was Americans that tried interesting ways of popping corn during the nineteenth century. Some threw corn seeds onto hot ashes, stirred, and then picked out the popped corn pieces. Others mixed corn with fat or butter and cooked it in a pan. (A)그들은 옥수수를 튀기는 것을 멋지고 재미있다고 생각했다.
A more popular way was cooking popcorn over an open fire in a wire box with a long wooden handle. The fanciest popcorn popper was invented by Charles Cretors in 1893, and before long many types of interesting poppers were seen in movie theaters and parks. Finally, an electric popcorn popper for the home was invented in 1925. Believe it or not, poppers were in high demand and were even made by middle school students in school clubs.

10 주어진 단어를 활용하여 밑줄 친 우리말 (A)를 영어로 쓰시오.

> think   excite   pop   wonderful

➡ _____

11 Where did popcorn poppers start to be seen after 1893? Answer in English with a full sentence.

➡ _____

_____

12 According to the passage, when was an electric popcorn popper for the home invented? Answer in English with a full sentence.

➡ _____

_____

01 주어진 문장을 'It ~ that' 강조 구문을 이용하여 괄호 안의 조건에 맞게 고쳐 쓰시오.

> Jake threw a stone at my dog in the park yesterday.

(1) (주어를 강조) _____

(2) (목적어를 강조) _____

(3) (장소를 강조) _____

(4) (때를 강조) _____

02 프레첼의 역사에 대한 다음 질문과 답변을 참고하여 프레첼의 역사를 소개하는 글을 완성하시오.

> **Q** : For how many years have people enjoyed the snack?
> **A** : People have enjoyed the snack for more than 1,600 years.
> **Q** : Where was it first found or made?
> **A** : It was first made in Italy.
> **Q** : Who tried interesting ways of enjoying it?
> **A** : People in Germany tried interesting ways of enjoying it.
> **Q** : Who else around the world has enjoyed making it?
> **A** : Americans as well as people in Europe have enjoyed making it.

> History of the Pretzel
> _____ is a popular snack around the world. People have enjoyed it _____
> _____. It was _____ that the snack was first made, and it was _____
> that _____. In addition to people _____, many people around
> the world have enjoyed this tasty snack. _____.

단원별 모의고사

01 다음 짝지어진 단어의 관계가 같도록 빈칸에 알맞은 말을 고르시오.

> ancient : modern = _____ : hostility

① bloom
② decoration
③ historian
④ goodwill
⑤ inventor

02 다음 영영풀이에 해당하는 말을 주어진 철자로 시작하여 쓰시오.

(1) b_____ : a wide round container that is open at the top
(2) c_____ : a large natural hole in the side of a cliff
(3) d_____ : a period of time when a particular family ruled a country
(4) g_____ : kind feelings towards or between people

03 다음 주어진 단어를 이용해 빈칸을 완성하시오.

> • In ancient China, people popped corn to tell fortunes for the coming year and their daughters' future _____.

➡ _____ (marry)

04 다음 대화의 빈칸에 공통으로 들어가기에 적절한 것은?

> A: _____ do you like my hamburger?
> B: I just love it. _____ tasty!
> A: Thanks. I'm glad you like.

① What
② How
③ Which
④ When
⑤ Where

[05~07] 다음 대화를 읽고 물음에 답하시오.

> Minji: Your cookies all look tasty.
> Jinho: Thanks. (A)Would you like to try some?
> Minji: Thanks, let me try one.
> Jinho: Here you go. ... (B)그거 어떠니?
> Minji: It's so sweet. I just love it.
> Jinho: I'm glad you like it.

05 위 대화의 밑줄 친 (A)와 바꾸어 쓸 수 있는 것을 <u>모두</u> 고르시오.

① Would you make some?
② Would you like some?
③ How would you be glad?
④ Please try some cookies.
⑤ Why don't you tell me?

06 위 대화의 밑줄 친 (B)에 해당하는 표현을 가장 잘 나타낸 것은?

① How would you try it?
② How would you bake it?
③ Why do you have it?
④ How do you like it?
⑤ Why would you think it?

07 위 대화의 내용과 일치하지 <u>않는</u> 것은?

① Jinho has made some cookies.
② Jinho wants Minji to try the cookie.
③ Minji thinks it's too sweet.
④ Minji is satisfied with the cookie.
⑤ Jinho is pleased that Minji likes the cookie.

[08~10] 다음 대화를 읽고 물음에 답하시오.

Nara: (A)핫 초콜릿 좀 먹을래, Junha?

Junha: Sure, I haven't had it for ages!... Mmm. (ⓐ)

Nara: How do you like it? (ⓑ)

Junha: I like it a lot. You are very good at making hot chocolate. (ⓒ)

Nara: Thanks. (B) 네가 좋아한다니 기뻐. By the way, did you know that chocolate was once called the "drink of the gods"?

Junha: Was it really? (ⓓ)

Nara: Yes, chocolate was first enjoyed by the emperor of the Aztec Empire, and it was once called xoco-latl, "drink of the gods."

Junha: (ⓔ) Well, thanks for the gods' drink, Nara.

Nara: You are welcome!

08 주어진 단어를 배열하여 (A), (B)의 우리말에 해당하는 영어 문장을 쓰시오.

(A) (you, hot, like, some, would, chocolate)

➡ _____

(B) (it, like, glad, you, I'm)

➡ _____

09 ⓐ~ⓔ 중에서 다음 문장이 들어가기에 적절한 곳은?

> That's surprising!

① ⓐ ② ⓑ ③ ⓒ ④ ⓓ ⑤ ⓔ

10 위 대화를 읽고 대답할 수 없는 것은?

① Who is good at making hot chocolate?
② Did Junha have hot chocolate often?
③ Was Junha satisfied with the chocolate?
④ Who told the origin of chocolate?
⑤ Why did Nara make hot chocolate?

[11~13] 다음 방송을 읽고 물음에 답하시오.

W: (A)_____ do you like the school lunch? (B)_____ would you like to have for your lunch? We'd like to have your cool ideas on the school lunch menu. (C)_____ don't you visit www.mslunch.ms.kr and answer the questions about your school lunch? (D) 우리는 여러분의 응답을 고대합니다. (we're, forward, get, answers)

11 빈칸 (A), (B), (C)에 들어가기에 가장 적절한 것으로 짝지어진 것은?

(A)	(B)	(C)
① What – How – What
② How – What – Why
③ How – Why – What
④ What – How – Why
⑤ Why – What– How

12 What will the students do after listening this announcement?

① They will go to the cafeteria to have lunch.
② They will talk about the cool ideas about the site.
③ They will go to the web site and answer the questions.
④ They will look forward to answering the questions.
⑤ They will go to the restaurant and have lunch.

13 주어진 단어들을 활용하여 밑줄 친 (D)의 우리말에 해당하는 영어 문장을 쓰시오.

➡ _____

14 다음 중 밑줄 친 'It ～ that'의 쓰임이 나머지와 <u>다른</u> 것은?

① <u>It</u> was him <u>that</u> I met at that time.
② <u>It</u> was the house <u>that</u> she wanted to visit.
③ <u>It</u> was she <u>that</u> called him last night.
④ <u>It</u> is the car <u>that</u> she cleans every morning.
⑤ <u>It</u> is true <u>that</u> he finally visited the island.

15 다음 중 어법상 <u>어색한</u> 것은?

① They thought chocolate "the drink of the gods".
② I consider Darwin a great scientist.
③ We believe him honestly.
④ She wants them to arrive here on time.
⑤ He made them keep quiet.

16 다음 우리말을 영어로 적절하게 옮긴 것은?

> 우리는 그녀가 훌륭한 예술가라고 믿는다.

① We believe her to a great artist.
② We consider she is a great artist.
③ We think a great artist for her.
④ We believe her to be a great artist.
⑤ We believe she will be a great artist.

17 'It ～ that' 구문을 사용하여 다음 문장의 밑줄 친 부분을 강조하는 문장으로 다시 쓰시오.

> (1) Hana met Nara <u>at the bus stop</u>.
> (2) Columbus discovered America <u>in 1492</u>.

(1) It was _____ .
(2) It was _____ .

[18~22] 다음 글을 읽고 물음에 답하시오.

Native Americans not only loved eating corn but also enjoyed the game of popping corn. ① Corn seeds were thrown on hot stones over a fire. ② Then they popped and bloomed into white flowers. ③ Native Americans used popcorn for decoration as well. ④ Their teenage girls used popped corn to decorate clothes. ⑤ The Aztecs made corn decorations for the statues of the god of rain. They thought popcorn a symbol of good health and goodwill. They believed that they would be protected by (A)_____ spirits when they wore decorations made with (B)_____ corn.

18 단어 'pop'을 어법에 맞게 빈칸 (A)와 (B)에 쓰시오.

➡ (A)_____ (B)_____

19 ①～⑤ 중 주어진 문장이 들어가기에 가장 적절한 곳은?

> The game was to catch and enjoy the flowery snacks.

①   ②   ③   ④   ⑤

20 What did Native Americans do with corn? Answer in English with three sentences.

➡ _____

_____

_____

21 Who made corn decorations for the statues of the god of rain? Answer in English and use the phrase 'It ~ that.'

➡ _____

_____

22 다음 중 위 글의 내용과 일치하는 것은?

① Native Americans neither ate corn nor enjoyed the game of popping corn.

② The Aztecs thought popcorn a symbol of wealth.

③ Native Americans didn't decorate their clothes.

④ Popcorn was a symbol of goodwill to the Aztecs.

⑤ Corn decorations were made for the statues of the god of rain by Native Americans.

[23~25] 다음 글을 읽고 물음에 답하시오.

In addition to Native Americans, many other people around the world enjoyed this tasty snack. The Chinese, as well as people in Sumatra and India, made popcorn long before Columbus arrived in the West Indies. In ancient China, people popped corn to tell (A)fortunes for the coming year and their daughters' future marriage. In the Song Dynasty, Chinese people invented large pot-shaped popping machines to pop corn, and these machines are still used by street poppers today.

23 다음 중 밑줄 친 (A)fortunes의 의미로 가장 적절한 것은?

① poverty   ② wealth

③ property   ④ luck

⑤ means

24 When were large pop-shaped popping machines invented? Answer in English with a full sentence.

➡ _____

25 다음 중 위 글을 읽고 답할 수 있는 것은?

① When was the first popcorn found in China?

② What did ancient Chinese people do for a living?

③ What did people in Sumatra and India mainly eat?

④ Why did people in ancient China pop corn?

⑤ How much was the popping machine which was invented in the Song Dynasty?

Lesson 3

What Makes Us Shop?

 의사소통 기능

- 경고하기
  Make sure you don't spend too much money.
- 의도 묻기
  Are you thinking of watching a movie?

 언어 형식

- 관계대명사 what
  Many teens like to do **what** their favorite celebrities do.

- 사역동사 make
  The signs **make** them **believe** that it is the last chance to grab the cool products.

Words & Expressions

Key Words

- **air**[ɛər] 명 공기, 대기, 분위기
- **appreciation**[əprì:ʃiéiʃən] 명 감상
- **attack**[ətǽk] 동 공격하다
- **booth**[bu:θ] 명 점포
- **brand-new**[brǽndnju] 형 완전히 새로운
- **celebrity**[səlérəti] 명 유명한 사람
- **celebrity brand** 유명인 브랜드
- **collection**[kəlékʃən] 명 수집품
- **consumer**[kənsú:mər] 명 소비자
- **cool**[ku:l] 형 멋있는
- **cute**[kju:t] 형 귀여운
- **elder sister** 누나, 언니
- **empty-handed**[émptihændid] 형 빈손으로
- **featuring**[fí:tʃəriŋ] 형 특징으로 하는
- **flash sale** 반짝 세일
- **floor**[flɔːr] 명 바닥, 층
- **grab**[græb] 동 움켜쥐다
- **helpful**[hélpfəl] 형 도움이 되는, 유익한
- **high-end**[háiend] 형 명품의, 고급의
- **hurt**[həːrt] 동 다치다
- **include**[inklú:d] 동 포함하다
- **incredibly**[inkrédəbli] 부 믿을 수 없을 정도로
- **instead**[instéd] 부 대신에
- **knee**[ni:] 명 무릎
- **limited edition** 한정판
- **lively**[láivli] 형 생생한, 활발한
- **pet**[pet] 동 만지다 명 반려동물
- **pocket money** 용돈
- **presentation**[prèzəntéiʃən] 명 발표
- **product**[prádʌkt] 명 상품
- **receipt**[risí:t] 명 영수증
- **recommend**[rèkəménd] 동 추천하다
- **repeat**[ripí:t] 동 반복하다
- **rest stop** 휴게소
- **return**[ritə́:rn] 동 반품하다
- **sale sign** 판매 게시물
- **seat belt** 안전벨트
- **sign**[sain] 명 간판, 게시물
- **slippery**[slípəri] 형 미끄러운
- **steal**[sti:l] 동 훔치다 명 도루, 공짜
- **suffer**[sʌ́fər] 동 겪다
- **swimsuit**[swimsut] 명 수영복
- **taste**[teist] 동 맛보다
- **traditional**[trədíʃənl] 형 전통적인
- **treasure**[tréʒər] 명 보물
- **trend**[trend] 명 유행

Key Expressions

- **be careful** 조심하다
- **be on** 켜지다
- **be willing to** 기꺼이 ~하려고 하다
- **break habit** 습관을 바꾸다
- **calm down** 진정하다
- **carry around** 들고 다니다
- **cool off** 진정하다
- **cut down** 줄이다
- **due to** ~ 때문에
- **get closer to** ~에 가까이 가다
- **get tired** 피곤해지다
- **get to** ~에 가다
- **give it a try** 시도해 보다
- **give up** 포기하다
- **look around** 둘러보다
- **look out for** ~을 조심하다
- **make a noise** 떠들다
- **now or never** 지금이 아니면 절대 못 한다
- **put on** ~을 신다, ~을 착용하다
- **sell like hot cakes** 불티나게 팔리다
- **sign out** 로그아웃하다
- **stick to** ~을 계속하다, ~을 고수하다
- **take off** 이륙하다
- **watch out for** ~을 조심하다

Word Power

※ 서로 비슷한 뜻을 가진 어휘
- □ **attack** 공격하다 – **charge** 공격하다
- □ **collect** 수집하다 – **gather** 모으다
- □ **hurt** 다치다 – **injure** 다치다
- □ **pocket money** 용돈 – **allowance** 용돈
- □ **product** 상품 – **commodity** 상품
- □ **repeat** 반복하다 – **replay** 반복하다

- □ **celebrity** 유명한 사람 – **star** 유명한 사람
- □ **consumer** 소비자 – **customer** 고객
- □ **lively** 활발한 – **cheerful** 활발한
- □ **presentation** 발표 – **demonstration** 발표
- □ **return** 반품하다 – **refund** 환불하다
- □ **suffer** 겪다 – **undergo** 겪다

※ 서로 반대의 뜻을 가진 어휘
- □ **attack** 공격하다 ↔ **defend** 방어하다
- □ **grab** 움켜쥐다 ↔ **let go** 놓아주다
- □ **include** 포함하다 ↔ **exclude** 제외하다
- □ **save** 저축하다 ↔ **spend** 쓰다
- □ **stay** 머무르다 ↔ **depart** 떠나다

- □ **consumer** 소비자 ↔ **producer** 생산자
- □ **hurt** 다치다 ↔ **heal** 치료하다
- □ **lively** 활발한 ↔ **gloomy** 우울한
- □ **wet** 젖은 ↔ **dry** 마른
- □ **traditional** 전통적인 ↔ **modern** 현대적인

※ 동사 – 명사
- □ **appreciate** 감상하다 – **appreciation** 감상
- □ **consume** 소비하다 – **consumption** 소비
- □ **present** 발표하다 – **presentation** 발표
- □ **repeat** 반복하다 – **repetition** 반복

- □ **collect** 수집하다 – **collection** 수집품
- □ **include** 포함하다 – **inclusion** 포함
- □ **produce** 생산하다 – **product** 상품

※ 명사 – 형용사
- □ **inclusion** 포함 – **inclusive** 포괄적인
- □ **repetition** 반복 – **repetitive** 반복적인
- □ **tradition** 전통 – **traditional** 전통적인

- □ **liveliness** 활발함 – **lively** 생생한, 활발한
- □ **taste** 맛 – **tasty** 맛좋은

English Dictionary

- □ **appreciation** 감상
  → pleasure you feel when you realize something is good 어떤 것이 좋다고 깨달을 때 느끼는 즐거움
- □ **attack** 공격하다
  → to deliberately use violence to hurt a person or damage a place 어떤 사람을 해치거나 장소를 손상 주기 위해 의도적으로 폭력을 사용하다
- □ **brand-new** 신상품
  → new and not yet used 새것이고 아직 사용되지 않은
- □ **celebrity** 유명한 사람
  → a famous living person 살아 있는 유명한 사람
- □ **high-end** 고급의
  → more expensive and of better quality than other products of the same type 같은 유형의 다른 상품보다 더 비싸고 품질이 좋은

- □ **consumer** 소비자
  → someone who buys and uses products 상품을 구입하여 사용하는 사람
- □ **include** 포함하다
  → to make someone or something part of a larger group 어떤 사람이나 어떤 것을 큰 집단의 한 부분으로 만들다
- □ **knee** 무릎
  → the joint that bends in the middle of your leg 다리 중간에 있는 구부러지는 관절
- □ **take off** 이륙하다
  → rise into the air from the ground 지상에서 공중으로 올라가다
- □ **treasure** 보물
  → a group of valuable things such as gold, silver, jewels 금, 은, 보석 같은 소중한 것들의 집합

01 다음 주어진 문장의 (A)와 (B)에 들어가기에 적절한 것으로 짝지어진 것은?

> • Are you thinking of throwing them (A)_____?
> • After 24 hours of cooling (B)_____, come back and see if you still want it.

	(A)	(B)			(A)	(B)
①	from – away			②	for – away	
③	out – from			④	with – for	
⑤	away – off					

02 다음 짝지어진 단어의 관계가 같도록 빈칸에 알맞은 단어를 고르시오.

> celebrity : star = _____ : gather

① attack ② hurt ③ include
④ collect ⑤ produce

03 다음 중 〈보기〉에 있는 단어를 사용하여 자연스러운 문장을 만들 수 <u>없는</u> 것은?

> ┤ 보기 ├
> take celebrities try featuring

① Many teens like to do what their favorite _____ do.
② Why don't you give it a _____ and get rich?
③ The planes can't _____ off due to a heavy snow.
④ Make a shopping list and _____ it around.
⑤ The most popular collections include character stickers, and goods _____ pop stars.

04 다음 빈칸에 들어갈 말로 적절한 것을 고르시오.

> Many teens are _____ buy what the stars use.

① would like ② ask to
③ willing to ④ doubt to
⑤ get to

05 다음 중 밑줄 친 부분의 뜻풀이가 바르지 <u>않은</u> 것은?

① <u>Instead</u>, hit "Add To Cart" and sign out. (마침내)
② They think celebrity brands will make them <u>cool</u>. (멋있는)
③ There's an online <u>flash sale</u> on new sneakers. (반짝 세일)
④ This completes my <u>collection</u>. (수집품)
⑤ Please help me <u>grab</u> a pair of smeakers. (움켜쥐다)

06 다음 영영풀이에 해당하는 단어를 고르시오.

> to deliberately use violence to hurt a person or damage a place

① include ② produce ③ attack
④ stay ⑤ spend

07 다음 중 밑줄 친 부분의 쓰임이 어색한 것은?

① What's your <u>favorite</u> color?
② Make sure you don't <u>make</u> any noise.
③ They are so cute. Let's <u>get away from</u> them.
④ N-girls are wearing a <u>brand-new</u> jacket.
⑤ Here are three shopping <u>tips</u> to live by.

01 다음 주어진 단어를 이용해 빈칸을 완성하시오.

> If you can't find anything on the list, walk out empty-handed. You will feel _____ light.

➡ _____ (incredible)

02 다음 짝지어진 단어의 관계가 같도록 빈칸에 알맞은 말을 쓰시오.

> include : exclude = _____ : defend

03 다음 빈칸에 알맞은 단어를 <보기>에서 골라 쓰시오.

> ┤ 보기 ├
> high-end   suffer   hot cakes   give

(1) Make sure you don't _____ up in the middle.

(2) They _____ from FOMO, Fear of Missing Out.

(3) When a product sells like _____, some people want to get it.

(4) I can get _____ sneakers for 70% off. It's a steal.

04 다음 밑줄 친 단어와 의미가 같은 단어를 쓰시오. (주어진 철자로 시작할 것)

> What do you do first when you get your pocket money?

➡ a_____

05 다음 영영풀이에 해당하는 말을 주어진 철자로 시작하여 쓰고, 알맞은 것을 골라 문장을 완성하시오. (문장에 쓸 때는, 필요하면 적절한 형태로 바꾸어 쓰시오.)

> • a_____ : to deliberately use violence to hurt a person or damage a place
> • b_____ : new and not yet used
> • c_____ : a famous living person

(1) A new _____ appeared on the Internet last year.

(2) If you freeze in place, a dog usually won't _____.

(3) I prefer a _____ car to a used one.

06 다음 빈칸에 공통으로 들어가기에 적절한 단어를 쓰시오.

> • Calm _____! You'll have better luck next time.
> • He cut _____ his time to one hour and five minutes.

07 다음 우리말에 맞게 빈칸에 알맞은 말을 쓰시오.

(1) 동전이 너무 많으면 들고 다니기가 아주 무거워요.
➡ Too many coins are too heavy to _____ _____.

(2) 우리는 계획을 고수해야 해.
➡ We have to _____ _____ the plan.

(3) 그는 소비자 제품을 테스트하는 사람으로 일한다.
➡ He works as a _____ product tester.

(4) 길을 횡단할 때는 자동차에 주의해라.
➡ When you cross a street, look _____ _____ cars.

Conversation

① 경고하기

Make sure you don't spend too much money. (돈을 너무 많이 쓰지 않도록 명심하세요.)

- "Make sure you don't ~"는 상대방에게 ~하지 않도록 확실히 하라는 뜻으로 경고할 때 쓰는 표현이다. 이 표현은 상대방에게 좋지 않은 것을 하지 말라고 충고할 때도 쓸 수 있다. "Don't ~"를 사용하여 직접적으로 단호하게 경고를 표현하거나, "(Please) Be careful not to ~"를 사용하여 완곡하게 경고를 표현할 수도 있다.

- 상대방이 잊어버리지 않도록 중요한 일에 대해 강한 당부 또는 경고하는 의미를 나타낼 수 있는 "Make sure ~"는 동사원형을 사용할 때는 "Make sure to+동사원형 ~"이 되고, 주어와 동사가 있는 절이 왔을 때는 "Make sure (that) 주어+동사 ~"의 구문이 된다. "~을 반드시 하지 말 것"을 강하게 당부하거나 경고할 경우에는 "Make sure not to+동사원형 ~" 또는 "Make sure (that) you don't ~"를 사용할 수 있다.

- "~을 확실히 하라, ~을 반드시 하라"의 뜻으로, "I think you should ~", "Try to ~", "Be sure to/(that) ~"을 통해서도 강한 당부, 충고, 경고의 의미를 나타낼 수 있다.

- Make sure you don't stay up all night working. (일을 하느라 밤을 새지 않도록 해.)
- Don't waste your time complaining about minor things. (너의 시간을 사소한 것들에 불평하며 낭비하지 마.)

경고하기

- Make sure you don't ~. ~하지 않도록 명심해라.
- Don't ~. ~하지 마라
- Be careful not to ~. ~하지 않도록 조심해라.
- Watch out for ~! / Look out for ~! ~을 조심해라!
- I think you should ~ . 나는 네가 ~해야 한다고 생각해.
- Try to ~ . ~하려고 애써라.
- Be sure to/that ~ . 반드시 ~해라.

핵심 Check

1. 다음 대화의 밑줄 친 부분을 완성하시오.

> **B:** Ouch!
>
> **W:** Are you all right, Jinsu?
>
> **B:** No, I'm not. I hurt my knee.
>
> **W:** <u>여기는 바닥이 항상 미끄러워. 뛰지 않도록 명심해.</u> (make, run, don't 포함)

➡ The floor is always slippery here. _____

② 의도 묻기

Are you thinking of watching a movie? (너 영화 보려고 하는 거니?)

- "Are you thinking of ~?"는 상대방의 말이나 행동을 보고, 그 사람의 의도를 물을 때 쓰는 표현이다. 이 말은 상대방이 자신이 의도한 것을 말하는 건지(또는 행동하려는 건지) 자세히 물어서 확인하고자 할 때 쓰는 표현이다. "Do you intend to ~?"(~을 의도하는 거니?) 또는 "Do you want to ~?"(~하고 싶니?)에 해당하는 의미이다.

- 이 표현 외에도 상대방의 행동이나 말의 의도를 묻는 표현은 다양하다. 단순히 앞으로의 의도를 물어 보는 의미로 think 대신에 go, plan, consider 등을 사용하여 "Are you going to ~?" 또는 "Are you planning to ~?", "Are you considering ~?"을 쓰기도 하고 "Will you ~?"를 쓸 수도 있다.

- "~을 의미하는 거니?"라는 의미로 상대방의 의도를 물어 볼 때는 "Do you mean ~?"으로 표현한다. 이에 대한 대답으로는 "That's what I mean.", "No. That's not what I mean." 등이 있다. "What do you mean?(무슨 뜻이야?)", "What do you mean by that?(그건 무슨 뜻이니?)", "I see what you mean.(네가 말하는 뜻을 알겠어.)" 등으로도 상대방의 의도를 묻거나 상대방의 의도에 대해 말할 수 있다.

의도 묻기

- Are you thinking of ~? ~할 생각이니?
- Are you planning to ~? ~할 거니?
- Are you going to ~? ~할 예정이니?
- Are you considering ~? ~할 생각이니?
- Will you ~? ~할 거니?
- Do you mean ~? ~을 말하는 거니?
- What do you mean by that? 그것은 무슨 말이니?

핵심 Check

2. 다음 밑줄 친 말 대신 쓰기에 적절하지 <u>않은</u> 것은?

> G: I cleaned my room and found some old T-shirts.
> B: What are you going to do with them? <u>Are you thinking of throwing them away?</u>
> G: No. I will make an eco bag out of them.
> B: That's a good idea!

① Are you considering throwing them away?

② Are you planning to throw them away?

③ Are you going to throw them away?

④ Will you throw them away?

⑤ What do you mean by throwing them away?

Listen & Speak 1 A-1

G: They are so cute. Let's ❶get closer to them.

M: OK. But ❷be careful, and do not pet them.

G: Why not?

M: Because they may attack you.

소녀: 동물들이 너무 귀여워요. 우리 더 가까이 가요.
남자: 그래. 하지만 조심해. 만지면 안 돼.
소녀: 왜 안 돼요?
남자: 동물들이 너를 공격할 수도 있으니까.

❶ get은 "~에 가다, 도착하다"의 의미를 가진다. "get closer"는 "더 가까이 가다"의 의미가 된다.
❷ "be careful"은 상대방에게 경고하는 의미이다. "반드시 ~해라"의 의미로 "Make sure ~"라고 하지만 "Be careful."(조심해.)을 통해서 경고의 의미를 전달하기도 한다.

Check(√) True or False

(1) The girl is petting the animals. T ☐ F ☐

(2) The man tells the girl not to pet the animals. T ☐ F ☐

Conversation

Seho: Oh! It's almost closing time. Hurry up!

Semi(Seho's sister) : Calm down, Seho. ❶We've got everything.

Seho: No. I need to visit Sneaker Ground. They're having a sale there.

Semi: ❷What? Are you thinking of getting sneakers?

Seho: Yes. I can get high-end sneakers for 70% off. It's a steal.

Semi: Well, ❸it was just a week ago that you bought blue sneakers there. Have you even put them on?

Seho: No. They don't match any of my pants.

Semi: You see? ❹Make sure you don't repeat the same mistake.

Seho: I see what you mean, but it's now or never. I can't miss out.

Semi: You are impossible.

세호: 앗! 문 닫을 시간이 거의 다 됐네. 서둘러!
세미(세호 누나): 진정해, 세호야. 우리 다 샀어.
세호: 아니야. Sneaker Ground에 가야 돼. 거기 지금 세일 중이거든.
세미: 뭐? 너 운동화 살 생각이니?
세호: 응. 명품 운동화를 70% 할인에 살 수 있어. 공짜나 다름없어.
세미: 글쎄, 네가 거기에서 파란 운동화 산 것이 고작 일주일 전이야. 그거 신어나 봤어?
세호: 아니. 그 운동화는 내가 가진 바지 중 어떤 것과도 어울리지 않아.
세미: 알겠지? 똑같은 실수를 저지르지 않도록 명심해.
세호: 누나 뜻이 뭔지는 알겠는데, 이런 기회는 다시 오지 않아. 놓칠 수 없어.
세미: 너 정말 못 말리겠네.

❶ 현재완료(have got)를 써서 '(필요한 모든 것을) 샀다'라고 표현하고 있다.
❷ 신발 매장에 들르겠다는 세호의 말에 놀란 누나는 "What?"이라고 물은 후 "Are you thinking of ~?" 표현을 써서 그의 의도를 다시 묻고 있다.
❸ 운동화를 그 매장에서 샀던 것이 바로 일주일밖에 안 되었다는 사실을 강조하기 위해서 it was와 that 사이에 'just a week ago'를 썼다.
❹ 'Make sure ~'표현을 써서 세호에게 같은 실수를 반복하지 말라고 경고하고 있다. 여기서 똑같은 실수는 바로 둘이 앞에서 말한 내용(지난주에 산 운동화에 어울리는 바지가 없다고 아직 신어보지도 못한 것)을 말한다.

Check(√) True or False

(3) Seho wants to buy new pants. T ☐ F ☐

(4) Seho's sister is satisfied with Seho's shopping habit. T ☐ F ☐

Listen & Speak 1 A-2

B: Ouch!

W: Are you all right, Jinsu?

B: No, I'm not. I hurt my knee.

W: ❶The floor is always slippery here.
❷Make sure you don't run.

❶ slippery는 "미끄러운"이라는 뜻이다.
❷ "Make sure that ～"에서 접속사 that이 생략된 형태이다.

Listen & Speak 1 A-3

B: Excuse me. Where is the restroom?

W: It's over there. But you can't use it now.

B: Oh. ❶Why not?

W: ❷We're taking off soon. Make sure you stay
in your seat when the seat belt sign is on.

❶ "Why not?"은 "왜 안 되나요?"의 의미로 안 되는 이유를 묻고 있다.
❷ "We're taking off soon."은 "비행기가 곧 이륙합니다."의미로 현재진행형으로 가까운 미래를 나타내고 있다.

Listen & Speak 1 B

A: Now, ❶we're getting to the rest stop. Any
questions?

B: Yes. Can I go to the snack stands?

A: Of course, but make sure you don't spend
too much money.

B: OK. Thanks.

❶ "we're getting"은 가까운 미래를 나타내는 의미로 쓰인 현재진행형이다.

Listen & Speak 2 A-1

G: I cleaned my room and ❶found some old
T-shirts.

B: What are you going to do with them? ❷Are
you thinking of throwing them away?

G: No. I will ❸make an eco bag out of them.

B: That's a good idea!

❶ 동사 found는 cleaned와 병렬이 되어 I를 공통의 주어로 하고 있다.
❷ "Are you thinking of ～?"는 "～할 작정이니?"의 의미로 상대의 의도를 묻고 있다.
❸ "make A out of B"는 "B로 A를 만들다"의 의미로 out of는 재료를 나타낸다.

Listen & Speak 2 A-2

B: What are you doing?

G: I'm ❶looking for the receipt for my new watch.

B: Why? Are you thinking of returning it?

G: Yes. ❷It suddenly stopped working.

❶ "look for ～"는 "～을 찾다"의 의미이다.
❷ "stop -ing"는 "～하기를 중단하다"의 의미로 시계가 작동을 멈추었다는 의미이다.

Listen & Speak 2 B

A: ❶Which floor are you going to?

B: I'm going to the third floor.

A: ❷Are you thinking of watching a movie?

B: No, I'm not. I'm thinking of playing with dogs.

❶ 건물에서 "어느 층"이라고 물어볼 때는 "which floor"라고 한다.
❷ "Are you thinking of ～?"는 "～할 작정이니?"의 의미로 상대의 의도를 묻고 있다. "Are you planning to watch a movie?"에 해당한다.

Real Life Task Step 1

B: What do you do first when you get your pocket
money? ❶I always save 30 percent of my
pocket money. How do I do this? ❷I cut down
my spending on ice cream and soft drinks. ❸
Why don't you give it a try and get RICH?
Make sure you don't give up in the middle.

❶ "I always save ～"는 평소에 늘 하고 있는 습관을 나타낸다.
❷ "cut down"은 "줄이다"의 의미이다.
❸ "Why don't you give it a try and get RICH?"는 상대에게 권하는 의미이다.

Real Life Task Step 2

A: ❶How did you like the presentation?

B: It was very helpful. I need to do something
to save money.

A: Are you thinking of cutting down your
spending?

B: Yes, I am. I'll spend less on clothes.

A: Good for you, but make sure you don't give
up your style.

❶ "How did you like ～?"는 상대에게 만족했는지 여부를 묻는 말이다.

● 다음 우리말과 일치하도록 빈칸에 알맞은 말을 쓰시오.

Listen & Speak 1 A-1

G: They are _____ cute. Let's _____ _____ to them.

M: OK. But _____ _____, and do not _____ them.

G: _____ not?

M: Because they may _____ you.

Listen & Speak 1 A-2

B: Ouch!

W: _____ you _____ right, Jinsu?

B: No, I'm not. I _____ my _____.

W: The _____ is always _____ here. _____ _____ you don't _____.

Listen & Speak 1 A-3

B: Excuse me. _____ is the restroom?

W: It's _____ there. But you _____ _____ it now.

B: Oh. Why not?

W: We're _____ _____ soon. Make _____ you _____ in your seat when the seat _____ _____ is _____.

Listen & Speak 1 B

A: Now, we're _____ to the _____ stop. Any _____?

B: Yes. _____ I go to the snack stands?

A: Of course, but _____ _____ you don't _____ too much money.

B: OK. Thanks.

Listen & Speak 2 A-1

G: I _____ my room and _____ some old T-shirts.

B: _____ are you going to do _____ them? Are you _____ _____ _____ them away?

G: No. I will _____ an eco bag _____ _____ them.

B: That's a good idea!

Listen & Speak 2 A-2

B: What are you doing?

G: I'm _____ _____ the _____ for my new watch.

B: Why? Are you _____ _____ _____ it?

G: Yes. It suddenly _____ working.

Listen & Speak 2 B

A: _____ _____ are you going to?

B: I'm _____ to the third floor.

A: Are you _____ _____ watching a movie?

B: No, I'm not. I'm _____ of playing with dogs.

Conversation

Seho: Oh! It's almost _____ time. Hurry up!

Semi(Seho's sister): _____ down, Seho. We've _____ everything.

Seho: No. I need to visit Sneaker Ground. They're _____ a sale there.

Semi: What? Are you _____ of _____ sneakers?

Seho: Yes. I can _____ high-end sneakers _____ 70% off. It's a _____.

Semi: Well, it was just a week ago _____ you _____ blue sneakers there. Have you _____ _____ them on?

Seho: No. They don't _____ any of my pants.

Semi: You see? _____ _____ you don't _____ the same mistake.

Seho: I see _____ you mean, but it's _____ _____ never. I can't miss _____.

Semi: You are _____.

세호: 앗! 문 닫을 시간이 거의 다 됐네. 서둘러!
세미(세호 누나): 진정해, 세호야. 우리 다 샀어.
세호: 아니야. Sneaker Ground에 가야 돼. 거기 지금 세일 중이거든.
세미: 뭐? 너 운동화 살 생각이니?
세호: 응. 명품 운동화를 70% 할인에 살 수 있어. 공짜나 다름없어.
세미: 글쎄, 네가 거기에서 파란 운동화 산 것이 고작 일주일 전이야. 그거 신어나 봤어?
세호: 아니. 그 운동화는 내가 가진 바지 중 어떤 것과도 어울리지 않아.
세미: 알겠지? 똑같은 실수를 저지르지 않도록 명심해.
세호: 누나 뜻이 뭔지는 알겠는데, 이런 기회는 다시 오지 않아. 놓칠 수 없어.
세미: 너 정말 못 말리겠네.

Real Life Task Step 1

B: What do you do first when you _____ your pocket money? I always _____ 30 percent of my pocket money. How do I do this? I _____ _____ my spending _____ ice cream and soft drinks. Why _____ you give it a _____ and get RICH? Make _____ you don't _____ _____ in the middle.

Real Life Task Step 2

A: _____ did you like the presentation?

B: It was very _____. I need to do something to save money.

A: Are you _____ of _____ down your spending?

B: Yes, I am. I'll spend _____ on clothes.

A: Good for you, but _____ _____ you don't _____ up your style.

01 다음 대화의 빈칸에 들어갈 말로 적절하지 <u>않은</u> 것을 고르시오.

> G: They are so cute. Let's get closer to them.
> M: OK. But _____.
> G: Why not?
> M: Because they may attack you.

① be careful, and do not pet them
② I think you should not pet them
③ don't pet them
④ don't forget to pet them
⑤ make sure you don't pet them

02 다음 대화의 순서가 바르게 배열된 것을 고르시오.

> B: Ouch!
> (A) No, I'm not. I hurt my knee.
> (B) Are you all right, Jinsu?
> (C) The floor is always slippery here. Make sure you don't run.

① (A) – (C) – (B)   ② (B) – (A) – (C)
③ (B) – (C) – (A)   ④ (C) – (A) – (B)
⑤ (C) – (B) – (A)

[03~04] 다음 대화를 읽고 물음에 답하시오.

> B: Excuse me. Where is the restroom?
> W: It's over there. But you can't use it now.
> B: Oh. Why not?
> W: We're taking off soon. (A)<u>안전벨트 표시등이 켜지면 반드시 자리에 앉아 계셔야 합니다.</u>

03 주어진 단어를 포함하여 (A)의 우리말을 영어로 쓰시오. (7 words)

➡ _____ when the seat belt sign is on.

(make, stay, sure, in)

04 위 대화의 내용과 일치하는 것은?

① They are in an express train.
② The boy can use the restroom at the moment.
③ After landing, the boy can use the restroom.
④ When the seat belt sign is on, they can't move around.
⑤ The boy knows how to control the plane.

[01~03] 다음 대화를 읽고 물음에 답하시오.

A: Now, we're (A)_____ the rest stop. Any questions?
B: Yes. Can I go to the snack stands?
A: Of course, but (B)make sure you don't spend too much money.
B: OK. Thanks.

01 빈칸 (A)에 들어가기에 가장 적절한 것은?

① walking around
② getting to
③ running from
④ driving through
⑤ climbing onto

02 위 글의 밑줄 친 (B) 대신 쓰기에 적절한 것은?

① you have to spend much money
② watch out for not spending money
③ be careful not spend too much money
④ make sure you spend much money
⑤ be sure not to spend too much money

03 위 대화의 내용과 일치하는 것은?

① 두 사람은 비행기를 타고 있다.
② A는 소년의 아버지이다.
③ 아마도 소년은 간식에 돈을 쓸 것이다.
④ 소년을 저축을 하는 이유를 묻고 있다.
⑤ 버스는 휴게소에 멈추지 않고 지나갈 예정이다.

[04~06] 다음 대화를 읽고 물음에 답하시오.

G: I cleaned my room and found some old T-shirts.
B: What are you going to do with them? ⓐ Are you thinking of throwing them (A)____?
G: No. I will make an eco bag (B)____ them.
B: That's a good idea!

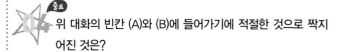

04 위 대화의 빈칸 (A)와 (B)에 들어가기에 적절한 것으로 짝지어진 것은?

① from – without
② around – to
③ with – by
④ of – on
⑤ away – out of

05 밑줄 친 ⓐ와 바꿔 쓸 수 있는 것은?

① Are you considering throwing
② Are you making to throw
③ Are you expect to throw
④ Are you making sure of throwing
⑤ What are you going to throw

06 According to the dialogue, which one is TRUE?

① The girl cleaned her room for a long time.
② The girl didn't like the T-shirt because it was too old.
③ The girl is going to recycle the old T-shirt.
④ The boy didn't wear the T-shirt.
⑤ The T-shirt was old but in good condition.

[07~08] 다음 대화를 읽고 물음에 답하시오.

B: What are you doing?
G: I'm looking for the receipt for my new watch.
B: Why? Are you thinking of (A)_____ it?
G: Yes. It suddenly stopped working.

07 위 대화의 빈칸 (A)에 들어가기에 적절한 것은?

① buying
② returning
③ wearing
④ fixing
⑤ calling

08 위 대화를 읽고 대답할 수 있는 것은?

① What is the girl looking for?
② Why did the boy ask the girl?
③ How will the boy repair the watch?
④ What does the girl want to buy?
⑤ Where did the girl buy the watch?

[09~10] 다음 대화를 읽고 물음에 답하시오.

A: (A)_____ floor are you going to?
B: I'm going to the second floor.
A: Are you thinking of having pizza?
B: (B)_____ I'm thinking of eating popcorn.

09 위 대화의 내용으로 보아, 빈칸 (A)에 들어가기에 적절한 것은?

① What
② Where
③ Which
④ How
⑤ Why

10 위 대화의 내용으로 보아 빈칸 (B)에 적절한 것은?

① Yes, you may.
② Yes, we have.
③ Yes, I will.
④ No, I haven't.
⑤ No, I'm not.

[11~12] 다음 대화를 읽고 물음에 답하시오.

G: How did you like the presentation?
B: It was very helpful. I need to do something to save money.
G: Are you thinking of (A)_____ your spending?
B: Yes, I am. I'll buy fewer snacks and drinks.
G: Good for you, but make sure you don't get too hungry.

11 위 대화의 빈칸 (A)에 들어가기에 적절한 것은?

① stopping considering
② using more time
③ increasing the amount of
④ making an effort
⑤ cutting down

12 According to the dialogue, which one is NOT true?

① The girl is asking the boy about the presentation.
② The boy thinks the presentation was helpful to him.
③ The girl will buy fewer snacks.
④ The boy needs to do something to save money.
⑤ The girl tells the boy not to get too hungry.

[01~04] 다음 대화를 읽고 물음에 답하시오.

Seho: Oh! It's almost closing time. Hurry up!
Semi(Seho's sister): Calm down, Seho. We've ⓐgot everything.
Seho: No. I need to visit Sneaker Ground. They're having a sale there.
Semi: What? Are you ⓑthinking of getting sneakers?
Seho: Yes. I can get high-end sneakers for 70% off. It's a ⓒsteal.
Semi: Well, (A)it was just a week ago what you bought blue sneakers there. Have you even ⓓput them on?
Seho: No. They don't match any of my pants.
Semi: You see? (B)똑같은 실수를 저지르지 않도록 명심해.(make, repeat)
Seho: I see what you mean, but it's now or never. I ⓔcan miss out.
Semi: You are impossible.

01 밑줄 친 ⓐ~ⓔ 중에서 내용상 어색한 것의 번호를 쓴 후 바로 잡아 쓰시오.

➡ _____

02 밑줄 친 (A) 문장에서 어법상 어색한 부분을 고쳐 다시 쓰시오.

➡ _____

03 주어진 단어를 포함하여 밑줄 친 (B)에 해당하는 영어 문장을 완성하시오. (8 words)

➡ _____

04 위 대화에서 다음 설명에 해당하는 표현을 찾아 쓰시오.

used to say that if someone does not do something now, they will not get another chance to do it

➡ _____

[05~07] 다음 대화를 읽고 물음에 답하시오.

G: How did you like the presentation?
B: It was very helpful. I need to do something to save money.
G: Are you thinking of cut down your spending?
B: Yes, I am. I'll spend more on clothes.
G: Good for you, but (A) 그래도 네 스타일은 포기하지 않도록 해. (make, give up, sure, style)

05 위 대화의 흐름상 어색한 문장을 올바른 내용으로 고치시오.

➡ _____
_____

06 위 대화에서 어법상 어색한 문장을 고쳐 다시 쓰시오.

➡ _____
_____

07 주어진 단어를 포함하여, 밑줄 친 (A)에 해당하는 표현을 완성하시오. (8 words)

➡ _____

Grammar

① 관계대명사 what

> Many teens like to do **what** their favorite celebrities do.
> (많은 십대들은 그들이 좋아하는 유명인들이 하는 것을 하고 싶어 한다.)

- 형태: what+(주어+)동사
  의미: ~하는 것

- 관계대명사 what은 별도의 선행사가 없고, 그 자체에 선행사를 포함하고 있는 관계대명사이기 때문에 형용사절이 아니라 명사절을 유도한다. 선행사가 별도로 없기 때문에 해석할 때는 '~하는 것, ~하는 일' 등으로 해석한다.
  - **what** is important 중요한 것
  - **what** he bought 그가 구입한 것
  - I found **what** she had lost. (what she had lost는 동사 found의 목적어가 되는 명사절)

- 명사절을 유도하는 관계대명사 what은 주격 또는 목적격이어서 명사절 속에서 주어, 목적어 역할을 한다.
  - He picked up **what** was on the table. 그는 테이블 위에 있는 것을 집어들었다.(관계대명사 what은 동사 was의 주어 역할을 하는 주격관계대명사이다.)
  - He couldn't understand **what** she said. 그는 그녀가 말하는 것을 이해할 수 없었다.(관계대명사 what은 동사 said의 목적어 역할을 하는 목적격 관계대명사이다.)

- 관계대명사 what이 포함된 관용적인 표현
  - what one has (사람이) 가진 것, 그의 재산
  - what one is 현재의 그 사람 (사람 됨됨이, 인격)
  - what is better 더욱 좋은 것은
  - what is worse 더욱 나쁜 것은

핵심 Check

1. 다음 괄호 안에서 어법상 적절한 것을 고르시오.
   (1) He didn't show me (that / what) she had brought.
   (2) (That / What) he painted made us surprised.
   (3) He didn't read the message (that / what) she had sent to him.

2. 다음 중 밑줄 친 부분의 쓰임이 나머지와 <u>다른</u> 하나는?
   ① <u>What</u> I need is a computer.
   ② Would you tell me <u>what</u> happened last night?
   ③ <u>What</u> he said was perfectly true.
   ④ They don't like <u>what</u> he wrote.
   ⑤ That is just <u>what</u> I want to say.

② 「주어+동사+목적어+목적격보어」 구문

The signs **make** them **believe** that it is the last chance to grab the cool products.
(게시물들은 지금이 좋은 상품을 살 수 있는 마지막 기회라고 그들이 믿게 만든다.)

- 형태: "주어+사역동사(make/have/let)+목적어+동사원형(목적격보어)"
  의미: ~에게 …하도록 만들다/시키다

- ask, allow, advise, enable, expect, want, tell 등의 동사는 목적격보어로 부정사를 쓸 때는 '동사+목적어+to부정사'로 '~에게 …하도록 하다'의 의미를 나타내지만, 사역동사 make, let, have를 쓸 때는 목적격보어로 to 없는 원형부정사를 쓴다. 지각동사 feel, hear, see, watch 등은 목적격보어로 원형부정사나 분사를 취한다. "~을 …하게 만들다"의 의미일 때는 "make+목적어+목적격보어(형용사/명사)"의 구문이 된다.
  - She **made** them **stay** in the house. (그녀는 그들이 집에 머물러 있도록 했다.)
  - I **had** Ted **get up** early in the morning. (나는 Ted가 아침에 일찍 일어나도록 했다.)
  - He **let** them **watch** TV after dinner. (그는 저녁식사 후에 그들이 TV를 보도록 허락했다.)

- 동사 help는 목적격보어로 부정사를 쓸 때는 to 있는 부정사와 to가 없는 원형부정사를 모두 쓸 수 있다. 사역의 의미를 가지는 get을 쓸 때는 'get+목적어+to부정사'의 형태로 '~에게 …하도록 시키다'의 의미가 된다.
  - He **got** them **to be** quiet. (그는 그들에게 조용히 하도록 했다.)
  - I **helped** them **(to) do** the homework. (나는 그들이 숙제하는 것을 도와주었다.)

- 사역동사의 목적격보어로 원형부정사를 쓸 때는 목적어의 능동적인 동작을 나타낸다. 사역동사의 목적어가 수동의 입장으로 당하는 내용일 때는 목적격보어로 과거분사를 쓴다.
  - The book **made** him **interested** in insects.
  - She **had** her car **repaired** yesterday.

핵심 Check

3. 다음 괄호 안에서 어법상 적절한 것을 고르시오.

(1) His injury made his father (get / to get) worried.

(2) His parents will let him (go / to go) to the party.

(3) My father asked me (clean / to clean) the room.

4. 다음 중 어법상 올바른 문장은?

① I couldn't make him went out.

② Tom always makes her laughs.

③ Mom made me taking out the garbage.

④ She made me wake up early in the morning,

⑤ Your advice made me to decide to study harder.

01 다음 중 어법상 어색한 문장은?

① I don't know what I should do.
② I live in a house that has five rooms.
③ This is a robot what can do my homework.
④ He is the man who gave me flowers.
⑤ Look at the windows which you have broken!

02 다음 빈칸에 들어갈 말이 순서대로 바르게 나열된 것은?

• Everyone knows _____ he loves you. • Please show me _____ you bought for me. • He is talking about the car _____ he bought.

① that – what – that
② that – which – which
③ that – that – which
④ who – what – which
⑤ who – which – which

03 다음 중 밑줄 친 부분이 어법상 올바른 것은?

① David always makes us <u>laugh</u>.
② Dad made me <u>watered</u> the flowers.
③ Tim's dad made him <u>cleaned</u> the floor.
④ Mom made me <u>washed</u> the dishes.
⑤ Dad made me <u>helping</u> an old lady on the street.

04 다음 빈칸에 들어갈 말로 알맞은 것은?

Mom had me _____ out the garbage while cleaning the house.

① take
② turn
③ make
④ to make
⑤ to take

 01 다음 중 밑줄 친 부분의 쓰임이 어색한 것은?

① She made him <u>clean</u> the room.
② He had us <u>wait</u> in the room.
③ His father let him <u>play</u> video games.
④ She allowed us <u>go</u> home early.
⑤ They helped us <u>to move</u> the table.

02 다음 중 밑줄 친 부분의 쓰임이 나머지와 다른 하나는?

① I can't believe <u>what</u> he said.
② I will do <u>what</u> makes you happy.
③ I think <u>what</u> Mina told me is a lie.
④ <u>What</u> I want for dinner is spaghetti.
⑤ Do you know <u>what</u> she will ask?

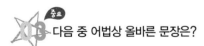 다음 중 어법상 올바른 문장은?

① I don't like that she bought at the mart.
② Show me the thing what is in your bag.
③ She has been reading the book what she bought.
④ I have been watching what she sent to me.
⑤ He was very surprised to hear what he had won the contest.

 04 다음 중 어법상 어색한 문장의 개수는?

ⓐ That's not what I want for my birthday.
ⓑ Did you hear that he said?
ⓒ She knows that you are ill in bed.
ⓓ He can't understand that he wrote.
ⓔ Did you receive what he had sent to you?

① 1개   ② 2개   ③ 3개   ④ 4개   ⑤ 5개

05 다음 중 어법상 어색한 문장은?

① I had John buy some bread.
② Jane makes David drive her car.
③ He had his car fix by an engineer.
④ They let Sam play computer games.
⑤ Doing yoga helps me to relieve stress.

06 다음 빈칸에 들어갈 수 없는 것은?

Mrs. Baker _____ her husband do the dishes.

① let   ② made   ③ wanted
④ had   ⑤ helped

 다음 중 밑줄 친 부분의 용법이 나머지 넷과 다른 것은?

① I <u>made</u> them clean the restroom.
② She will <u>make</u> me clean the windows again.
③ The movie <u>made</u> everyone cry.
④ My father <u>made</u> me a new desk as a gift.
⑤ Mr. Park always <u>makes</u> people laugh out loud.

08 다음 중 빈칸에 들어갈 동사의 형태가 바른 것끼리 묶인 것은?

> (A) I made my students _____ (believe) my idea.
> (B) I had the box _____ (deliver) to the office.
> (C) She helped me _____ (do) the dishes.

	(A)	(B)	(C)
①	believed	delivered	do
②	believe	deliver	do
③	believe	delivered	to do
④	believed	deliver	do
⑤	to believe	deliver	to do

09 다음 중 어법상 올바른 문장은?

① That she told him was a lie.
② I bought what I wanted to buy.
③ The boy eats only that he likes.
④ There is some truth in that he says.
⑤ This is the song what I want to listen to.

10 다음 문장을 영어로 바르게 옮긴 것은?

> 담임 선생님께서 우리에게 교실을 청소하도록 시키셨다.

① My homeroom teacher make us clean our classroom.
② My homeroom teacher made us clean our classroom.
③ My homeroom teacher made we clean our classroom.
④ My homeroom teacher make us cleaned our classroom.
⑤ My homeroom teacher made us to clean our classroom.

11 다음 중 빈칸에 들어갈 말이 <u>다른</u> 하나는? (대 · 소문자 무시)

① _____ I need is something to drink.
② This is _____ you need when you open tins of food.
③ Never put off till tomorrow _____ you can do today.
④ I didn't like _____ my brother had bought at the store.
⑤ Sean loves the dog _____ is lying on the chair.

12 다음 빈칸에 공통으로 들어갈 말로 알맞은 것은?

> (1) This is not _____ I want to see.
> (2) You can enjoy _____ you want to do.

① who   ② when   ③ that
④ what   ⑤ where

13 다음 중 밑줄 친 부분의 쓰임이 <보기>와 같은 것으로 짝지어진 것은?

> ─┤ 보기 ├─
> My teacher <u>makes</u> us keep the rules in school.

㉮ She <u>makes</u> students bring their books.
㉯ She doesn't allow students to <u>make</u> a noise in class.
㉰ The teacher <u>makes</u> students do their homework.
㉱ She <u>makes</u> us happy when she smiles.
㉲ Let me help you to <u>make</u> a cake for her.

① ㉮, ㉯   ② ㉮, ㉰
③ ㉯, ㉰, ㉱   ④ ㉮, ㉯, ㉰
⑤ ㉯, ㉰, ㉲

14 다음 중 어법상 올바른 문장을 고르면?

① My father let me to use his phone.
② She helped him to choose some new clothes.
③ Have him to come early.
④ Jake made his brother to wash the dishes.
⑤ Jane can make any broken machine working again.

 다음 중 밑줄 친 단어와 쓰임이 같은 것은?

> Nothing will <u>make</u> me change my mind.

① What <u>makes</u> you say that?
② She <u>made</u> coffee for me.
③ He <u>made</u> a lot of movies.
④ I <u>made</u> up my mind.
⑤ What time do you <u>make</u> it?

 다음 중 밑줄 친 What[what]의 쓰임이 나머지 넷과 다른 것은?

① I had the best party ever, thanks to my friends. And I got <u>what</u> I wanted for my birthday.
② <u>What</u> you should do is to check everything before you leave your house.
③ I'm sorry but I need to check what you have. Show me <u>what</u> you have in your pocket.
④ Do you know that girl? I want to know <u>what</u> her name is.
⑤ Last week when the accident happened, Robert said <u>what</u> everyone expected he would say.

17 다음 중 빈칸에 들어갈 말이 나머지와 다른 하나는?

① The shop didn't have _____ I wanted.
② I know _____ her address is.
③ _____ he wants to be is a designer.
④ Everything _____ they said was true.
⑤ _____ kind of music do you like?

18 다음 중 어법상 올바른 문장의 개수는?

> ⓐ It is the last chocolate what I have now.
> ⓑ Every girl like to play with dolls.
> ⓒ Reading books is that he does in his free time.
> ⓓ Mom took my dog that was sick to the dog hospital.

① 0개 ② 1개 ③ 2개 ④ 3개 ⑤ 4개

19 다음 빈칸에 공통으로 들어갈 말로 알맞은 것은?

> • I don't agree with _____ you just said.
> • My little sister showed me _____ she had painted.

① where ② which ③ how
④ when   ⑤ what

[01~02] 다음 주어진 두 문장을 관계대명사 what을 이용하여 한 문장으로 바꿔 쓰시오.

01
Did Jisu tell me the truth? Well, I think it's a lie.

➡ I think _____.

02 중요
I gave something to Jessica. It became her favorite friend.

➡ _____ became her favorite friend.

[03~04] 다음 우리말을 관계대명사 what을 이용하여 영작하시오. (단, 괄호 안의 단어를 문장에 맞는 형태로 적절히 활용할 것)

03
내가 필요한 것은 마실 것이다. (something, drink)

➡ _____

04 중요
나는 그가 말하는 것을 이해할 수 없었다. (can't, understand, say)

➡ _____

[05~06] 다음 〈보기〉와 같이, 문장이 같은 의미가 되도록 주어진 단어를 활용하여 다시 쓰시오.

┌─ 보기 ─┐
Don't stop him from doing what he wants. (let)

➡ Let him do what he wants.
└────────┘

05
He looks older when he wears the hat. (make)

➡ The hat _____.

06 중요
Mom told me to look for her smartphone. (have)

➡ _____

07 다음 주어진 단어들을 사용하여 우리말과 같은 뜻이 되도록 문장을 만드시오. (필요한 경우 단어를 변형하여 사용)

우리 엄마는 항상 내가 우유를 사오도록 시키신다.

(I, make, always, buy, some milk)

→ My mom _____.

[08~10] 다음 문장을 관계대명사 what을 이용한 문장으로 바꿔 쓰시오.

08

The thing that she said was true.

➡ _____ _____ _____ w a s true.

09 중요

Tell me the thing which you want.

➡ Tell me _____ _____ _____ .

10

The victims received the things which they needed.

➡ The victims received _____ _____ _____ .

11 고난이도

다음 우리말과 의미가 같도록 주어진 〈조건〉에 맞게 영작하시오.

당신이 해야 할 것은 그것들 모두를 확인하는 것이다.

┌── 조건 ──┐
• 'should, check, what, all of them'을 활용할 것.
• 10단어의 문장으로 완성하고 필요하면 단어의 형태를 변형할 것

➡ _____

12 다음 우리말을 영작하시오. (단, 'what'을 반드시 포함할 것)

이것은 어제 내가 산 것이다.

➡ _____

13 중요

다음 우리말과 같은 의미가 되도록 괄호 안의 단어를 이용하여 빈칸에 알맞은 말을 쓰시오.

어머니는 내가 컴퓨터 게임을 못하게 하셨다. (let)

➡ My mother _____ computer games.

[14~15] 다음 그림을 보고 괄호 안의 단어를 재배열하여 문장을 완성하시오. (한 칸에 한 단어만 쓸 것)

14

Jane's mom _____ _____ _____ _____ _____ .

(Jane, had, dishes, the, wash)

15 고난이도

Ms. Baker _____ _____ _____ _____ _____ _____ .

(made, his, wash, her, son, hands)

Reading

What Makes You Shop?

What makes you shop? Do you buy only what you really need?
　　　　사역동사+목적어+동사원형(~가 V하게 하다)　　　　　　관계대명사(~하는 것)
Read on and think about your shopping habits.

Mina: Look at that!

Somin: Wow! N-girls are wearing a brand-new jacket.

Mina: It looks very cute. I have to have one just like it.
　　　　　　　　　　　　　　　　　　a brand-new jacket

Somin: Me, too.

Many teens like to do what their favorite celebrities do. They are more
　　　　　　　　　= doing　관계대명사(~하는 것)
than willing to buy what the stars use. They want to look like their heroes.
be willing to V: (기꺼이) ~할 의향이 있다 (more than은 강조)　　　　　　　~처럼 보이다
They think celebrity brands will make them cool, happy, and popular.
　　　　　　　　　　　　　　make+목적어+형용사: ~를 …하게 만들다

Somin: Can you help me, Inho?

Inho: Sure. What's up?

Somin: There's going to be an online flash sale on new sneakers. Please

help me grab a pair.
help+목적어+(to) 동사원형: ~가 V하는 것을 돕다
Inho: Okay, I'll click like crazy.
　　　　　　미친 듯이, 맹렬히
When a product sells like hot cakes, some people often feel that they
자동사(팔리다) sell like hot cakes: 불티나게 팔리다　　　　　　명사절 접속사
won't be able to get it if they are not fast enough. They suffer from
　　　　　조건의 부사절 접속사　　　　← fast를 수식
FOMO, Fear of Missing Out, when they see sales signs such as *Limited*
　　　　FOMO와 동격　　　　　　　　　　　　= like
Edition and *Flash Sale*. The signs make them believe that it is the last
　　　　　　　사역동사+목적어+동사원형(~가 V하게 하다)
chance to grab the cool products. Then, getting quick-selling goods
형용사적 용법(chance 수식)　　　　　　　동명사(주어)
becomes more like winning a game than spending money.
동명사 주어 단수취급　　동명사(like의 목적어)

* 다음 문장이 본문의 내용과 일치하면 T, 일치하지 않으면 F를 쓰시오.

1　People buy only what they really need.　□

2　Teens like to buy things that their friends wear.　□

3　Buying quick-selling goods is like winning a game.　□

brand-new: 신제품의
be willing to ~: 기꺼이 ~하다, ~할 의향이 있다
hero: 영웅
brand: 상표, 상품
flash sale: (짧은 기간 동안 하는) 반짝 세일
grab 움켜쥐다
crazy 미친
product 상품
pair: 한 쌍[켤레]
suffer from: ~을(주로 어려움이나 고통을) 겪다
limited: 한정된, 제한된
edition: (한 번에 출시, 출간되는) 판, 호

Inho: What a pick!

Mina: Did you get it, Inho?

Inho: Yeah, finally. This completes my collection.

Mina: Good for you!

Collecting popular things is one of the hottest trends among young
동명사 주어   단수취급   one of the 최상급+복수명사(가장 ~한 것들 중 하나)

consumers. The most popular collections include character stickers,

baseball card sets, and goods featuring pop stars. Teen consumers
상품   현재분사

enjoy getting more and more of these, because the idea of *more is*
동명사를 목적어로 취하는 동사   이유의 부사절을 이끄는 접속사(~ 때문에)

better makes them happy.
주어 the idea에 수의 일치

What celebrity brands have you bought? What quick-selling goods
경험을 묻는 현재완료

have you grabbed? What character stickers have you collected? Are

you happy with what you have bought, grabbed, and collected? If
관계대명사(~하는 것)

you are happy with them, that's all right. If you aren't, however, you
what you have bought. grabbed. and collected

should try to be a smarter shopper.
~하기 위해 애쓰다

Here are three shopping tips to live by.
three shopping tips에 수의 일치   to부정사의 형용사적 용법

TIP 01. STICK TO A LIST

Make a shopping list and carry it around. Run into a store and get
a shopping list

what you need. If you can't find anything on the list, walk out empty-
= the thing that   빈손으로

handed. You will feel incredibly light.

TIP 02. COOL OFF FOR A DAY

When you shop online, don't click "Buy Now." Instead, hit "Add To

Cart" and sign out. After 24 hours of cooling off, come back and see

if you still want it.
명사절 접속사(~인지 아닌지)

TIP 03. FIND OLD TREASURES

Whenever you want to buy something new, go through your
접속사(~할 때마다)   -thing으로 끝나는 대명사는 형용사의 수식을 뒤에서 받음

closet and see what you have. Find old treasures and enjoy a new
옷장에서 찾은 입을 만한 옷

appreciation for them.
old treasures

---

pick: 고르기, 선택
complete: 완료하다, 완성하다
collection: 수집, 수집품
trend: 경향, 추세
include: 포함하다
feature: ~의 특징을 그리다
quick-selling: 빨리 팔리는
shopper: 구매자
live by: ~에 따라서 살다
stick to: ~을 고수하다
incredibly: 믿을 수 없을 정도로, 엄청
나게
cool off: 진정하다, 식다
instead: 대신에
go through: ~을 살펴보다
appreciation: 감상, 감사

● 우리말을 참고하여 빈칸에 알맞은 말을 쓰시오.

What Makes You Shop?

1 What makes you _____? Do you buy only _____ _____ _____ _____?

2 Read _____ and think about your _____ _____.

3 Mina: Look _____ that!
Somin: Wow! N-girls _____ _____ a brand-new jacket.
Mina: It looks very _____. I have _____ _____ _____ just like it.
Somin: Me, _____.

4 Many teens like to do _____ _____ _____ _____ _____.

5 They are _____ _____ willing _____ _____ what the stars _____.

6 They want to _____ _____ their _____.

7 They think celebrity brands will _____ _____ _____, _____, and _____.

8 Somin: _____ you _____ me, Inho?
Inho: Sure. _____ _____?
Somin: There's going to be an _____ _____ _____ on new sneakers. Please _____ me _____ a pair.
Inho: Okay, I'll click _____ _____.

9 When a product _____ _____ _____ _____, some people often feel _____ they won't be able to get it _____ they are _____ _____ _____.

10 They _____ _____ FOMO, Fear of Missing Out, _____ they see sales signs _____ _____ *Limited Edition* and *Flash Sale*.

11 The signs _____ them _____ that it is the last _____ _____ _____ the cool products.

12 Then, getting quick-selling goods _____ _____ _____ winning a game _____ spending money.

무엇이 여러분을 쇼핑하게 합니까?

1 무엇이 여러분을 쇼핑하게 합니까? 여러분은 정말로 필요한 것만을 삽니까?

2 읽어 가며 여러분의 쇼핑 습관에 대해 생각해 보십시오.

3 미나: 저것 좀 봐!
소민: 와! N-girls가 신상품 재킷을 입고 있네.
미나: 정말 귀여워 보여. 나도 그것과 꼭 같은 것을 하나 가지고 있어야만 되겠어.
소민: 나도 그래.

4 많은 십대들은 좋아하는 유명인이 하는 것을 하기 좋아합니다.

5 그들은 스타들이 사용하는 것을 기꺼이 사고자 합니다.

6 그들은 그들의 영웅처럼 보이기를 원합니다.

7 그들은 유명인 브랜드가 그들을 멋지고 행복하며 인기 있게 만들 것이라고 생각합니다.

8 소민: 나 도와줄 수 있어, 인호야?
인호: 물론이지. 무슨 일이야?
소민: 새로운 운동화의 온라인 반짝 판매가 있을 예정이야. 부탁인데, 내가 한 켤레를 손에 넣도록 도와줘.
인호: 알겠어. 내가 열심히 클릭할게.

9 한 상품이 불티나게 팔릴 때, 어떤 사람들은 그들이 충분히 재빠르지 않으면 그것을 얻을 수 없을 것이라고 흔히 느낍니다.

10 그들은 '한정판'이나 '반짝 판매'와 같은 판매 게시물을 보면, FOMO(놓치는 것에 대한 두려움)를 겪습니다.

11 그 게시물들은 그들로 하여금 그것이 그 멋진 상품들을 손에 넣을 마지막 기회라고 믿게 만듭니다.

12 그러면, 빨리 팔리는 물건을 사는 것은 돈을 쓰는 것이라기보다는 게임에서 이기는 것과 같아집니다.

13
Inho: What _____ _____!

Mina: Did you get _____, Inho?

Inho: Yeah, _____. This _____ my collection.

Mina: Good _____ you!

14 _____ popular things _____ one of the _____ _____ among young _____.

15 The most popular _____ _____ character stickers, baseball card sets, and goods _____ pop stars.

16 Teen consumers enjoy _____ more and more of these, _____ the idea _____ *more is better* makes them happy.

17 What celebrity brands _____ you _____? What quick-selling goods _____ you _____? What character stickers _____ you _____?

18 Are you happy with _____ you _____ _____, _____, and _____?

19 If you are happy _____ _____, that's _____.

20 If you _____, _____, you should try _____ _____ a smarter shopper.

21 Here _____ three shopping tips _____ _____ _____ _____.

22 TIP 01. _____ _____ A LIST.

23 Make a _____ _____ and carry _____ around. _____ _____ a store and get _____ you need.

24 If you can't find _____ _____ _____ _____, walk out _____. You will feel _____ _____.

25 TIP 02. COOL OFF FOR A DAY.

26 When you shop _____, don't click "Buy Now." _____, hit "Add To Cart" and _____ _____.

27 After 24 hours of _____ _____, come back and see _____ you _____ _____ _____.

28 TIP 03. FIND _____ _____.

29 _____ you want to buy _____ _____, _____ _____ your closet and see _____ you have. Find old treasures and enjoy _____ _____ _____ _____ _____.

---

13 인호: 정말 잘 골랐네!
미나: 너 그거 손에 넣었어, 인호야?
인호: 응, 마침내. 이것이 내 수집품을 완성하네.
미나: 잘됐네!

14 인기 있는 것들을 모으는 것은 젊은 소비자들 사이에서 가장 인기 있는 유행 중 하나입니다.

15 가장 인기 있는 수집품으로 캐릭터 스티커, 야구 카드 세트, 팝 스타를 특징으로 삼는 상품 등이 있습니다.

16 십대 소비자들은 이것들을 점점 더 많이 가지는 것을 즐기는데, '많을수록 좋다'라는 생각이 그들을 행복하게 만들어 주기 때문입니다.

17 어떤 유명인 상표를 구입해 보셨습니까? 어떤 빨리 팔리는 상품을 손에 넣어 보셨습니까? 어떤 캐릭터 스티커를 수집해 보셨습니까?

18 여러분이 구입하고 손에 넣고 수집한 것에 만족하십니까?

19 여러분들이 그것들에 만족한다면, 괜찮습니다.

20 그러나 여러분이 그것들에 만족하지 않는다면, 여러분은 더 똑똑한 구매자가 되려고 노력해야 합니다.

21 여기 생활 속에서 지켜야 할 세 가지 구매 팁이 있습니다.

22 조언 01 목록을 고수하세요.

23 쇼핑 목록을 작성하고 휴대하세요. 상점 안으로 달려가서 필요한 것을 얻으세요.

24 목록에 있는 것을 찾을 수 없다면, 빈손으로 걸어 나오세요. 믿을 수 없을 정도로 경쾌한 기분을 느끼게 될 거예요.

25 조언 02 하루 동안 진정해 보세요.

26 온라인 쇼핑을 할 때 "바로 구입"을 클릭하지 마세요. 대신, "장바구니에 추가"를 누르고 로그아웃 하세요.

27 24시간 동안 진정한 이후에, 돌아와서 여전히 그것을 원하는지 확인해 보세요.

28 조언 03 오래된 보물들을 찾으세요.

29 새로운 물건을 사고 싶을 때마다 옷장을 살펴보고 갖고 있는 물건을 확인해 보세요. 오래된 보물들을 찾고 그것들을 새롭게 감상하며 즐기세요.

● 우리말을 참고하여 본문을 영작하시오.

What Makes You Shop?

1 무엇이 여러분을 쇼핑하게 합니까? 여러분은 정말로 필요한 것만을 삽니까?

➡ _____

2 읽어 가며 여러분의 쇼핑 습관에 대해 생각해 보십시오.

➡ _____

3 미나: 저것 좀 봐! / 소민: 와! N-girls가 신상품 재킷을 입고 있네.

미나: 정말 귀여워 보여. 나도 그것과 꼭 같은 것을 하나 가지고 있어야만 되겠어. / 소민: 나도 그래.

➡ _____

4 많은 십대들은 좋아하는 유명인이 하는 것을 하기 좋아합니다.

➡ _____

5 그들은 스타들이 사용하는 것을 기꺼이 사고자 합니다.

➡ _____

6 그들은 그들의 영웅처럼 보이기를 원합니다.

➡ _____

7 그들은 유명인 브랜드가 그들을 멋지고 행복하며 인기 있게 만들 것이라고 생각합니다.

➡ _____

8 소민: 나 도와줄 수 있어, 인호야? / 인호: 물론이지. 무슨 일이야?

소민: 새로운 운동화의 온라인 반짝 판매가 있을 예정이야. 부탁인데, 내가 한 켤레를 손에 넣도록 도와줘.
／ 인호: 알겠어. 내가 열심히 클릭할게.

➡ _____

_____

_____

9 한 상품이 불티나게 팔릴 때, 어떤 사람들은 그들이 충분히 재빠르지 않으면 그것을 얻을 수
없을 것이라고 흔히 느낍니다.

➡ _____

_____

10 그들은 '한정판'이나 '반짝 판매'와 같은 판매 게시물을 보면, FOMO(놓치는 것에 대한 두려움)를 겪습니다.

➡ _____

_____

11 그 게시물들은 그들로 하여금 그것이 그 멋진 상품들을 손에 넣을 마지막 기회라고 믿게 만듭니다.

➡ _____

12 그러면, 빨리 팔리는 물건을 사는 것은 돈을 쓰는 것이라기보다는 게임에서 이기는 것과 같아집니다.

➡ _____

13 인호: 정말 잘 골랐네! / 미나: 너 그거 손에 넣었어, 인호야?
인호: 응, 마침내. 이것이 내 수집품을 완성하네. / 미나: 잘됐네!
➡ _____
_____

14 인기 있는 것들을 모으는 것은 젊은 소비자들 사이에서 가장 인기 있는 유행 중 하나입니다.
➡ _____

15 가장 인기 있는 수집품으로 캐릭터 스티커, 야구 카드 세트, 팝 스타를 특징으로 삼는 상품 등이 있습니다.
➡ _____

16 십대 소비자들은 이것들을 점점 더 많이 가지는 것을 즐기는데, '많을수록 좋다'라는 생각이 그들을
행복하게 만들어 주기 때문입니다.
➡ _____

17 어떤 유명인 상표를 구입해 보셨습니까? 어떤 빨리 팔리는 상품을 손에 넣어 보셨습니까? 어떤 캐릭터 스
티커를 수집해 보셨습니까?
➡ _____
_____

18 여러분이 구입하고 손에 넣고 수집한 것에 만족하십니까?
➡ _____

19 여러분들이 그것들에 만족한다면, 괜찮습니다.
➡ _____

20 그러나 여러분이 그것들에 만족하지 않는다면, 여러분은 더 똑똑한 구매자가 되려고 노력해야 합니다.
➡ _____

21 여기 생활 속에서 지켜야 할 세 가지 구매 팁이 있습니다.
➡ _____

22 조언 01 목록을 고수하세요.
➡ _____

23 쇼핑 목록을 작성하고 휴대하세요. 상점 안으로 달려가서 필요한 것을 얻으세요.
➡ _____

24 목록에 있는 것을 찾을 수 없다면, 빈손으로 걸어 나오세요. 믿을 수 없을 정도로 경쾌한 기분을 느끼게 될 거예요.
➡ _____

25 조언 02 하루 동안 진정해 보세요.
➡ _____

26 온라인 쇼핑을 할 때 "바로 구입"을 클릭하지 마세요. 대신, "장바구니에 추가"를 누르고 로그아웃 하세요.
➡ _____

27 24시간 동안 진정한 이후에, 돌아와서 여전히 그것을 원하는지 확인해 보세요.
➡ _____

28 조언 03 오래된 보물들을 찾으세요.
➡ _____

29 새로운 물건을 사고 싶을 때마다 옷장을 살펴보고 갖고 있는 물건을 확인해 보세요. 오래된 보물들을
찾고 그것들을 새롭게 감상하며 즐기세요.
➡ _____
_____

[01~03] 다음 글을 읽고 물음에 답하시오.

What makes you shop? Do you buy only what you really need? Read on and think about your shopping habits.

Mina: Look at that!

Somin: Wow! N-girls are wearing a brand-new jacket.

Mina: It looks very cute. I have to have one just like it.

Somin: Me, too.

Many teens like to do what their favorite celebrities do. They are more than willing to buy what the stars use. They want to look like their heroes. They think celebrity brands will make them (A)_____.

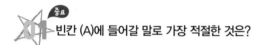

01 빈칸 (A)에 들어갈 말로 가장 적절한 것은?

① terrible, unhappy, and ugly
② boring, fortunate, and unhappy
③ satisfied, cool, and rich
④ cool, happy, and popular
⑤ happy but lonely

02 다음 중 위 글의 내용과 일치하는 것은?

① Mina is not interested in N-girls.
② Somin wants to buy a jacket like what N-girls are wearing.
③ Many teens don't want to buy what the stars use.
④ Mina doesn't think N-girls' jacket cute.
⑤ Many teens want to be heroes.

서답형
03 What do many teens like to do?

➡ _____

[04~06] 다음 글을 읽고 물음에 답하시오.

Somin: Can you help me, Inho?

Inho: Sure. What's up?

Somin: There's going to be an online flash sale on new sneakers. Please help me grab a pair.

Inho: Okay, I'll click like crazy.

When a product sells like hot cakes, some people often feel that they won't be able to get it (A)_____ they are not fast enough. They suffer from FOMO, (B)_____, when they see sales signs such as *Limited Edition* and *Flash Sale*. The signs make them believe that it is the last chance to grab the cool products. Then, getting (C)quick-selling goods becomes more like winning a game than spending money.

04 빈칸 (A)에 들어갈 말로 가장 적절한 것은?

① because   ② although   ③ so
④ if   ⑤ unless

05 다음 중 빈칸 (B)에 들어갈 말로 가장 적절한 것은?

① Fear of Most Originality
② Full of Making Out
③ Fear of Missing Out
④ Full of Missing Out
⑤ Function of Making Out

서답형
06 다음은 밑줄 친 (C)의 의미이다. 빈칸에 알맞은 말을 쓰시오.

Quick-selling goods are products labeled like _____ or _____.

[07~09] 다음 글을 읽고 물음에 답하시오.

Inho: What a pick!

Mina: Did you get it, Inho?

Inho: Yeah, finally. This (A)[lacks / completes] my collection.

Mina: Good for you!

  Collecting popular things is one of the hottest trends among young consumers. The most popular collections (B)[include / conclude] character stickers, baseball card sets, and goods featuring pop stars. Teen consumers enjoy ⓐ＿＿＿ (C)[less and less / more and more] of these, because the idea of *more is better* makes them happy.

  What celebrity brands have you bought? What quick-selling goods have you grabbed? What character stickers have you collected? Are you happy with what you have bought, grabbed, and collected? If you are happy with them, that's all right. If you aren't, however, you should try to be a smarter shopper.

서답형

07 동사 get을 어법에 맞게 빈칸 ⓐ에 쓰시오.

➡ ＿＿＿＿＿＿＿＿＿＿＿

08 (A)~(C)에서 글의 흐름상 옳은 것끼리 바르게 짝지은 것은?

① lacks – include – less and less

② lacks – conclude – less and less

③ completes – include – less and less

④ completes – conclude – more and more

⑤ completes – include – more and more

서답형

09 다음과 같이 풀이되는 말을 위 글에서 찾아 쓰시오.

> someone who is famous, especially in areas of entertainment such as films, music, writing, or sport

➡ ＿＿＿＿＿＿＿＿＿＿＿

[10~12] 다음 글을 읽고 물음에 답하시오.

Here are three shopping tips to live by.

TIP 01. STICK TO A LIST

  Make a shopping list and carry it around. Run into a store and get what you need. If you can't find anything on the list, walk out empty-handed. You will feel incredibly light.

TIP 02. COOL OFF FOR A DAY

  When you shop online, don't click "Buy Now." Instead, hit "Add To Cart" and sign out. After 24 hours of cooling off, come back and see if you still want it.

TIP 03. FIND OLD TREASURES

  Whenever you want to buy something new, go through your closet and see what you have. Find (A)old treasures and enjoy a new appreciation for them.

서답형

10 밑줄 친 (A)의 의미를 우리말로 쓰시오.

➡ ＿＿＿＿＿＿＿＿＿＿＿

11 다음 중 위 글의 내용을 바르게 이해한 사람은?

① Amelia: I will make a shopping list and keep it in my room.

② Brian: In addition to the shopping list, I will buy more to be a smart consumer.

③ Chris: I will click "Buy Now" as soon as I see it.

④ David: If there isn't what I want in the mall, I will just walk out without buying anything.

⑤ Eden: I will click everything I see.

서답형

12 What should we do after making a shopping list?

➡ ＿＿＿＿＿＿＿＿＿＿＿

[13~16] 다음 글을 읽고 물음에 답하시오.

What makes you shop? Do you buy only what you really need? Read on and think about your shopping habits.

Mina: Look at that!

Somin: Wow! N-girls are wearing a brand-new jacket.

Mina: It looks very cute. I have to have one just like it.

Somin: Me, too.

Many teens like to do (A)＿＿＿ ①their favorite celebrities do. ②They are more than willing to buy what the stars use. ③They want to look like ④their heroes. They think celebrity brands will make ⑤them cool, happy, and popular.

13 다음 중 빈칸 (A)에 들어갈 말로 가장 적절한 것은?

① that   ② if   ③ what
④ whom   ⑤ which

14 ①~⑤ 중 지칭하는 바가 <u>다른</u> 하나는?

①   ②   ③   ④   ⑤

15 다음 중 위 글을 읽고 답할 수 있는 것은?

① How many members are there in N-girls?
② Where are Mina and Somin talking?
③ How much is the brand-new jacket?
④ What are N-girls wearing?
⑤ How many jackets does Mina have?

16 What do many teens want to look like? Answer in English with a full sentence.

➡ _____

[17~19] 다음 글을 읽고 물음에 답하시오.

Somin: Can you help me, Inho?

Inho: Sure. What's up?

Somin: There's going to be an online flash sale on new sneakers. Please help me grab a pair.

Inho: Okay, I'll click like crazy.

When a product (A)<u>sells like hot cakes</u>, some people often feel that they won't be able to get it if they are not fast enough. They suffer from FOMO, Fear of Missing Out, when they see sales signs such as *Limited Edition and Flash Sale*. The signs make them believe that it is the last chance to grab the cool products. Then, getting quick-selling goods becomes more like winning a game than spending money.

17 밑줄 친 (A)의 의미로 가장 적절한 것은?

① is sold by people who like hot cakes
② is easy to make hot cakes
③ is easy to sell hot cakes
④ is famous but not tasty
⑤ is sold quickly in great quantities

18 What does Somin want to buy? Answer in English with nine words.

➡ _____

19 Choose the one who suffers from FOMO.

① Colin: I am not interested in limited edition.
② Becky: Although I can't buy the product labeled as 'Flash Sale', I don't care.
③ Thomas: If I don't hurry, I won't get the product that I want to buy.
④ Jason: I am not into quick-selling products.
⑤ Juho: There will be many chances to grab cool products.

[20~22] 다음 글을 읽고 물음에 답하시오.

Inho: What a pick!

Mina: Did you get it, Inho?

Inho: Yeah, finally. This completes my collection.

Mina: Good for you!

Collecting popular things ①is one of the hottest ②trends among young consumers. The most popular collections include character stickers, baseball card sets, and goods ③featured pop stars. Teen consumers enjoy getting more and more of ④these, because the idea of *more is better* makes them happy.

What celebrity brands have you bought? What quick-selling goods have you grabbed? What character stickers have you collected? Are you happy with what you have bought, grabbed, and collected? If you are happy with (A)them, that's all right. If you ⑤aren't, however, you should try to be a smarter shopper.

20 ①~⑤ 중 어법상 바르지 않은 것은?

① ② ③ ④ ⑤

서답형
21 밑줄 친 (A)가 가리키는 것을 위 글에서 찾아 쓰시오.

➡ _____

중요
22 다음 중 위 글을 읽고 답할 수 있는 것은?

① What does Inho collect?

② How many collections does Inho have?

③ Where does Inho get the thing which completes his collection?

④ What is one of the hottest trends among young consumers?

⑤ What should we do to become a smarter shopper?

[23~26] 다음 글을 읽고 물음에 답하시오.

Here are three shopping tips to live by.

TIP 01. STICK TO A LIST

Make a shopping list and carry it around. Run into a store and ①get what you need. If you can't find anything on the list, walk out ②empty-handed. You will feel incredibly ③light.

TIP 02. COOL OFF FOR A DAY

When you shop online, don't click "Buy Now." Instead, hit "Add To Cart" and ④sign in. After 24 hours of cooling off, come back and see if you still want it.

TIP 03. FIND OLD TREASURES

Whenever you want to buy ⑤something new, go (A)_____ your closet and see what you have. Find old treasures and enjoy a new appreciation for them.

중요
23 다음 중 빈칸 (A)에 들어갈 말로 가장 적절한 것은?

① after ② on ③ about

④ through ⑤ for

24 ①~⑤ 중 글의 흐름상 어색한 것은?

① ② ③ ④ ⑤

서답형
25 위 글의 내용에 맞게 빈칸에 알맞은 말을 쓰시오.

_____ _____ _____ _____ in your closet is a better idea than buying new one whenever you want to.

서답형
26 What shouldn't we click when we shop online? Answer in English with five words.

➡ _____

[01~03] 다음 글을 읽고 물음에 답하시오.

What makes you shop? Do you buy only what you really need? Read on and think about your shopping habits.

Mina: Look at that!

Somin: Wow! N-girls are wearing a brand-new jacket.

Mina: It looks very cute. I have to have one just like it.

Somin: Me, too.

Many teens like to do what their favorite celebrities do. They are more than willing to buy what the stars use. They want to look like their heroes. They think celebrity brands will make them cool, happy, and popular.

01
What do we need to think about when we read the passage? Answer in English with a full sentence.

➡ _____

02
What are Somin and Mina looking at? Answer by using the words below.

(at / wearing)

➡ _____

03
주어진 단어를 활용하여 다음 물음에 완전한 문장의 영어로 답하시오.

Q: What are many teens more than willing to buy? (their) (12 words)

➡ _____
_____

[04~06] 다음 글을 읽고 물음에 답하시오.

Somin: Can you help me, Inho?

Inho: Sure. What's up?

Somin: There's going to be an online flash sale on new sneakers. (A)부탁인데, 내가 한 켤레를 손에 넣도록 도와줘.

Inho: Okay, I'll click like crazy.

When a product sells like hot cakes, some people often feel that they won't be able to get (B)it if they are not fast enough. They suffer from FOMO, Fear of Missing Out, when they see sales signs such as *Limited Edition* and *Flash Sale*. The signs make them believe that it is the last chance to grab the cool products. Then, getting quick-selling goods becomes more like winning a game than spending money.

04
주어진 단어를 활용하여 밑줄 친 우리말 (A)를 영어로 쓰시오.

(please / help / grab)

➡ _____

05
밑줄 친 (B)가 의미하는 것을 10자 이내의 우리말로 쓰시오.

➡ _____

06
According to the passage, what do people believe when they see sales signs such as *Flash Sale*?

➡ _____
_____

[07~09] 다음 글을 읽고 물음에 답하시오.

Inho: What a pick!

Mina: Did you get it, Inho?

Inho: Yeah, finally. This completes my collection.

Mina: Good for you!

Collecting popular things is one of the hottest trends among young consumers. The most popular collections include character stickers, baseball card sets, and goods featuring pop stars. Teen consumers enjoy getting more and more of these, because the idea of *more is better* makes them happy.

What celebrity brands have you bought? What quick-selling goods have you grabbed? What character stickers have you collected? (A)여러분이 구입하고 손에 넣고 수집한 것에 만족하십니까? If you are happy with them, that's all right. If you aren't, however, you should try to be a smarter shopper.

07 Write the reason why teen consumers enjoy more and more of popular collections. Use the phrase 'It's because.'

➡ _____

_____

08 What do the most popular collections include? Answer in English with a full sentence.

➡ _____

_____

09 주어진 단어를 활용하여 밑줄 친 우리말 (A)를 영어로 쓰시오.

(happy with) (11 words)

➡ _____

_____

[10~13] 다음 글을 읽고 물음에 답하시오.

Here are three shopping tips to live by.

TIP 01. STICK TO A LIST

Make a shopping list and carry it around. Run into a store and get (A)_____ you need. If you can't find anything on the list, walk out empty-handed. You will feel incredibly light.

TIP 02. COOL OFF FOR A DAY

When you shop online, don't click "Buy Now." Instead, hit "Add To Cart" and sign out. After 24 hours of cooling off, come back and see if you still want (B)it.

TIP 03. FIND OLD TREASURES

Whenever you want to buy something new, go through your closet and see (C)_____ you have. Find old treasures and enjoy a new appreciation for them.

10 빈칸 (A)와 (C)에 공통으로 들어가는 말을 쓰시오.

➡ _____

11 밑줄 친 (B)가 의미하는 것을 우리말로 쓰시오.

➡ _____

12 How will you feel if you don't buy things that is not on your shopping list? Answer in English with a full sentence.

➡ _____

13 다음 Andy의 글을 읽고 적절한 조언을 위 글에서 찾아 쓰시오.

Andy: I am thinking of buying the bread just because it has stickers that I collect. But buying the bread is not on my shopping list. What should I do?

➡ _____

Listen & Speak 2 B

A: Which floor are you going to?
어느 층으로

B: I'm going to the second floor.

A: Are you thinking of having pizza?
~하려고 하는 거니?(의도를 묻는 말)

B: No, I'm not. I'm thinking of eating popcorn.

구문해설 · floor 바닥, (건물의) 층, second floor 2층

해석

A: 몇 층을 가시나요?

B: 저는 2층에 갑니다.

A: 피자를 먹으려고 하시나요?

B: 아니요. 팝콘을 먹으려고요.

Real-Life Task Step 3

We are thinking of cutting down our spending to save money.
"저축하기 위하여"의 의미로 목적을 나타내는 부사적 용법이다.

Nara will spend less on clothes.
little의 비교급

Seho will buy fewer snacks and drinks.
few의 비교급/셀 수 있는 것의 수가 적을 때는 few를 쓴다.

Jina will come to school by bicycle, not by bus.

구문해설 · cut down ~을 줄이다 · spend on ~에 (돈을) 쓰다 · by bicycle 자전거를 타고

우리는 돈을 절약하기 위해서 지출을 줄이려고 합니다.
나라는 옷을 덜 살 것입니다.
세호는 간식과 음료를 덜 살 것입니다.
지나는 버스가 아닌 자전거를 타고 등교할 것입니다.

Before I Read

FLASH SALE
SPECIAL OFFER FOR SMART CONSUMERS.
전치사(~를 위한)

50% OFF ON CELEBRITY BRANDS FOR THIS WEEKEND ONLY.
할인해서

GRAB THESE NEW GOODS BEFORE THEY SELL OUT.
these new goods를 지칭

구문해설 · consumer: 소비자 · celebrity: 유명인사, 연예인 · offer: 제공하다, 제의하다 · grab: 붙잡다, (~할 기회를) 잡다 · sell out: 다 팔리다

반짝 세일
똑똑한 소비자들을 위한 특별한 할인.
유명인 브랜드를 이번 주말에만 50% 할인된 가격으로.
다 팔리기 전에 이 새 상품들을 가져가세요.

Words & Expressions

01 다음 문장에 공통으로 들어가기에 가장 적절한 것은?

> • We're taking _____ soon. Make sure you stay in your seat when the seat belt sign is on.
> • After 24 hours of cooling _____, come back and see if you still want it.

① away   ② off

③ forward   ④ behind

⑤ from

02 빈칸에 알맞은 단어를 〈보기〉에서 골라 쓰시오.

> ┤ 보기 ├
> knee   helpful   consumer   celebrity

(1) She became a TV _____.

(2) Companies should consider _____ rights.

(3) She made _____ comments on my work.

(4) I fell over and hurt my _____.

03 다음 영영풀이에 해당하는 단어를 고르시오.

> to make someone or something part of a larger group or set

① decorate   ② include

③ match   ④ pet

⑤ product

Conversation

04 다음 대화의 빈칸에 들어갈 말로 알맞은 것은?

> **A:** Now, we're getting to the rest stop. Any questions?
> **B:** Yes. Can I look around?
> **A:** Of course, but _____ you don't go far from your group.
> **B:** OK. Thanks.

① be famous

② make sure

③ don't be serious

④ you need

⑤ you don't have to

[05~07] 다음 대화를 읽고 물음에 답하시오.

> **G:** I cleaned my room and found some old T-shirts.
> **B:** What are you going to do with them? _____ throwing them away?
> **G:** No. I will make an eco bag out of them.
> **B:** That's a good idea!

05 위 대화의 빈칸에 들어가기에 적절한 것은?

① How about

② Why don't you

③ Do you want to

④ Would you like to

⑤ Are you thinking of

06 What will the girl do with the old T-shirts?

① She will throw them away.

② She will clean the room with them.

③ She wants to find some old T-shirts.

④ She will make an eco bag out of them.

⑤ She is going to buy some new T-shirts.

07 위 대화의 내용과 일치하는 것은?

① The boy was cleaning the house.

② The boy found some old T-shirts.

③ The boy asks the girl what she will do with the old T-shirts.

④ The girl will throw the old T-shirts away.

⑤ The boy wants to make an eco bag.

[08~10] 다음 대화를 읽고 물음에 답하시오.

Seho: Oh! It's almost closing time. Hurry up!

Semi(Seho's sister): Calm down, Seho. We've got everything.

Seho: No. I need to visit Sneaker Ground. They're having a sale there.

Semi: What? (A) Are you thinking of getting sneakers?

Seho: Yes. I can get high-end sneakers for 70% off. It's a steal. (B)

Semi: Well, it was just a week ago that you bought blue sneakers there. (C)

Seho: No. They don't match any of my pants. (D)

Semi: You see? ⓐ_____

Seho: I see what you mean, but it's now or never. (E) I can't miss out.

Semi: You are impossible.

08 위 대화의 (A) ~ (E) 중에서 다음 주어진 문장이 들어가기에 적절한 곳은?

> Have you even put them on?

① (A)   ② (B)   ③ (C)   ④ (D)   ⑤ (E)

09 위 대화의 빈칸 ⓐ에 들어가기에 적절한 것은?

① Why don't you repeat the same mistake?

② Make sure you don't repeat the same mistake.

③ What do you want by making the same mistake again?

④ How many pairs of sneakers do you want to have?

⑤ Who had the same sneakers as these?

10 위 대화의 내용과 일치하지 않는 것은?

① Seho wants to visit Sneaker Ground.

② They are having a sale at Sneaker Ground.

③ Seho is going to buy a new pair of sneakers.

④ Seho already bought a new pair of sneakers just a week ago.

⑤ Seho thinks he can get the new sneakers later.

11 다음 대화의 빈칸에 들어가기에 적절한 것은?

> B: Which shop are you going to visit?
> G: I'm going to visit the sneaker shop.
> B: Are you thinking of getting new sneakers?
> G: No, I'm not. _____

① I need a new pair of sneakers.

② I heard they are having a big sale.

③ My sneakers are very old.

④ I will show you the way to the shop.

⑤ I'm thinking of getting a refund.

12 다음 주어진 말에 이어질 대화의 순서가 바르게 배열된 것을 고르시오.

> A: How did you like the presentation?
> B: It was very helpful. I need to do something to save money.
> (A) Yes, I am. I'll spend less on clothes.
> (B) Are you thinking of cutting down your spending?
> (C) Good for you, but make sure you don't give up your style.

① (A) – (C) – (B)   ② (B) – (A) – (C)

③ (B) – (C) – (A)   ④ (C) – (A) – (B)

⑤ (C) – (B) – (A)

Grammar

13 다음 중 어법상 어색한 문장을 모두 고르면?

① We like the chair which he made.

② That's not what I was trying to say.

③ I love the book that you gave me yesterday.

④ This is not the movie what I want to see.

⑤ Which she said on the phone made me upset.

14 다음 중 밑줄 친 부분의 쓰임이 나머지 넷과 다른 것은?

① He <u>made</u> me wash the dishes.

② The black suit <u>made</u> Kate look thin.

③ My mom <u>made</u> spaghetti this evening.

④ The wind <u>made</u> the picture fall on the floor.

⑤ He <u>made</u> them create a new invention every month.

15 다음 주어진 문장의 밑줄 친 부분과 같은 용법으로 쓰인 것을 두 개 고르면?

> Show me <u>what</u> you have in your bag.

① Please read me <u>what</u> she sent to you.

② <u>What</u> do you want for your birthday?

③ I want to know <u>what</u> time he will come.

④ That is exactly <u>what</u> she wanted to say.

⑤ <u>What</u> do you think she wants to buy?

16 다음 질문에 대한 답을 관계대명사 what을 이용하여 쓰시오. (괄호 안에 주어진 단어를 사용할 것)

> Q: Is this the book which you want to read?
> A: Yes, _____. (it, what)

17 다음 중 어법상 <u>어색한</u> 문장의 개수는?

> ⓐ I don't understand what you just said.
> ⓑ Can you tell me what you have in mind?
> ⓒ This is not what you told us.
> ⓓ Everything what they said was true.
> ⓔ The shop didn't have that I wanted.

① 1개　　　② 2개　　　③ 3개
④ 4개　　　⑤ 5개

18 다음 중 밑줄 친 부분이 어법상 <u>어색한</u> 것은?

① Tell me <u>what</u> you did yesterday morning.
② We should have the right to express <u>that</u> we have in mind.
③ That makes us think about <u>what</u> we have to be careful about in the future.
④ The movie helps us remind <u>that</u> we lost so many things during the last few years.
⑤ Look at the many findings <u>that</u> have helped people develop the new world of communication.

19 다음 〈보기〉에서 어법상 옳은 문장을 <u>모두</u> 고른 것은?

> ┤ 보기 ├
> ⓐ Who made him do the dishes?
> ⓑ She had her house painted yesterday.
> ⓒ She asked them step aside.
> ⓓ Let me to use your computer for just an hour.
> ⓔ Did you let them to go out?

① ⓐ, ⓔ　　　　② ⓒ, ⓔ
③ ⓐ, ⓑ　　　　④ ⓑ, ⓓ, ⓔ
⑤ ⓑ, ⓒ, ⓓ

20 다음 중 어법상 올바른 문장을 고르면?

① I will have her to call you.
② They had me repeated the story.
③ Skipping breakfast made me feel hungry.
④ At last, my mom had my sister cleaning her room.
⑤ Dad will let me to go to the movies this weekend.

[21~22] 다음 글을 읽고 물음에 답하시오.

Somin: Can you help me, Inho?
Inho: Sure. What's up?
Somin: There's going to be an online flash sale on new sneakers. Please help me grab a pair.
Inho: Okay, I'll click like crazy.

　When a product sells like hot cakes, some people often feel that they won't be able to get it if they are not fast enough. They suffer from FOMO, Fear of Missing Out, when they see sales signs such as *Limited Edition* and *Flash Sale*. The signs make them believe that it is the last chance to grab the cool products. Then, getting quick-selling goods becomes more like winning a game than spending money.

21 다음 중 위 글의 내용과 일치하는 것은?

① Somin doesn't care about whether she gets the new sneakers or not.
② Inho doesn't want to help Somin.
③ Somin wants to buy new sneakers at a shop by herself.
④ Somin thinks that if she is not fast enough, she won't get new sneakers.
⑤ Inho thinks that Somin will be fast enough to get the shoes.

22 What does FOMO stand for? Answer in English with a full sentence.

➡ _____

[23~26] 다음 글을 읽고 물음에 답하시오.

> Inho: What a pick!
> Mina: Did you get it, Inho?
> Inho: Yeah, ①finally. This completes my collection.
> Mina: Good for you!
>
>   Collecting popular things ②is one of the hottest ③trend among young consumers. The most popular collections include character stickers, baseball card sets, and goods featuring pop stars. Teen consumers enjoy getting more and more of these, because the idea of (A)_____ makes them ④happy.
>   What celebrity brands have you bought? What quick-selling goods have you grabbed? What character stickers have you collected? Are you happy with what you have bought, grabbed, and collected? If you are happy with ⑤them, that's all right. If you aren't, however, you should try to be a smarter shopper.

23 다음 중 빈칸 (A)에 들어갈 말로 가장 적절한 것은?

① *less is necessary*　② *more is worse*

③ *more is better*　④ *nothing is better*

⑤ *better is less*

24 ①~⑤ 중 어법상 바르지 <u>않은</u> 것은?

① ② ③ ④ ⑤

25 다음 중 위 글을 읽고 답할 수 있는 것은?

① What does Inho's collection look like?

② What is the hottest trend among adults?

③ What do most young consumers like to wear?

④ What does Inho complete?

⑤ Why do teenagers like to collect things?

26 What do the most popular collections include? Answer in English with a full sentence.

➡ _____

_____

[27~29] 다음 글을 읽고 물음에 답하시오.

> This is what I bought last week, a smart watch.
> (A) Now, let me write what I don't like about the product. It has a very small screen, so it is difficult to read the time.
> (B) All in all, I'm not satisfied, and this makes me give the product only one star.
> (C) I'd like to begin with what I like about the product. It counts my steps, so it helps me get enough exercise.

27 자연스러운 글이 되도록 (A)~(C)를 바르게 나열하시오.

➡ _____

28 Write the reason why it is difficult to read the time with the smart watch. Use the phrase 'It's because.'

➡ _____

29 다음 중 위 글의 내용과 일치하는 것은?

① The writer bought the smart watch last month.

② The writer likes the smart watch because it counts his heart beating.

③ The writer feels satisfied with the smart watch.

④ The writer has bad eyesight.

⑤ The smart watch helps the writer get enough exercise.

01 출제율 95%

다음 짝지어진 단어의 관계가 같지 않은 것은?

① useful – helpful
② reply – answer
③ collect – gather
④ hurt – injure
⑤ consumer – producer

02 출제율 85%

다음 주어진 문장의 (A)와 (B)에 공통으로 들어가기에 적절한 것은?

(A) A: I'll spend less on clothes.
    B: Good for you, but make sure you don't give _____ your style.
(B) You should use your imagination to come _____ with a good idea.

① with   ② from   ③ up
④ by   ⑤ for

03 출제율 100%

다음 중 〈보기〉에 있는 단어를 사용하여 자연스러운 문장을 만들 수 없는 것은?

┤ 보기 ├
carry around   cool off
cut down on   due to

① The accident was _____ the high speed.
② She will _____ teaching next year.
③ He will _____ his umbrella all day.
④ The doctor told him to _____ his drinking.
⑤ We dived into the river to _____.

04 출제율 90%

다음 대화의 빈칸에 들어가기에 적절한 것은?

A: Now, we're getting to the rest stop. Any questions?
B: Yes. Can I meet my friend on another bus?
A: Of course, but _____.
   (물론이에요, 하지만 늦지 않게 돌아오도록 하세요.)
B: OK. Thanks.

① why don't you come earlier
② make sure you don't come earlier
③ how about coming late
④ make sure you don't come late
⑤ make sure you don't go too far

[05~07] 다음 대화를 읽고 물음에 답하시오.

B: Let's get into the wave pool. (A)
G: Wait! (B)
B: Do you mean the round one over there? (C)
G: Yes. (D) ⓐ들어가기 전에 구명조끼를 입어.(put, get, life jacket) (E) Make sure you don't miss any safety signs.

05 출제율 100%

(A) ~ (E) 중에서 다음 문장이 들어가기에 적절한 곳은?

Don't you see that sign?

① (A)   ② (B)   ③ (C)   ④ (D)   ⑤ (E)

06 출제율 90%

ⓐ의 밑줄 친 우리말에 해당하는 영어 문장을 완성하시오. (주어진 표현을 반드시 포함할 것)

➡ _____

07 According to the dialogue, which one is NOT true?

① The boy wants to get into the wave pool.

② The girl tells the boy to read the sign.

③ The two are talking about a round sign.

④ Before getting in, they have to put on a life jacket.

⑤ They have to miss safety signs.

[08~10] 다음 대화를 읽고 물음에 답하시오.

> Seho: Oh! It's almost closing time. Hurry up!
>
> Semi(Seho's sister): (A)_____, Seho. We've got everything.
>
> Seho: No. I need to visit Sneaker Ground. They're having a sale there.
>
> Semi: What? Are you thinking of getting sneakers?
>
> Seho: Yes. I can get high-end sneakers for 70% off. It's a steal.
>
> Semi: Well, (B)네가 거기에서 파란 운동화 산 것이 고작 일주일 전이야. Have you even put them on?
>
> Seho: No. They don't match any of my pants.
>
> Semi: You see? Make sure you don't repeat the same mistake.
>
> Seho: I see what you mean, but it's now or never. I can't miss out.
>
> Semi: You are impossible.

08 위 대화의 빈칸 (A)에 들어가기에 가장 적절한 것은?

① Get down

② Calm down

③ Turn down

④ Put down

⑤ Run down

09 위 대화의 밑줄 친 (B)에 해당하는 영어 문장으로 적절한 것은?

① it was just a week ago that you bought blue sneakers there.

② it was just a week ago what you bought blue sneakers there.

③ just a week ago it was that you bought blue sneakers there.

④ it was that just a week ago you bought blue sneakers there.

⑤ was it just a week ago that you bought blue sneakers there.

10 위 대화를 읽고 대답할 수 없는 것은?

① Which floor is Sneaker Ground on?

② What does Seho want to buy?

③ When did Seho buy blue sneakers?

④ What's the name of the sneaker shop?

⑤ How much discount do they give on high-end sneakers?

11 다음 중 어법상 올바른 문장을 고르면?

① Please let me going home now.

② I had my brother mails the letter.

③ Sad stories always make me cried.

④ My mom had us to walk the dog.

⑤ The teacher made the students line up.

12 다음 중 밑줄 친 부분의 용법이 나머지 넷과 다른 것은?

① I <u>made</u> them water the flowers.

② She will <u>make</u> me do the dishes again.

③ The movie <u>made</u> everyone cry until the end.

④ My father <u>made</u> me a new desk as a gift.

⑤ Mr. Park always <u>makes</u> people laugh out loud.

13 다음 〈보기〉의 밑줄 친 부분의 쓰임이 같은 것끼리 짝지어 진 것을 고르면? (출제율 95%)

┌─── 보기 ───┐
ⓐ Let me know <u>what</u> time it is.
ⓑ She will give Jack <u>what</u> she is making.
ⓒ That's not <u>what</u> I was trying to say.
ⓓ <u>What</u> are your opinions about the topic?
ⓔ You can bring <u>what</u> you like to eat there.
└────────┘

① ⓐ, ⓑ, ⓒ   ② ⓑ, ⓒ, ⓔ
③ ⓒ, ⓓ, ⓔ   ④ ⓐ, ⓑ, ⓒ, ⓔ
⑤ ⓐ, ⓒ, ⓓ, ⓔ

14 다음 밑줄 친 부분 중 어법상 옳은 것은? (출제율 90%)

① The teacher let us <u>to go</u> out to play.
② David felt the waves <u>to touch</u> his feet.
③ They helped us <u>to solve</u> the difficult problem.
④ You have to make her <u>to come</u> out of her room first.
⑤ We always enjoy <u>to watch</u> movies when exams are over.

[15~17] 다음 글을 읽고 물음에 답하시오.

What (A)_____ you shop? Do you buy only what you really need? Read on and think about your shopping habits.

Mina: Look at that!

Somin: Wow! N-girls are wearing a brand-new jacket.

Mina: It looks very cute. I have to have one just like it.

Somin: Me, too.

Many teens like to do what their favorite celebrities do. They are more than willing to buy what the stars use. They want to look like their heroes. They think celebrity brands will (B)_____ them cool, happy, and popular.

15 빈칸 (A)와 (B)에 동사 make를 어법에 맞게 쓰시오. (출제율 90%)

➡ (A) _____, (B) _____

16 다음 중 위 글의 내용과 일치하는 것은? (출제율 95%)

① N-girls are Somin's friends.
② Somin already has many jackets.
③ This is about people's shopping habit.
④ N-girls are wearing brand-new pants.
⑤ Somin and Mina are N-girls' heroes.

17 Why do teens buy what their celebrities use? (출제율 100%)

① Because celebrities make them buy the products.
② Because they want to make money.
③ Because they want to show off.
④ Because they believe the products are cheap.
⑤ Because they want to look like their favorite stars.

[18~22] 다음 글을 읽고 물음에 답하시오.

Here are three shopping tips to live (A)_____.

TIP 01. STICK TO A LIST

Make a shopping list and carry it around. Run into a store and get what you need. If you can't find anything on the list, walk out empty-handed. You will feel incredibly light.

TIP 02. COOL OFF FOR A DAY

When you shop online, don't click "Buy Now." Instead, hit "Add To Cart" and sign out. After 24 hours of cooling off, come back and see if you still want it.

TIP 03. FIND OLD TREASURES

Whenever you want to buy something new, go through your closet and see what you have. Find old treasures and enjoy a new appreciation for them.

출제율 90%

18 다음 중 빈칸 (A)에 들어갈 말로 가장 적절한 것은?

① on   ② by   ③ in   ④ at   ⑤ to

출제율 100%

19 다음 중 위 글을 읽고 답할 수 있는 것은?

① How many items should be there on a shopping list?
② How long should we cool off when we do off-line shopping?
③ What should we do if we can't find anything on our list?
④ What should we buy when we do off-line shopping?
⑤ How long does it take to shop online?

출제율 95%

20 According to the passage, how does a shopping list help us?

① It makes us feel uncomfortable.
② It helps us to buy what we really need.
③ It makes us spend much more money.
④ It helps us to find our old treasures.
⑤ It makes us add many items to the cart.

출제율 90%

21 What should we do whenever we want to buy something new? Answer in English with a full sentence.

➡ _____

_____

출제율 95%

22 다음은 반짝 세일 물건을 사려고 하는 친구에게 할 조언이다. 위 글의 내용에 맞게 빈칸에 알맞은 말을 쓰시오.

Calm down. You are suffering from FOMO, Fear of Missing Out. Why don't you add it to the cart and _____ _____ _____ _____ _____?

01 다음 짝지어진 단어의 관계가 같도록 주어진 철자로 시작하여 빈칸에 알맞은 말을 쓰시오.

consumer : producer – i_____ : exclude

02 다음 문장의 빈칸에 공통으로 들어갈 알맞은 단어를 쓰시오.

- They are so cute. Let's _____ closer to them.
- I think "BUY 1, _____ 1 FREE" is the most interesting.
- Make sure you call me as soon as you _____ there.

[03~04] 다음 대화를 읽고 물음에 답하시오.

B: Let's get ⓐ_____ the wave pool.
G: Wait! Don't you see that sign?
B: (A)저기 있는 동그란 것 말이야?
G: Yes. Put ⓑ_____ a life jacket before you get in. Make sure you don't miss any safety signs.

03 위 대화의 밑줄 친 (A)에 해당하는 영어 문장을 완성하시오. (보기의 단어를 모두 포함할 것)

보기
mean   over   round

➡ _____

04 위 대화의 빈칸 ⓐ와 ⓑ에 들어가기에 적절한 한 단어를 각각 쓰시오.

➡ ⓐ _____ ⓑ _____

05 다음 〈보기〉와 같도록 관계대명사 what을 사용하여 대화를 완성하시오. (적절한 대명사를 사용할 것)

보기
A: Is this the sandwich that your mom made for you?
B: Yes, it is what she made for me.

A: Is this the hat that Kate wanted to buy?
B: Yes, it is _____.

06 다음 글 (A)를 읽고 (B)의 빈칸을 완성하시오. (단, make를 적절한 형태로 반드시 포함하여 쓸 것)

(A) When Joe was feeling sad, Kate told him some funny stories. He felt much better after he listened to her stories.

(B) Dear Kate,
Thank you for your funny stories. Your stories _____ _____ _____ much better when I was feeling sad.
Love, Joe

Somin: Can you help me, Inho?

Inho: Sure. What's up?

Somin: There's going to be ①an online flash sale on new sneakers. Please help me grab a pair.

Inho: Okay, I'll ②click like crazy.

When a product sells like hot cakes, some people often feel that they won't be able to get it if they ③are fast enough. They suffer from FOMO, Fear of Missing Out, when they see sales signs such as *Limited Edition* and *Flash Sale*. The signs make them believe that it is ④ the last chance to grab the cool products. Then, getting (A)quick-selling goods becomes more like ⑤winning a game than spending money.

07 ①~⑤ 중 글의 흐름상 어색한 것을 바르게 고쳐 쓰시오.

➡ _____ 번 ➡ _____

08 According to the passage, when do people suffer from FOMO? Answer in English with a full sentence.

➡ _____

_____

09 다음은 밑줄 친 (A)를 설명하는 말이다. 글의 내용에 맞게 빈칸에 알맞은 말을 쓰시오.

> Quick-selling goods are things labeled '_____' or '_____.'

[10~12] 다음 글을 읽고 물음에 답하시오.

This is what I bought last week, a smart watch. I'd like to begin with what I like about the product. It counts my steps, so it helps me get enough exercise. Now, let me write what I don't like about the product. It has a very small screen, so it is difficult to read the time. All in all, I'm not satisfied, and this makes me give the product only one star.

10 Write the reason why the writer like the smart watch.

➡ _____

_____

11 Why is it difficult to read the time with the smart watch? Answer in English and use the phrase 'It's because.'

➡ _____

12 How many stars did the writer give the product? Answer in English with a full sentence.

➡ _____

01 여러 나라에는 특정 상품을 판매하는 시장이 있습니다. 다음 게시물을 완성해 봅시다..

- Alkmaar Market (네덜란드)

  At the Alkmaar Market, they sell many kinds of _____ in the traditional way.

- Ka Faroshi Market (아프가니스탄)

  The Ka Faroshi Market sells _____ of different colors and sizes. They are popular among many people.

- Jagalchi Market 자갈치 시장 (한국)

  Visit the Jagalchi Market to taste fresh _____ and feel the lively air.

02 모둠별로 특정 상품을 판매하는 시장을 조사해 봅시다.

Have you ever visited the Ghazipur Market? It is in New Delhi, India. At the market, you can buy flowers from all around the world. Flowers are in full glory around 5 a. m.

[예시 답안] Have you ever visited the Chatuchak Market? It is in Bangkok, Thailand. This market has more than 15,000 booths. They sell goods from every part of Thailand. It is the largest market in Thailand and is visited by about 200,000 visitors each day it is open.

Market	City, Country	Special Goods	Further Information
Ghazipur Market	New Delhi, India	flowers from all around the world	If you want to see its full glory, you should get there around 5 a.m.

03 다음 표를 참고하여 구매 후기를 완성하시오.

What I bought	a pair of running shoes
What I like about the product	They are very comfortable, so I wear them often.
What I don't like about the product	The color is white, so they get dirty easily.
Stars	(□) not satisfied (☑) satisfied ★★★★☆

A pair of running shoes

This is what I bought. I'd like to begin with _____ _____. Now, let me write _____ _____. All in all, I'm _____, and this makes me give the product _____.

단원별 모의고사

01 다음 짝지어진 단어의 관계가 같도록 빈칸에 알맞은 말을 고르시오.

> include : exclude = _____ : gloomy

① incredible   ② common
③ lively   ④ slippery
⑤ friendly

02 다음 밑줄 친 단어와 바꿔 쓰기에 적절한 것은?

> She made <u>helpful</u> comments on my work.

① careful   ② cheerful
③ harmful   ④ useful
⑤ wonderful

03 다음 대화의 (A)~(C)에서 적절한 것으로 짝지은 것은?

> B: Ouch!
> W: Are you all right, Jinsu?
> B: No, I'm not. I (A)[hurt / kept] my knee.
> W: The floor is always (B)[shiny / slippery] here. Make sure you don't (C) [walk / run].

	(A)	(B)	(C)
①	hurt	shiny	walk
②	kept	shiny	walk
③	hurt	slippery	walk
④	kept	slippery	run
⑤	hurt	slippery	run

04 다음 영영풀이에 해당하는 말을 주어진 철자로 시작하여 쓰시오.

(1) k_____ : the joint that bends in the middle of your leg
(2) c_____ : a famous living person
(3) b_____ : new and not yet used

[05~06] 다음 대화를 읽고 물음에 답하시오.

> G: I cleaned my room and found some old T-shirts.
> B: (A)<u>What are you going to do with them?</u> Are you thinking of throwing them away?
> G: No. I will make an eco bag out of them.
> B: That's a good idea!

05 위 대화의 밑줄 친 (A)와 바꾸어 쓸 수 있는 것은?

① What are you going to buy?
② What are you planning to do with them?
③ What did you find in the room?
④ When are you going to clean the room?
⑤ What are you going to sell with them?

06 위 대화를 읽고 대답할 수 있는 것은?

① When was the girl cleaning the room?
② Where is the girl going to throw away the old T-shirts?
③ What did the girl find in her room?
④ What will the girl do with the eco bag?
⑤ Does the boy have an eco bag?

[07~10] 다음 대화를 읽고 물음에 답하시오.

Seho: Oh! It's almost closing time. Hurry up!

Semi(Seho's sister): Calm down, Seho. We've got everything.

Seho: No. I need to visit Sneaker Ground. They're having a sale there.

Semi: What? Are you (A)_____ of getting sneakers?

Seho: Yes. I can get high-end sneakers for 70% off. It's a steal.

Semi: Well, (가)네가 거기에서 파란 운동화 산 것이 고작 일주일 전이야. Have you even put them on?

Seho: No. They don't (B)_____ any of my pants.

Semi: You see? Make sure you don't repeat the same mistake.

Seho: I see (C)_____ you mean, but it's now or never. I can't miss out.

Semi: You are impossible.

07 위 대화에서 다음 설명에 해당하는 단어를 찾아 쓰시오.

> more expensive and of better quality than other products of the same type

➡ _____

08 위 대화의 밑줄 친 (가)를 영어로 옮길 때 다음 ⓐ, ⓑ에 들어가기에 적절한 것으로 짝지어진 것은?

> ⓐ_____ just a week ago ⓑ_____ you bought blue sneakers there.

	ⓐ	ⓑ
①	it was	what
②	that was	that
③	this was	which
④	it was	that
⑤	that was	what

09 위 대화의 (A), (B), (C)에 들어가기에 적절한 것은?

	(A)	(B)	(C)
①	thinking	match	what
②	planning	match	that
③	thinking	match	which
④	planning	go	that
⑤	thinking	go	what

10 다음 중 위 대화의 내용과 일치하는 것은?

① Seho thinks they've got everything.

② Semi wants to visit Sneaker Ground.

③ Seho bought blue sneakers last month.

④ At Sneaker Ground they are giving 70% discount.

⑤ If Seho buys the sneakers, he will never buy them again.

[11~12] 다음 대화를 읽고, 물음에 답하시오.

G: How did you like the presentation?

B: It was very helpful. I need to do something to (A)_____ money.

G: Are you thinking of cutting down your spending?

B: Yes, I am. I'll spend less on clothes.

G: Good for you, but make sure you don't give up your style.

11 위 대화의 빈칸 (A)에 들어가기에 적절한 것은?

① make   ② save   ③ spend

④ give   ⑤ send

12 Which one is TRUE according to the dialogue?

① They are talking before the presentation.

② The boy thinks the presentation was too long.

③ The girl is asking the boy the amount of money he wants to save.

④ The girl will buy some clothes.

⑤ The boy thinks he spent too much on his clothes.

13 다음 중 밑줄 친 What[what]의 쓰임이 나머지 넷과 다른 것은?

① That's exactly <u>what</u> I wanted to buy.

② <u>What</u> he says is not important.

③ <u>What</u> didn't you like about the movie?

④ <u>What</u> I need is just something to eat.

⑤ <u>What</u> I didn't like was the special effects.

14 다음 중 밑줄 친 부분의 어법이 어색한 것은?

① The unhappy story about the accident <u>made me cry</u>.

② The snow on the tree <u>made me feel</u> happy.

③ She <u>asked me to help</u> her with the work.

④ I <u>had my brother to fix</u> my camera.

⑤ Dad won't <u>let me go</u> to the movies this weekend.

15 다음 문장의 빈칸에 들어갈 형태로 알맞게 짝지어진 것은?

> • She let him _____ into a room. (go)
>
> • The cartoon makes me _____. (laugh)
>
> • _____ popular things is one of the hottest trends among young consumers. (collect)

① go	laugh	Collect
② go	laugh	Collecting
③ go	to laugh	Collect
④ going	to laugh	Collecting
⑤ going	laughing	Collect

16 다음 우리말을 각각 3단어의 영어로 완성하시오. (what을 반드시 포함할 것)

> **A:** 저는 당신이 원하는 것을 할게요.
>
> = I will do _____.
>
> **B:** 제가 원하는 것을 해 줄 수 있나요?
>
> = Can you do _____?

17 다음 중 어법상 어색한 문장은?

① Is this what you always listen to?

② He could not understand what she said.

③ What she wants to buy is that blue dress.

④ You can choose what you like to wear a shirt when you come to school.

⑤ You can enjoy what you want once a week.

[18~21] 다음 글을 읽고 물음에 답하시오.

> Inho: ①<u>What a pick!</u>
>
> Mina: Did you get it, Inho?
>
> Inho: Yeah, finally. This completes my collection.
>
> Mina: Good for you!
>
> (A) The most popular collections include character stickers, baseball card sets, and goods featuring pop stars.
>
> (B) Collecting popular things ②<u>are</u> one of the hottest trends among young consumers.
>
> (C) Teen consumers enjoy getting more and more of these, because the idea of *more is better* makes them ③<u>happy</u>.
>
> What celebrity brands ④<u>have you bought</u>?
>
> What quick-selling goods have you grabbed?
>
> What character stickers have you collected?

Are you happy with what you have bought, grabbed, and collected? If you are happy ⑤with them, that's all right. If you aren't, ⓐ_____, you should try to be a smarter shopper.

18 다음 중 빈칸 ⓐ에 들어갈 말로 가장 적절한 것은?

① for example ② therefore
③ once ④ however
⑤ that is to say

19 자연스러운 글이 되도록 (A)~(C)를 바르게 배열하시오.

➡ _____

20 ①~⑤ 중 어법상 바르지 <u>않은</u> 것은?

① ② ③ ④ ⑤

21 According to the passage, what should we do if we aren't happy with what we have bought, grabbed, and collected? Answer in English.

➡ _____

[22~25] 다음 글을 읽고 물음에 답하시오.

Here are three shopping tips to live by.
TIP 01. STICK TO A LIST
  Make a shopping list and carry it around. Run into a store and get what you need. If you can't find anything on the list, walk out empty-handed. You will feel incredibly light.
TIP 02. (A)_____
  When you shop online, don't click "Buy Now." Instead, hit "Add To Cart" and sign out. After 24 hours of cooling off, come back and see if you still want it.

TIP 03. FIND OLD TREASURES
  Whenever you want to buy something new, go through your closet and see what you have. Find old treasures and enjoy a new appreciation for them.

22 다음 중 밑줄 친 (A)에 들어갈 말로 가장 적절한 것은?

① COOL OFF YOUR PASSION
② DO NOT SHOP ONLINE
③ BUY SOMETHING RIGHT AWAY
④ COOL OFF FOR A DAY
⑤ ADD TO CART AS SOON AS POSSIBLE

23 What is the passage mainly talking about?

① how to live in the digital world
② some advice for choosing a job
③ how to do off-line shopping wisely
④ tips to find cheap online malls
⑤ how to be a smarter consumer

24 위 글의 내용에 맞게 빈칸에 알맞은 말을 쓰시오.

Click "_____" instead of
"_____"

25 위 글의 내용에 맞게 조언을 완성하시오.

Cindy wants to buy a new jacket that her favorite singer is wearing. She knows that she already has many jackets, but she thinks that it will make her cool. In this situation, what can you say to Cindy?
"Cindy, _____."

INSIGHT
on the textbook
교과서 파헤치기

※ 다음 영어를 우리말로 쓰시오.

01 around	22 loud
02 difficulty	23 interestingly
03 last	24 lunar
04 lonely	25 pleased
05 scary	26 bother
06 support	27 reply
07 turn	28 price
08 tear	29 meaning
09 opinion	30 midnight
10 mood	31 possibly
11 serve	32 fair
12 grader	33 passing
13 stressful	34 permission
14 order	35 get along with ~
15 least	36 lose one's temper
16 already	37 don't have to ~
17 view	38 get better
18 present	39 in my opinion
19 privacy	40 take a second look
20 trade	41 put up with ~
21 appreciate	42 get on one's nerve
	43 have a hard time -ing

※ 다음 우리말을 영어로 쓰시오.

01 이미, 벌써

02 생각, 의견

03 자정

04 괴롭히다, 귀찮게 굴다

05 일, 직업, 업

06 어려움

07 공정한, 공평한

08 진가를 알아보다, 고마워하다

09 무서운

10 차례, 순번

11 주문하다; 주문

12 지속되다

13 아마, 도저히

14 제공하다, 대접하다

15 사생활

16 (시간, 세월의) 경과, 흐름

17 가장 적게

18 외로운

19 기쁜

20 때때로, 가끔

21 대략, 약

22 시끄러운

23 스트레스가 많은

24 흥미롭게도

25 음력의

26 유일한, 단지

27 눈물, 울음

28 가격, 물가

29 웃음

30 지지하다

31 허락, 허가

32 대답; 대답하다

33 선물; 현재의, 참석한

34 기분

35 ~ 없이 지내다

36 화내다

37 (~와) 만나다

38 ~을 견디다, 참다

39 ~의 곁을 지키다

40 내 생각에는

41 다시 보다

42 결국 ~하게 되다

43 ~와 잘 지내다

※ 다음 영영풀이에 알맞은 단어를 <보기>에서 골라 쓴 후, 우리말 뜻을 쓰시오.

1 _____ : relating to the Moon: _____

2 _____ : the sound of people laughing: _____

3 _____ : the way you feel at a particular time: _____

4 _____ : to say that you agree with an idea: _____

5 _____ : a problem or something that causes trouble: _____

6 _____ : the state of being free from public attention: _____

7 _____ : to continue for a particular length of time: _____

8 _____ : to answer someone by saying or writing something: _____

9 _____ : treating everyone in a way that is right or equal: _____

10 _____ : one of the parents of your mother or father: _____

11 _____ : unhappy because you do not have anyone to talk to: _____

12 _____ : to make someone feel slightly worried, upset, or concerned: _____

13 _____ : a drop of liquid that comes from your eyes especially when you cry:
_____

14 _____ : an opportunity or responsibility to do or use something before or after
other people: _____

15 _____ : to understand how serious or important a situation or problem: _____

16 _____ : the act of allowing someone to do something, especially when this is
done by someone in a position of authority: _____

보기			
grandparent	mood	privacy	bother
tear	difficulty	lunar	turn
appreciate	reply	last	lonely
fair	support	laughter	permission

※ 다음 우리말과 일치하도록 빈칸에 알맞은 말을 쓰시오.

Listen & Speak 1 A-1

G: _____ you _____ this book?

B: Yes, I _____. The _____ is very _____.

G: Is it? _____ _____ _____, it's a _____ story.

B: Well, it _____ be.

소녀: 너 이 책 읽어봤니?
소년: 응, 읽어봤어. 이야기가 무척 무섭더라.
소녀: 그래? 내 생각에는 슬픈 이야기인데.
소년: 음, 그럴 수도 있지.

Listen & Speak 1 A-2

B: _____ you _____ this _____?

G: Yes, I _____. It's one of the _____ movies I've ever seen.

B: You _____ _____ _____ it a lot. To me, it's just an old movie.

G: _____ can you _____ say that? In my _____, it is just _____.

소년: 너 이 영화 봤니?
소녀: 응, 봤어. 내가 본 최고의 영화들 중 하나야.
소년: 그 영화 무척 좋아하는 것 같네. 나에겐 그건 그저 오래된 영화인데.
소녀: 어떻게 그런 말을 할 수 있어? 내 생각에, 그 영화는 정말 훌륭해.

Listen & Speak 1 A-3

B: _____ this _____ _____?

G: Well, I _____ it's beautiful.

B: Hmm ..., _____ _____ a _____ _____, there is something _____ _____ the painting.

G: Hey, you _____ have to _____ _____ me.

소년: 이 그림은 이상하지 않니?
소녀: 글쎄, 나는 아름답다고 생각하는데.
소년: 음, 다시 보니 그림에 뭔가 아름다운 것이 있군.
소녀: 이런, 내 의견에 동의하지 않아도 돼.

Listen & Speak 1 B

A: We are now _____ _____. This year is very _____!

B: You can _____ _____ again! _____ _____ we do to make this year special?

A: In my _____, we should _____ more _____.

B: You're _____. I think it's also _____ to read a lot of books.

A: 우리는 이제 3학년이야. 이번 해는 매우 중요해!
B: 정말 그래! 이번 해를 특별하게 보내기 위해 무엇을 해야 할까?
A: 내 생각에 우리는 더 많은 친구를 사귀어야 해.
B: 맞아. 많은 책을 읽는 것 또한 중요하다고 생각해.

Listen & Speak 2 A-1

G: Did you _____ that a new ice _____ store _____ last week?

B: _____. I _____ _____ _____ there.

G: _____ you? How _____ it?

B: The ice cream was _____.

G: _____ was the _____?

B: Well, it was very _____. I was not _____ _____ it.

소녀: 지난주에 새 아이스크림 가게가 개업했다는 것 들었니?
소년: 물론이지. 나는 이미 거기 가봤어.
소녀: 그랬어? 어땠어?
소년: 아이스크림은 훌륭했어.
소녀: 가격은 어땠어?
소년: 음, 가격은 매우 비쌌어. 나는 그것이 마음에 들지 않았어.

Listen & Speak 2 A-2

B: _____ are _____ _____ _____ people _____.

G: Yes, _____ are. It's been 30 minutes _____ we _____.

B: The _____ is so _____. I'm not _____ _____ it.

G: _____ _____ _____ people _____ _____. They are _____ _____ now.

B: _____ we come in _____?

G: Yes, we did. It's not _____.

Conversation B

Yujin: Did your family _____ _____ to _____ last weekend?

Seho: Yes, we did. The _____ was great, but my _____ is _____ big and _____.

Yujin: Really? _____ _____ is it?

Seho: There are _____ of us: my _____, my mom, my dad, two _____, and me.

Yujin: That is a _____ _____!

Seho: Well, I _____ like it _____ _____. There's no _____.

Yujin: I _____ _____ you're saying, but to me, it's _____ to _____ a big family. I sometimes feel _____ because I'm an _____ _____.

Seho: Yeah ..., I see _____ you _____.

Real Life Task Step 1

W: People often say, "I'm not _____ about my family." But we have a _____ story. We _____ 2,000 people, "With _____ do you feel happiest?" _____ _____ _____ of them _____ happiest when they are _____ their family. The second-largest _____ of people are happiest _____ their _____. _____, _____ 13% of the people we _____ feel happiest when _____.

Real Life Task Step 2

A: It's _____ to have a happy _____ to live a happy _____.

B: I _____. What _____ family members _____ to _____ a happy family?

A: In my _____, they should _____ to help one _____.

B: That's a _____ idea. I think they also _____ to be _____ to _____ _____. What _____ should they _____?

※ 다음 우리말에 맞도록 대화를 영어로 쓰시오.

Listen & Speak 1 A-1

G: _____

B: _____

G: _____

B: _____

소녀: 너 이 책 읽어봤니?
소년: 응, 읽어봤어. 이야기가 무척 무섭
　　　더라.
소녀: 그래? 내 생각에는 슬픈 이야기인데.
소년: 음, 그럴 수도 있지.

Listen & Speak 1 A-2

B: _____

G: _____

B: _____

G: _____

소년: 너 이 영화 봤니?
소녀: 응, 봤어. 내가 본 최고의 영화들
　　　중 하나야.
소년: 그 영화 무척 좋아하는 것 같네. 나
　　　에겐 그건 그저 오래된 영화인데.
소녀: 어떻게 그런 말을 할 수 있어? 내
　　　생각에, 그 영화는 정말 훌륭해.

Listen & Speak 1 A-3

B: _____

G: _____

B: _____

_____

G: _____

소년: 이 그림은 이상하지 않니?
소녀: 글쎄, 나는 아름답다고 생각하는데.
소년: 음, 다시 보니 그림에 뭔가 아름다
　　　운 것이 있군.
소녀: 이런, 내 의견에 동의하지 않아도 돼.

Listen & Speak 1 B

A: _____

B: _____

A: _____

B: _____

A: 우리는 이제 3학년이야. 이번 해는 매
　　우 중요해!
B: 정말 그래! 이번 해를 특별하게 보내
　　기 위해 무엇을 해야 할까?
A: 내 생각에 우리는 더 많은 친구를 사
　　귀어야 해.
B: 맞아. 많은 책을 읽는 것 또한 중요하
　　다고 생각해.

Listen & Speak 2 A-1

G: _____

B: _____

G: _____

B: _____

G: _____

B: _____

소녀: 지난주에 새 아이스크림 가게가 개
　　　업했다는 것 들었니?
소년: 물론이지. 나는 이미 거기 가봤어.
소녀: 그랬어? 어땠어?
소년: 아이스크림은 훌륭했어.
소녀: 가격은 어땠어?
소년: 음, 가격은 매우 비쌌어. 나는 그것
　　　이 마음에 들지 않았어.

Listen & Speak 2 A-2

B: _____

G: _____

B: _____

G: _____

B: _____

G: _____

소년: 여기 사람들이 많다.

소녀: 응, 그러네. 우리가 주문한지 30 분이 지났어.

소년: 서비스가 너무 느려. 나는 그것이 마음에 안 들어.

소녀: 저기 저 사람들 좀 봐. 저 사람들은 지금 음식을 받는걸.

소년: 우리가 더 빨리 오지 않았니?

소녀: 응, 그랬지. 이건 공평하지 않아.

Conversation B

Yujin: _____

Seho: _____

Yujin: _____

Seho: _____
_____

Yujin: _____

Seho: _____

Yujin: _____
_____

Seho: _____

유진: 지난 주말에 가족들과 식사하러 외출했니?

세호: 응, 했어. 음식은 아주 괜찮았는데, 우리 가족이 너무 많고 시끄러워.

유진: 정말? 얼마나 많은데?

세호: 일곱 명이야. 할아버지, 할머니, 엄마, 아빠, 남동생 두 명, 그리고 나.

유진: 정말 대가족이구나!

세호: 그런데 난 그게 맘에 안 들어. 사생활이 없거든.

유진: 무슨 말인지 알겠지만, 나는 대가족이 있는 것이 좋아. 나는 외동이라서 가끔 외롭거든.

세호: 그렇구나. 무슨 의미인지 알겠어.

Real Life Task Step 1

W: _____
_____
_____
_____
_____

W: 사람들은 종종 "난 내 가족이 마음에 안 들어."라고 말합니다. 그러나 우리에게는 다른 이야기가 있습니다. 우리는 2,000명의 사람들에게 "누구와 함께 있을 때 가장 행복하십니까?"라고 물었습니다. 절반 이상의 사람들이 가족과 함께 있을 때 가장 행복하다고 느낍니다. 그다음으로 많은 사람들이 그들의 친구와 함께 있을 때 가장 행복합니다. 흥미롭게도 우리가 조사한 사람들의 약 13퍼센트는 혼자 있을 때 가장 행복하다고 느낍니다.

Real Life Task Step 2

A: _____

B: _____

A: _____

B: _____
_____

A: 행복한 삶을 위해 행복한 가족을 갖는 것은 중요해.

B: 동의해. 행복한 가정생활을 위해 가족 구성원들이 무엇을 해야 할까?

A: 내 생각에 그들은 서로를 도우려고 노력해야 해.

B: 좋은 생각이야. 나는 그들이 또한 서로에게 친절해야 한다고 생각해. 그들은 또 무엇을 해야 할까?

※ 다음 우리말과 일치하도록 빈칸에 알맞은 것을 골라 쓰시오.

Family: Love It, Hate It, and Can't Do Without It

가족: 사랑하고, 미워하고, 그런데 없어서는 안 되는 것

1 The word *family* _____ _____ _____ _____ to different people.

A. have   B. meanings   C. different   D. may

1 가족이라는 말은 사람들마다 다른 의미를 가질 수 있습니다.

2 We asked our _____, " _____ are you _____ with your family?" Here are some of their _____.

A. how   B. replies   C. doing   D. readers

2 우리는 독자들에게 '가족과 어떻게 지내나요?'라고 물었습니다. 여기 그 대답들 중 몇 가지가 있습니다.

3 I often ask myself whether I_____ _____ with my family members, and more _____ than not, I'm not sure _____ I really do.

A. whether   B. along   C. often   D. get

3 나는 종종 가족들과 잘 지내는지 나 자신에게 물어보는데, 많은 경우에 잘 지내는지 확신하지 못한다.

4 _____ one _____, they _____ me _____ the time.

A. bother   B. for   C. all   D. thing

4 한 예를 들자면, 가족들은 나를 항상 귀찮게 한다.

5 My sister comes into my room _____ my _____ and shouts at me to _____ _____ on Sunday mornings.

A. permission   B. up   C. without   D. wake

5 언니는 일요일 아침에 허락도 없이 내 방에 들어와서 일어나라고 소리친다.

6 Next, Mom _____ me to _____ the dog, and then Dad _____ me to _____ my room.

A. tells   B. walk   C. asks   D. clean

6 그다음에는 엄마가 개를 산책시키라고 하시고, 그러고 나면 아빠가 방을 청소하라고 하신다.

7 They keep _____ _____ _____ _____ until I get angry at them.

A. nerves   B. on   C. getting   D. my

7 가족들은 내가 화가 날 때까지 내 신경을 건드린다.

8 But I always _____ _____ loving them because they have been with me _____ my _____, still stick by me now, and will continue to do so in the future.

Kamala, U.S.A

A. worst   B. up   C. at   D. end

8 하지만 결국엔 항상 가족들을 사랑하게 되는데, 그들은 내가 가장 어려울 때 함께 있어 주었고, 지금도 내 곁을 지키며, 앞으로도 계속해서 그럴 것이기 때문이다.   카말라, 미국

9 I _____ a room _____ my sister, _____ is two years _____ than me.

A. who   B. older   C. share   D. with

10 _____ she became a teenager, her _____ started _____ every _____.

A. changing   B. when   C. mood   D. minute

11 She would _____ her temper _____ _____ one moment and happily read a book or _____ a film the next.

A. nothing   B. lose   C. watch   D. over

12 It was _____ _____ me _____ _____ up with her.

A. to   B. difficult   C. put   D. for

13 Now it's my _____ to _____ a teenager. My sister is still one, but she is _____ _____.

A. getting   B. turn   C. better   D. be

14 Whenever I _____ my _____, she _____ to _____ me.

A. temper   B. tries   C. lose   D. support

15 I also understand her _____ than before _____ now I know _____ it feels _____ to be a teenager.

A. because   B. what   C. like   D. better

16 As we _____ to know each other better, we _____ greater love _____ each _____.

Rachel, Australia

A. toward   B. get   C. feel   D. other

17 My older brother, _____ _____ university this year, is the _____ _____.

A. child   B. entered   C. golden   D. who

18 He is a _____ _____ at home and a perfect _____ _____ school.

A. perfect   B. at   C. son   D. student

19 _____ to _____, it is really stressful to have _____ a _____ brother.

A. say   B. such   C. needless   D. shining

20 Well, in _____, he is not _____ and is _____ at one thing that I am _____ at.

A. great   B. fact   C. poor   D. perfect

---

9 나는 언니와 방을 함께 쓰는데, 언니는 나보다 두 살이 많다.

10 언니는 십대가 되었을 때, 기분이 매분마다 바뀌기 시작했다.

11 어느 순간 갑자기 아무것도 아닌 일에 화를 내다가 바로 다음 순간 즐겁게 책을 읽거나 영화를 보곤 했다.

12 나는 언니를 견디기가 힘들었다.

13 이젠 내가 십대가 될 차례이다. 언니도 아직 십대이지만 점점 나아지고 있다.

14 내가 화를 낼 때마다 언니는 나를 지지해 주려고 노력한다.

15 지금은 나도 십대라는 것이 어떤 느낌인지 알기 때문에 예전보다 언니를 더 잘 이해한다.

16 우리가 서로를 잘 알아 갈수록 우리는 서로에게 더 큰 사랑을 느낀다.   레이첼, 호주

17 우리 형은 올해 대학에 들어갔는데, 누구에게나 사랑받는 아들이다.

18 형은 집에서는 완벽한 아들이고 학교에서는 완벽한 학생이다.

19 말할 필요도 없이, 그렇게 눈부신 형이 있다는 것은 정말 골치 아픈 일이다.

20 하지만 사실 형도 완벽하지 않고, 내가 잘하는 일에는 형편없다.

21 He has no _____ for fashion, and I always help him _____ he has a _____ time _____ clothes for a date.

A. choosing   B. eye   C. hard   D. whenever

22 I feel _____ when he _____ me _____ my help and _____ my fashion sense.

A. for   B. pleased   C. appreciates   D. thanks

23 It is not always _____ for me to live with the perfect brother, and I _____ in "every man for his _____ _____."

Minsu, Korea

A. trade   B. believe   C. difficult   D. own

24 Kamala, Rachel, and Minsu all have _____ _____ _____ in their family _____.

A. life   B. own   C. their   D. difficulties

25 _____ the _____ time, they love their families and _____ special _____ in them.

A. meanings   B. same   C. find   D. at

26 What story _____ you _____ us _____ your _____?

A. would   B. tell   C. family   D. about

27 A FAMILY

A family

is _____ of love and tears,

laughter and _____.

It _____ stronger

with the _____ of time.

A. made   B. passing   C. grows   D. years

21 형은 패션을 보는 눈이 없어서, 데이트에 입을 옷을 고르는 걸 어려워할 때마다 내가 항상 그를 도와준다.

22 형이 내 도움을 고마워하고 내 패션 감각을 알아줄 때 기분이 좋다.

23 완벽한 형과 함께 사는 것이 항상 어려운 일은 아니며, "굼벵이도 구르는 재주가 있다."는 것을 나는 믿는다.   민수, 한국

24 Kamala, Rachel, 그리고 민수 모두에게 가족생활의 어려움이 있습니다.

25 그와 동시에 그들은 자신들의 가족을 사랑하고 그 안에서 특별한 의미를 찾고 있습니다.

26 여러분은 여러분 가족에 대해 어떤 이야기를 할 건가요?

27 가족

가족은
사랑과 눈물
웃음과 세월로 만들어집니다.
가족은 시간의 흐름과 함께
점점 더 강해집니다.

※ 다음 우리말과 일치하도록 빈칸에 알맞은 것을 골라 쓰시오.

Family: Love It, Hate It, and Can't Do Without It

1 The word *family* _____ _____ _____ _____ to _____ people.

2 We asked our readers, "_____ are you _____ with your family?" _____ are some of _____ _____.

3 I often _____ myself _____ I _____ _____ _____ my family members, and _____ _____ _____ _____, I'm _____ _____ _____ I really do.

4 _____ _____ _____, they _____ me all the time.

5 My sister _____ _____ my room _____ my _____ and _____ _____ me _____ _____ _____ on Sunday mornings.

6 Next, Mom _____ me _____ _____ the dog, and then Dad _____ _____ _____ _____ my room.

7 They _____ _____ _____ _____ _____ _____ until I get _____ _____ them.

8 But I always _____ _____ _____ them because they have been with me _____ _____ _____, still stick by me now, and will continue _____ _____ _____ in the future.

Kamala, U.S.A

9 I _____ a room with my sister, _____ _____ two years _____ _____ _____.

10 _____ she became a teenager, _____ _____ started _____ _____.

11 She _____ _____ her temper _____ _____ one moment and happily _____ a book or _____ a film the next.

12 It was _____ _____ _____ _____ put up with her.

13 Now it's _____ _____ _____ _____ a teenager. My sister is still one, but she is _____ _____.

14 _____ I lose my temper, she _____ _____ _____ me.

가족: 사랑하고, 미워하고, 그런데 없어서는 안 되는 것

1 가족이라는 말은 사람들마다 다른 의미를 가질 수 있습니다.

2 우리는 독자들에게 '가족과 어떻게 지내나요?'라고 물었습니다. 여기 그 대답들 중 몇 가지가 있습니다.

3 나는 종종 가족들과 잘 지내는지 나 자신에게 물어보는데, 많은 경우에 잘 지내는지 확신하지 못한다.

4 한 예를 들자면, 가족들은 나를 항상 귀찮게 한다.

5 언니는 일요일 아침에 허락도 없이 내 방에 들어와서 일어나라고 소리친다.

6 그다음에는 엄마가 개를 산책시키라고 하시고, 그러고 나면 아빠가 방을 청소하라고 하신다.

7 가족들은 내가 화가 날 때까지 내 신경을 건드린다.

8 하지만 결국엔 항상 가족들을 사랑하게 되는데, 그들은 내가 가장 어려울 때 함께 있어 주었고, 지금도 내 곁을 지키며, 앞으로도 계속해서 그럴 것이기 때문이다.   카말라, 미국

9 나는 언니와 방을 함께 쓰는데, 언니는 나보다 두 살이 많다.

10 언니는 십대가 되었을 때, 기분이 매분마다 바뀌기 시작했다.

11 어느 순간 갑자기 아무것도 아닌 일에 화를 내다가 바로 다음 순간 즐겁게 책을 읽거나 영화를 보곤 했다.

12 나는 언니를 견디기가 힘들었다.

13 이젠 내가 십대가 될 차례이다. 언니도 아직 십대이지만 점점 나아지고 있다.

14 내가 화를 낼 때마다 언니는 나를 지지해 주려고 노력한다.

15 I also _____ her _____ _____ before _____ now I know _____ _____ _____ _____ to be a teenager.

16 As we _____ _____ _____ each other better, we _____ _____ _____ toward _____ _____ .

Rachel, Australia

17 My older brother, _____ _____ university this year, _____ _____ _____ _____ .

18 He is _____ _____ _____ at home and a _____ _____ _____ school.

19 _____ _____ _____ _____ , it is really _____ to have _____ _____ _____ _____ .

20 Well, in fact, he is not perfect and is _____ _____ one thing _____ I _____ _____ _____ .

21 He has _____ _____ _____ fashion, and I always help him _____ he has a _____ _____ _____ _____ for a date.

22 I feel _____ when he _____ me _____ my help and _____ my _____ _____ .

23 It is not always difficult _____ _____ _____ _____ _____ the perfect brother, and I _____ _____ "every man for his _____ _____ ."

Minsu, Korea

24 Kamala, Rachel, and Minsu all have _____ _____ _____ _____ in their _____ _____ .

25 _____ _____ _____ _____ _____ , they love their families and _____ _____ _____ in them.

26 What story _____ you _____ us about your family?

27 A FAMILY

A family

_____ _____ _____ love and _____ ,

_____ and _____ .

It _____ stronger

with the _____ _____ _____ .

15 지금은 나도 십대라는 것이 어떤 느낌인지 알기 때문에 예전보다 언니를 더 잘 이해한다.

16 우리가 서로를 잘 알아 갈수록 우리는 서로에게 더 큰 사랑을 느낀다. 레이첼, 호주

17 우리 형은 올해 대학에 들어갔는데, 누구에게나 사랑받는 아들이다.

18 형은 집에서는 완벽한 아들이고 학교에서는 완벽한 학생이다.

19 말할 필요도 없이, 그렇게 눈부신 형이 있다는 것은 정말 골치 아픈 일이다.

20 하지만 사실 형도 완벽하지 않고, 내가 잘하는 일에는 형편없다.

21 형은 패션을 보는 눈이 없어서, 데이트에 입을 옷을 고르는 걸 어려워할 때마다 내가 항상 그를 도와준다.

22 형이 내 도움을 고마워하고 내 패션 감각을 알아줄 때 기분이 좋다.

23 완벽한 형과 함께 사는 것이 항상 어려운 일은 아니며, "굼벵이도 구르는 재주가 있다."는 것을 나는 믿는다. 민수, 한국

24 Kamala, Rachel, 그리고 민수 모두에게 가족생활의 어려움이 있습니다.

25 그와 동시에 그들은 자신들의 가족을 사랑하고 그 안에서 특별한 의미를 찾고 있습니다.

26 여러분은 여러분 가족에 대해 어떤 이야기를 할 건가요?

27 가족

가족은

사랑과 눈물

웃음과 세월로 만들어집니다.

가족은 시간의 흐름과 함께 점점 더 강해집니다.

※ 다음 문장을 우리말로 쓰시오.

Family: Love It, Hate It, and Can't Do Without It

1 The word *family* may have different meanings to different people.

➡ _____

2 We asked our readers, "How are you doing with your family?" Here are some of their replies.

➡ _____

3 I often ask myself whether I get along with my family members, and more often than not, I'm not sure whether I really do.

➡ _____

4 For one thing, they bother me all the time.

➡ _____

5 My sister comes into my room without my permission and shouts at me to wake up on Sunday mornings.

➡ _____

6 Next, Mom asks me to walk the dog, and then Dad tells me to clean my room.

➡ _____

7 They keep getting on my nerves until I get angry at them.

➡ _____

8 But I always end up loving them because they have been with me at my worst, still stick by me now, and will continue to do so in the future.   Kamala, U.S.A.

➡ _____

_____

9 I share a room with my sister, who is two years older than me.

➡ _____

10 When she became a teenager, her mood started changing every minute.

➡ _____

11 She would lose her temper over nothing one moment and happily read a book or watch a film the next.

➡ _____

12 It was difficult for me to put up with her.

➡ _____

13 Now it's my turn to be a teenager. My sister is still one, but she is getting better.

➡ _____

14 Whenever I lose my temper, she tries to support me.

➡ _____

15 I also understand her better than before because now I know what it feels like to be a teenager.

➡ _____

16 As we get to know each other better, we feel greater love toward each other.

Rachel, Australia

➡ _____

17 My older brother, who entered university this year, is the golden child.

➡ _____

18 He is a perfect son at home and a perfect student at school.

➡ _____

19 Needless to say, it is really stressful to have such a shining brother.

➡ _____

20 Well, in fact, he is not perfect and is poor at one thing that I am great at.

➡ _____

21 He has no eye for fashion, and I always help him whenever he has a hard time choosing clothes for a date.

➡ _____

22 I feel pleased when he thanks me for my help and appreciates my fashion sense.

➡ _____

23 It is not always difficult for me to live with the perfect brother, and I believe in "every man for his own trade."

Minsu, Korea

➡ _____

24 Kamala, Rachel, and Minsu all have their own difficulties in their family life.

➡ _____

25 At the same time, they love their families and find special meanings in them.

➡ _____

26 What story would you tell us about your family?

➡ _____

27 A family / is made of love and tears, / laughter and years. / It grows stronger with the passing of time.

➡ _____

※ 다음 괄호 안의 단어들을 우리말에 맞도록 바르게 배열하시오.

Family: Love It, Hate It, and Can't Do Without It

1 (word / the / may / *family* / have / meanings / different / to / people. / different)

  ➡ _____

2 (asked / we / readers, / our / "how / you / are / doing / your / with / family?" // are / here / of / some / replies. / their)

  ➡ _____

  _____

3 (often / I / myself / ask / whether / get / I / along / with / family / my / members, / and / often / more / not, / than / I'm / sure / not / whether / really / do. / I)

  ➡ _____

  _____

4 (one / for / things, / bother / they / all / me / time. / the)

  ➡ _____

5 (sister / my / comes / my / into / room / my / without / permission / and / at / shouts / me / to / up / wake / on / mornings. / Sunday)

  ➡ _____

  _____

6 (next, / asks / Mom / to / me / the / walk / dog, / and / then / tells / Dad / to / me / clean / room. / my)

  ➡ _____

  _____

7 (keep / they / getting / my / on / nerves / until / get / I / at / angry / them.)

  ➡ _____

8 (I / but / always / up / end / loving / because / them / they / been / have / me / with / at / worst, / my / stick / still / me / by / now, / and / continue / will / do / to / so / the / future. / in) Kamala, U.S.A.

  ➡ _____

  _____

가족: 사랑하고, 미워하고, 그런데 없어서는 안 되는 것

1 가족이라는 말은 사람들마다 다른 의미를 가질 수 있습니다.

2 우리는 독자들에게 '가족과 어떻게 지내나요?'라고 물었습니다. 여기 그 대답들 중 몇 가지가 있습니다.

3 나는 종종 가족들과 잘 지내는지 나 자신에게 물어보는데, 많은 경우에 잘 지내는지 확신하지 못한다.

4 한 예를 들자면, 가족들은 나를 항상 귀찮게 한다.

5 언니는 일요일 아침에 허락도 없이 내 방에 들어와서 일어나라고 소리친다.

6 그다음에는 엄마가 개를 산책시키라고 하시고, 그러고 나면 아빠가 방을 청소하라고 하신다.

7 가족들은 내가 화가 날 때까지 내 신경을 건드린다.

8 하지만 결국엔 항상 가족들을 사랑하게 되는데, 그들은 내가 가장 어려울 때 함께 있어 주었고, 지금도 내 곁을 지키며, 앞으로도 계속해서 그럴 것이기 때문이다.   카말라, 미국

9 (share / I / room / a / my / with / sister, / is / who / years / two / than / older / me.)

➡ _____

10 (she / when / became / teenager, / a / mood / her / changing / started / minute. / every)

➡ _____

11 (would / she / her / lose / temper / nothing / over / moment / one / and / happily / a / read / book / or / a / watch / film / next. / the)

➡ _____

➡ _____

12 (was / it / difficult / me / for / to / up / put / her. / with)

➡ _____

13 (it's / now / turn / my / be / to / a / teenager. // sister / my / still / is / one, / she / but / getting / is / better.)

➡ _____

➡ _____

14 (I / whenever / lose / temper, / my / tries / she / support / to / me.)

➡ _____

15 (also / I / understand / better / her / than / because / before / I / now / what / know / feels / it / to / like / be / teenager. / a)

➡ _____

➡ _____

16 (we / as / to / get / each / know / better, / other / feel / we / greater / toward / love / other. / each)   Rachel, Australia

➡ _____

➡ _____

17 (older / my / brother, / entered / who / this / university / year, / the / is / child. / golden)

➡ _____

18 (is / he / perfect / a / son / home / at / and / perfect / a / student / school. / at)

➡ _____

19 (to / needless / say, / is / it / stressful / really / have / to / a / such / brother. / shining)

➡ _____

20 (in / well, / fact, / is / he / perfect / not / and / poor / is / at / thing / one / that / am / I / at. / great)

➡ _____

9 나는 언니와 방을 함께 쓰는데, 언니는 나보다 두 살이 많다.

10 언니는 십대가 되었을 때, 기분이 매분마다 바뀌기 시작했다.

11 어느 순간 갑자기 아무것도 아닌 일에 화를 내다가 바로 다음 순간 즐겁게 책을 읽거나 영화를 보곤 했다.

12 나는 언니를 견디기가 힘들었다.

13 이젠 내가 십대가 될 차례이다. 언니도 아직 십대이지만 점점 나아지고 있다.

14 내가 화를 낼 때마다 언니는 나를 지지해 주려고 노력한다.

15 지금은 나도 십대라는 것이 어떤 느낌인지 알기 때문에 예전보다 언니를 더 잘 이해한다.

16 우리가 서로를 잘 알아 갈수록 우리는 서로에게 더 큰 사랑을 느낀다.   레이첼, 호주

17 우리 형은 올해 대학에 들어갔는데, 누구에게나 사랑받는 아들이다.

18 형은 집에서는 완벽한 아들이고 학교에서는 완벽한 학생이다.

19 말할 필요도 없이, 그렇게 눈부신 형이 있다는 것은 정말 골치 아픈 일이다.

20 하지만 사실 형도 완벽하지 않고, 내가 잘하는 일에는 형편없다.

21 (has / he / eye / no / fashion, / for / I / and / help / always / him / whenever / has / he / time / a / hard / clothes / choosing / a / for / date.)

➡ _____

_____

22 (feel / I / when / pleased / he / me / thanks / for / help / my / appreciate / and / fashion / my / sense.)

➡ _____

_____

23 (is / it / always / not / difficult / me / for / live / to / with / perfect / the / brother, / I / and / believe / "every / in / man / his / for / trade." / own) Minsu, Korea

➡ _____

_____

24 (Rachel, / Kamala, / Minsu / and / have / all / own / their / difficulties / their / in / life. / family)

➡ _____

_____

25 (the / at / time, / same / love / they / their / and / families / special / find / in / meanings / them.)

➡ _____

_____

26 (story / what / you / would / us / tell / your / about / family?)

➡ _____

27 (family / a // made / is / love / of / tears, / and // years. / and / laughter // grows / it / with / stronger / passing / the / time / of)
     A family

➡ _____

_____

21 형은 패션을 보는 눈이 없어서, 데이트에 입을 옷을 고르는 걸 어려워할 때마다 내가 항상 그를 도와준다.

22 형이 내 도움을 고마워하고 내 패션 감각을 알아줄 때 기분이 좋다.

23 완벽한 형과 함께 사는 것이 항상 어려운 일은 아니며, "굼벵이도 구르는 재주가 있다."는 것을 나는 믿는다.   민수, 한국

24 Kamala, Rachel, 그리고 민수 모두에게 가족생활의 어려움이 있습니다.

25 그와 동시에 그들은 자신들의 가족을 사랑하고 그 안에서 특별한 의미를 찾고 있습니다.

26 여러분은 여러분 가족에 대해 어떤 이야기를 할 건가요?

27 가족

가족은
사랑과 눈물
웃음과 세월로 만들어집니다.
가족은 시간의 흐름과 함께
점점 더 강해집니다.

※ 다음 우리말을 영어로 쓰시오.

Family: Love It, Hate It, and Can't Do Without It

1 가족이라는 말은 사람들마다 다른 의미를 가질 수 있습니다.

➡ _____

2 우리는 독자들에게 '가족과 어떻게 지내나요?'라고 물었습니다. 여기 그 대답들 중 몇 가지가 있습니다.

➡ _____

3 나는 종종 가족들과 잘 지내는지 나 자신에게 물어보는데, 많은 경우에 잘 지내는지 확신하지 못한다.

➡ _____
_____

4 한 예를 들자면, 가족들은 나를 항상 귀찮게 한다.

➡ _____

5 언니는 일요일 아침에 허락도 없이 내 방에 들어와서 일어나라고 소리친다.

➡ _____

6 그다음에는 엄마가 개를 산책시키라고 하시고, 그러고 나면 아빠가 방을 청소하라고 하신다.

➡ _____

7 가족들은 내가 화가 날 때까지 내 신경을 건드린다.

➡ _____

8 하지만 결국엔 항상 가족들을 사랑하게 되는데, 그들은 내가 가장 어려울 때 함께 있어 주었고, 지금도 내 곁을 지키며, 앞으로도 계속해서 그럴 것이기 때문이다.

➡ _____
_____

Kamala, U.S.A.

9 나는 언니와 방을 함께 쓰는데, 언니는 나보다 두 살이 많다.

➡ _____

10 언니는 십대가 되었을 때, 기분이 매분마다 바뀌기 시작했다.

➡ _____

11 어느 순간 갑자기 아무것도 아닌 일에 화를 내다가 바로 다음 순간 즐겁게 책을 읽거나 영화를 보곤 했다.

➡ _____

12 나는 언니를 견디기 힘들었다.

➡ _____

13 이젠 내가 십대가 될 차례이다. 언니도 아직 십대이지만 점점 나아지고 있다.

➡ _____

14 내가 화를 낼 때마다 언니는 나를 지지해 주려고 노력한다.

➡ _____

15 지금은 나도 십대라는 것이 어떤 느낌인지 알기 때문에 예전보다 언니를 더 잘 이해한다.

➡ _____

16 우리가 서로를 잘 알아 갈수록 우리는 서로에게 더 큰 사랑을 느낀다.

➡ _____

Rachel, Australia

17 우리 형은 올해 대학에 들어갔는데, 누구에게나 사랑받는 아들이다.

➡ _____

18 형은 집에서는 완벽한 아들이고 학교에서는 완벽한 학생이다.

➡ _____

19 말할 필요도 없이, 그렇게 눈부신 형이 있다는 것은 정말 골치 아픈 일이다.

➡ _____

20 하지만 사실 형도 완벽하지 않고, 내가 잘하는 일에는 형편없다.

➡ _____

21 형은 패션을 보는 눈이 없어서, 데이트에 입을 옷을 고르는 걸 어려워할 때마다 내가 항상 그를 도와준다.

➡ _____

22 형이 내 도움을 고마워하고 내 패션 감각을 알아줄 때 기분이 좋다.

➡ _____

23 완벽한 형과 함께 사는 것이 항상 어려운 일은 아니며, "굼벵이도 구르는 재주가 있다."는 것을 나는 믿는다.

➡ _____

Minsu, Korea

24 Kamala, Rachel, 그리고 민수 모두에게 가족생활의 어려움이 있습니다.

➡ _____

25 그와 동시에 그들은 자신들의 가족을 사랑하고 그 안에서 특별한 의미를 찾고 있습니다.

➡ _____

26 여러분은 여러분 가족에 대해 어떤 이야기를 할 건가요?

➡ _____

가족

27 가족은 / 사랑과 눈물 / 웃음과 세월로 만들어집니다. / 가족은 시간의 흐름과 함께 / 점점 더 강해집니다.

A FAMILY

➡ _____

※ 다음 우리말과 일치하도록 빈칸에 알맞은 말을 쓰시오.

Listen & Speak 2 B

1. A: What do you _____ _____ _____ your family?
2. B: My father is a _____ _____.
3. A: Then, what do you _____ _____ _____ _____ _____?
4. B: I _____ _____ _____ a room _____ my brother. I'm _____ _____ _____ it.

1. A: 너희 가족에 대해 가장 좋은 점이 뭐니?
2. B: 우리 아빠는 요리를 아주 잘하셔.
3. A: 그러면, 너의 가족에 대해 가장 안 좋은 점은 뭐니?
4. B: 나는 형이랑 방을 같이 써야 해. 나는 그 점이 마음에 들지 않아.

Real Life Task Step 3

1. Family is a very _____ _____ of our happy _____, and _____ _____ many things family _____ _____ _____.
2. _____ _____ _____, it is _____ _____ _____ _____ a lot of conversations.
3. Next, ...

1. 가족은 우리의 행복한 삶에서 매우 중요한 부분이고, 가족 구성원들이 해야 할 많은 것들이 있습니다.
2. 우리의 의견으로는, 그들이 많은 대화를 하는 것이 중요합니다.
3. 다음으로는 …

Before I Read

1. _____ _____ I _____?
2. Q: When Mom and Dad _____ _____ me about my _____ _____, they _____ _____ _____ _____ and I _____ _____ my _____.
3. I don't know _____ _____ _____ _____ _____ so _____.
4. _____ _____ I _____?
5. A: Many teenagers _____ the _____ _____.
6. Try to just _____ _____ _____ and do your _____.
7. Then it will _____ _____ _____ or _____.

1. 내가 무엇을 해야 할까요?
2. Q: 엄마와 아빠가 계속 학업에 대해 물으면, 그들은 제 신경을 건드려서 저는 종종 화를 냅니다.
3. 제가 왜 그렇게 쉽게 화를 내는지 모르겠습니다.
4. 어떻게 해야 하나요?
5. A: 많은 십대들이 같은 문제를 가지고 있습니다.
6. 그냥 내버려두고 자신의 일을 하도록 하세요.
7. 그러면 조만간 나아질 것입니다.

※ 다음 우리말을 영어로 쓰시오.

Listen & Speak 2 B

1. A: 너희 가족에 대해 가장 좋은 점이 뭐니?

   ➡ _____

2. B: 우리 아빠는 요리를 아주 잘하셔.

   ➡ _____

3. A: 그러면, 너의 가족에 대해 가장 안 좋은 점은 뭐니?

   ➡ _____

4. B: 나는 형이랑 방을 같이 써야 해. 나는 그 점이 마음에 들지 않아.

   ➡ _____

Real Life Task Step 3

1. 가족은 우리의 행복한 삶에서 매우 중요한 부분이고, 가족 구성원들이 해야 할 많은 것들이 있습니다.

   ➡ _____

   _____

2. 우리의 의견으로는, 그들이 많은 대화를 하는 것이 중요합니다.

   ➡ _____

3. 다음으로는 …

   ➡ _____

Before I Read

1. 내가 무엇을 해야 할까요?

   ➡ _____

2. Q: 엄마와 아빠가 계속 학업에 대해 물으면, 그들은 제 신경을 건드려서 저는 종종 화를 냅니다.

   ➡ _____

   _____

3. 제가 왜 그렇게 쉽게 화를 내는지 모르겠습니다.

   ➡ _____

4. 어떻게 해야 하나요?

   ➡ _____

5. A: 많은 십대들이 같은 문제를 가지고 있습니다.

   ➡ _____

6. 그냥 내버려두고 자신의 일을 하도록 하세요.

   ➡ _____

7. 그러면 조만간 나아질 것입니다.

   ➡ _____

※ 다음 영어를 우리말로 쓰시오.

01 serve _____

02 ancient _____

03 ash _____

04 bowl _____

05 emperor _____

06 decoration _____

07 empire _____

08 goodwill _____

09 popular _____

10 sour _____

11 spicy _____

12 freshly _____

13 pot-shaped _____

14 historian _____

15 protect _____

16 dynasty _____

17 imagine _____

18 spirit _____

19 bloom _____

20 statue _____

21 marriage _____

22 stir _____

23 seed _____

24 originally _____

25 finally _____

26 tasty _____

27 flowery _____

28 once _____

29 popper _____

30 origin _____

31 slice _____

32 inventor _____

33 pleased _____

34 electric _____

35 by oneself _____

36 in addition to _____

37 before long _____

38 as well as _____

39 be made from _____

40 come up with _____

41 be served with _____

42 long before _____

43 not only ~ but also _____

※ 다음 우리말을 영어로 쓰시오.

01 동굴

02 왕조

03 전기의

04 기원

05 갓 ~한, 새롭게

06 고대의

07 원래, 최초에

08 재

09 씨앗

10 (음식을) 제공하다, 시중들다

11 꽃이 피다

12 매운, 향신료를 넣은

13 장식

14 꽃무늬의

15 젓다, 섞다

16 (우묵한) 그릇, 사발

17 영혼, 정령

18 황제

19 조각

20 제국

21 조각상

22 친선, 호의

23 보호하다

24 결혼, 결혼 생활

25 국수

26 발명가

27 신 맛이 나는

28 역사가, 사학자

29 (과거의) 이전에, 한때

30 상상하다

31 던지다

32 기쁜, 만족해하는

33 맛있는

34 항아리 모양의

35 ~하기 오래전에

36 ~로 만들어지다

37 ~을 생각해 내다

38 혼자서

39 ~와 함께 제공되다

40 오래지 않아, 얼마 후

41 그런데

42 ~ 이외에도

43 ~뿐만 아니라 …도

※ 다음 영영풀이에 알맞은 단어를 <보기>에서 골라 쓴 후, 우리말 뜻을 쓰시오.

1 _____ : decorated with pictures of flowers: _____

2 _____ : of or from a long ago: _____

3 _____ : a person who has invented something: _____

4 _____ : the soft grey powder that remains after burning: _____

5 _____ : a large natural hole in the side of a cliff: _____

6 _____ : to get to the place you are going to: _____

7 _____ : to come suddenly or unexpectedly out: _____

8 _____ : a type of light soft shoe with a rubber sole: _____

9 _____ : a round metal container that you use for cooking: _____

10 _____ : a period of time when a particular family ruled a country: _____

11 _____ : kind feelings towards or between people: _____

12 _____ : a wide round container that is open at the top: _____

13 _____ : the place or situation in which something begins to exist: _____

14 _____ : an image of a person or animal that is made in solid material: _____

15 _____ : the small hard part produced by a plant, from which a new plant can grow:
_____

16 _____ : a long thin piece of food made from a mixture of flour, water, and eggs:
_____

보기			
seed	cave	arrive	noodle
origin	pop	ancient	statue
ash	bowl	dynasty	inventor
flowery	goodwill	pan	sneakers

※ 다음 우리말에 맞도록 대화를 영어로 쓰시오.

해석

Listen & Speak 1 A-1

G: You've _____ a new _____, _____ _____?

B: Yes, I _____.

G: _____ do you _____ it?

B: I _____ like it _____ _____.

소녀: 너 새 전화기 생겼구나, 그렇지 않니?
소년: 응, 그래.
소녀: 그거 어때?
소년: 전혀 마음에 들지 않아.

Listen & Speak 1 A-2

B: I _____ these _____ _____ a birthday _____!

G: _____ _____ they look! _____ do you _____ _____?

B: I _____ _____ them.

소년: 나 이 운동화를 생일 선물로 받았어.
소녀: 정말 멋져 보인다! 마음에 드니?
소년: 정말 마음에 들어.

Listen & Speak 2 A-1

B: _____ you _____ _____ soup?

G: Yes, I'd love some.

B: _____ you go. ... _____ do you _____ it?

G: It's _____ and _____. I just love it.

B: I'm _____ you _____ _____.

소년: 수프 좀 드시겠어요?
소녀: 네, 좀 먹고 싶어요.
소년: 여기 있습니다. … 어때요?
소녀: 뜨겁고 달콤하네요. 정말 좋습니다.
소년: 좋아하시니 기뻐요.

Listen & Speak 2 A-2

G: Did you _____ this _____ _____ _____?

B: Yes, I did.

G: It _____ just _____.

B: Thanks. I'm _____ you _____ it.

소녀: 혼자서 이 그릇을 만들었어요?
소년: 응, 그랬어요.
소녀: 정말 멋져 보여요.
소년: 고마워요. 좋아해서 기뻐요.

Listen & Speak 2 A-3

G: _____ do you _____ this _____ painting?

B: I just love it. Thanks.

G: I'm very _____ you _____ it.

소녀: 이 페이스 페인팅이 어때요?
소년: 정말 좋아요. 고맙습니다.
소녀: 좋아하셔서 정말 기쁘군요.

Conversation

Nara: _____ you _____ some hot _____, Junha?

Junha: _____, I _____ _____ it for _____! ... Mmm.

Nara: _____ do you _____ it?

Junha: I like it a _____. You are very _____ _____ making hot chocolate.

나라: 핫 초콜릿 좀 먹을래, 준하야?
준하: 물론이지, 오랫동안 먹지 못했어!
    … 음.
나라: 어떠니?
준하: 정말 좋아. 너 핫 초콜릿을 만드는
    재주가 정말 좋구나.

Nara: _____. I'm _____ you like it. _____ the _____, did you know that chocolate was _____ _____ the "drink of the gods"?

Junha: Was it _____?

Nara: Yes, chocolate was first _____ by the _____ of the Aztec Empire, and it was _____ _____ xoco-latl, "drink of _____ gods."

Junha: That's _____! Well, _____ for the gods' drink, Nara.

Nara: You are _____!

Real Life Task Step 1

W: _____ do you _____ the school lunch? _____ would you like to _____ for your lunch? We'd _____ to have your _____ ideas on the school lunch menu. _____ _____ you visit www. mslunch.ms.kr and _____ the questions about your school lunch? We're _____ _____ _____ _____ your answers.

Real Life Task Step 2

A: _____ do you _____ on your Monday _____ menu?

B: I _____ ice cream and _____ juice. How do you _____ my menu?

A: That _____ great. I _____ it _____ _____.

B: I'm _____ you _____ _____.

Check My Progress 1

G: You've _____ a new _____, Minsu?

B: Yes, I have. This is my birthday _____ from my mother.

G: _____ _____ _____ her! How do you like it?

G: I like it _____ _____. I like the _____.

G: Your _____ color is blue, _____ _____?

B: Yes, it is.

Real Life Task Step 2

G: Did you _____ all of _____ _____ _____?

B: Yes, I did.

G: They _____ just _____.

B: Thanks. Would you _____ _____ _____ some cake?

G: Sure.

B: How _____ you like it?

G: I just love this.

B: Thanks. I'm so _____ you _____ _____.

나라: 고마워. 네가 좋아한다니 기뻐. 그런데, 너 초콜릿이 한때 "신들의 음료"라고 불렸던 것을 아니?

준하: 정말 그랬니?

나라: 응, 초콜릿은 처음에 아즈텍 제국의 황제에 의해 즐겨졌고, 한때 xoco-latl, 즉 "신들의 음료"라고 불렸어.

준하: 그것 놀라운데! 어쨌든, 신들의 음료에 대해 고마워, 나라야.

나라: 천만에!

여자: 학교 점심은 어떤가요? 점심으로 무엇을 원하나요? 학교 점심 메뉴에 대해 여러분의 좋은 의견을 원합니다. www.mslunch.ms.kr을 방문하여 학교 점심에 대한 질문에 답해 주시겠어요? 여러분의 응답을 고대합니다.

A: 월요일 간식 메뉴에 무엇이 있니?

B: 아이스크림과 사과 주스가 있어. 내 메뉴 어때?

A: 그거 멋지네. 정말 좋아.

B: 네가 좋아한다니 기뻐

소녀: 민수야, 새 가방 생겼구나?

소년: 응, 그래. 이거 우리 엄마께서 주신 생일 선물이야.

소녀: 네 엄마 정말 친절하시구나! 가방이 어때?

소년: 정말 좋아. 나는 색상이 마음에 들어.

소녀: 네가 가장 좋아하는 색깔은 파란색이지, 그렇지 않니?

소년: 응, 맞아.

소녀: 이거 네가 다 직접 구웠니?

소년: 응, 내가 했어.

소녀: 정말 맛있어 보인다.

소년: 고마워. 케이크 좀 먹어 볼래?

소녀: 좋아.

소년: 어때?

소녀: 이거 정말 맛있다.

소년: 고마워. 네가 좋아하니 정말 기뻐.

대화문 Test

※ 다음 우리말과 일치하도록 빈칸에 알맞은 말을 쓰시오.

Listen & Speak 1 A-1

G: _____

B: _____

G: _____

B: _____

소녀: 너 새 전화기 생겼구나, 그렇지 않니?
소년: 응, 그래.
소녀: 그거 어때?
소년: 전혀 마음에 들지 않아.

Listen & Speak 1 A-2

B: _____

G: _____

B: _____

소년: 나 이 운동화를 생일 선물로 받았어.
소녀: 정말 멋져 보인다! 마음에 드니?
소년: 정말 마음에 들어.

Listen & Speak 2 A-1

B: _____

G: _____

B: _____

G: _____

B: _____

소년: 수프 좀 드시겠어요?
소녀: 네, 좀 먹고 싶어요.
소년: 여기 있습니다. … 어때요?
소녀: 뜨겁고 달콤하네요. 정말 좋습니다.
소년: 좋아하시니 기뻐요.

Listen & Speak 2 A-2

G: _____

B: _____

G: _____

B: _____

소녀: 혼자서 이 그릇을 만들었어요?
소년: 응, 그랬어요.
소녀: 정말 멋져 보여요.
소년: 고마워요. 좋아해서 기뻐요.

Listen & Speak 2 A-3

G: _____

B: _____

G: _____

소녀: 이 페이스 페인팅이 어때요?
소년: 정말 좋아요. 고맙습니다.
소녀: 좋아하셔서 정말 기쁘군요.

Conversation

Nara: _____

Junha: _____

Nara: _____

Junha: _____

나라: 핫 초콜릿 좀 먹을래, 준하야?
준하: 물론이지, 오랫동안 먹지 못했어!
    … 음.
나라: 어떠니?
준하: 정말 좋아. 너 핫 초콜릿을 만드는
    재주가 정말 좋구나.

...

Nara: _____
_____

Junha: _____

Nara: _____
_____

Junha: _____

Nara: _____

Real Life Task Step 1

W: _____
_____
_____
_____

Real Life Task Step 2

A: _____

B: _____

A: _____

B: _____

Check My Progress 1

G: _____

B: _____

G: _____

B: _____

G: _____

B: _____

Real Life Task Step 2

G: _____

B: _____

G: _____

B: _____

G: _____

B: _____

G: _____

B: _____

나라: 고마워. 네가 좋아한다니 기뻐. 그런데, 너 초콜릿이 한때 "신들의 음료"라고 불렸던 것을 아니?

준하: 정말 그랬니?

나라: 응, 초콜릿은 처음에 아즈텍 제국의 황제에 의해 즐겨졌고, 한때 xoco-latl, 즉 "신들의 음료"라고 불렸어.

준하: 그것 놀라운데! 어쨌든, 신들의 음료에 대해 고마워, 나라야.

나라: 천만에!

여자: 학교 점심은 어떤가요? 점심으로 무엇을 원하나요? 학교 점심 메뉴에 대해 여러분의 좋은 의견을 원합니다. www.mslunch.ms.kr을 방문하여 학교 점심에 대한 질문에 답해 주시겠어요? 여러분의 응답을 고대합니다.

A: 월요일 간식 메뉴에 무엇이 있니?

B: 아이스크림과 사과 주스가 있어. 내 메뉴 어때?

A: 그거 멋지네. 정말 좋아.

B: 네가 좋아한다니 기뻐

소녀: 민수야, 새 가방 생겼구나?

소년: 응, 그래. 이거 우리 엄마께서 주신 생일 선물이야.

소녀: 네 엄마 정말 친절하시구나! 가방이 어때?

소년: 정말 좋아. 나는 색상이 마음에 들어.

소녀: 네가 가장 좋아하는 색깔은 파란색이지, 그렇지 않니?

소년: 응, 맞아.

소녀: 이거 네가 다 직접 구웠니?

소년: 응, 내가 했어.

소녀: 정말 맛있어 보인다.

소년: 고마워. 케이크 좀 먹어 볼래?

소녀: 좋아.

소년: 어때?

소녀: 이거 정말 맛있다.

소년: 고마워. 네가 좋아하니 정말 기뻐.

※ 다음 우리말과 일치하도록 빈칸에 알맞은 것을 골라 쓰시오.

1 Pop! Pop! Pop! _____ you _____ the _____ of _____ made popcorn?

    A. smell   B. don't   C. freshly   D. love

2 It is one of the _____ _____ snacks around the world, and _____ believe that people have _____ it for more than 5,000 years.

    A. popular   B. historians   C. most   D. enjoyed

3 _____ was in Central America _____ corn was _____ _____, and it was in caves in New Mexico that the first popcorn was found.

    A. grown   B. it   C. originally   D. that

4 Native Americans _____ _____ loved eating corn _____ _____ enjoyed the game of popping corn.

    A. also   B. not   C. but   D. only

5 Corn _____ were _____ _____ hot stones _____ a fire.

    A. over   B. seeds   C. on   D. thrown

6 Then they _____ and _____ _____ white flowers.

    A. into   B. popped   C. bloomed

7 The game was _____ _____ and _____ the _____ snacks.

    A. enjoy   B. catch   C. flowery   D. to

8 Native Americans _____ popcorn _____ _____ as _____.

    A. well   B. for   C. used   D. decoration

9 Their teenage girls _____ popped corn _____ _____ _____.

    A. clothes   B. used   C. decorate   D. to

10 The Aztecs _____ corn _____ for the _____ of the god of rain.

    A. statues   B. made   C. decorations

1 펑! 펑! 펑! 당신은 갓 만들어진 팝콘의 냄새를 좋아하지 않나요?

2 그것은 전 세계에서 가장 인기 있는 간식 중 하나이고, 역사가 들은 사람들이 5,000년 이상 그것을 즐겨 왔다고 믿고 있습니다.

3 옥수수가 본래 재배된 곳은 중앙 아메리카였고, 최초의 팝콘이 발견된 곳은 뉴멕시코의 동굴 안이었습니다.

4 아메리카 원주민들은 옥수수 먹는 것을 좋아했을 뿐만 아니라 옥수수를 튀기는 게임도 즐겼습니다.

5 옥수수 씨는 불 위의 뜨거운 돌들 위로 던져졌습니다.

6 그 다음 그것들은 펑 소리를 내며 튀겨졌고 하얀 꽃 모양으로 피어났습니다.

7 그 게임은 그 꽃 모양의 간식을 잡아서 즐기는 것이었습니다.

8 아메리카 원주민들은 팝콘을 장식을 위해서도 사용했습니다.

9 그들의 십 대 소녀들은 튀겨진 옥수수를 옷을 장식하는 데 사용했습니다.

10 아즈텍족 사람들은 비의 신 조각상을 위해 옥수수 장식품을 만들었습니다.

11 They _____ popcorn a _____ of good _____ and _____ .

    A. goodwill   B. symbol   C. health   D. thought

12 They believed _____ they would be _____ by popping _____ when they wore _____ made with popped corn.

    A. spirits   B. decorations   C. protected   D. that

13 _____ _____ to Native Americans, many other people _____ the world enjoyed this _____ snack.

    A. tasty   B. addition   C. around   D. in

14 The Chinese, _____ _____ as people in Sumatra and India, made popcorn _____ _____ Columbus arrived in the West Indies.

    A. well   B. before   C. as   D. long

15 In _____ China, people popped corn to tell _____ for the _____ year and their daughters' future _____ .

    A. fortunes   B. ancient   C. coming   D. marriage

16 In the Song Dynasty, Chinese people _____ large _____ popping _____ to pop corn, and these machines are still _____ by street poppers today.

    A. used   B. invented   C. machines   D. pot-shaped

17 It was Americans that tried interesting _____ _____ popping corn _____ the nineteenth _____ .

    A. during   B. ways   C. of   D. century

18 Some _____ corn seeds _____ hot ashes, stirred, and then _____ _____ the popped corn pieces.

    A. out   B. threw   C. picked   D. onto

19 Others _____ corn _____ _____ or butter and _____ it in a pan.

    A. fat   B. cooked   C. mixed   D. with

11 그들은 팝콘을 좋은 건강과 호의의 상징으로 생각했습니다.

12 그들은 튀겨진 옥수수로 만든 장식들을 달면 불쑥 나타나는 정령에 의해 보호받을 것이라고 믿었습니다.

13 아메리카 원주민 외에도, 전 세계의 많은 다른 사람들이 이 맛있는 간식을 즐겼습니다.

14 수마트라인과 인도인뿐 아니라 중국인들도 콜럼버스가 서인도 제도에 도착하기 훨씬 이전부터 팝콘을 만들었습니다.

15 고대 중국에서, 사람들은 다음 해와 그들의 딸들의 장래의 혼사를 점치기 위해 옥수수를 펑 소리를 내며 튀겼습니다.

16 송나라 왕조에서, 중국 사람들은 옥수수를 튀기기 위해 커다란 항아리 모양의 팝콘 튀기는 기계를 발명하였고, 이 기계는 오늘날에도 길거리에서 팝콘 만드는 이들에 의해 사용되고 있습니다.

17 19세기 동안 옥수수를 튀기는 흥미로운 방법들을 시도해 본 것은 바로 미국인들이었습니다.

18 이들 중 일부는 뜨거운 잿더미 위로 옥수수 씨를 던지고, 뒤섞은 다음, 펑 터져 나온 옥수수 알갱이들을 집어냈습니다.

19 다른 이들은 옥수수를 기름이나 버터와 섞고 이를 납작한 냄비에 요리하였습니다.

20 They _____ popping corn _____ and _____ .

    A. wonderful   B. thought   C. exciting

21 A more _____ way was _____ popcorn _____ an open fire in a wire box with a long _____ handle.

    A. over   B. wooden   C. cooking   D. popular

22 The _____ popcorn popper was _____ by Charles Cretors in 1893, and before long many _____ of interesting poppers were _____ in movie theaters and parks.

    A. invented   B. seen   C. types   D. fanciest

23 _____, an _____ popcorn popper for the home _____ _____ in 1925.

    A. was   B. finally   C. electric   D. invented

24 Believe it or not, poppers were in _____ _____ and were even _____ _____ middle school students in school clubs.

    A. demand   B. made   C. high   D. by

25 _____ do you _____ your popcorn? Sweet, _____, or _____?

    A. like   B. spicy   C. how   D. hot

26 Next time you enjoy popcorn, _____ _____ as a Native American, an _____ Chinese _____, or an inventor.

    A. person   B. imagine   C. ancient   D. yourself

27 _____ a _____ of popcorn, you can be a Native American and make pretty _____ or be an ancient Chinese person and tell _____.

    A. decorations   B. bowl   C. fortunes   D. with

28 Or better still, _____ _____ you be an inventor and _____ up _____ a new popper for your favorite popcorn?

    A. with   B. don't   C. why   D. come

20 그들은 옥수수를 튀기는 것을 멋지고 재미있다고 생각했습니다.

21 보다 인기 있는 방법은 팝콘을 긴 나무 손잡이가 있는 철사 상자 안에 넣어 덮개가 없는 불에서 요리하는 방법이었습니다.

22 가장 멋진 팝콘 튀기는 기계는 1893년 Charles Cretors에 의해 발명되었는데, 오래지 않아 많은 종류의 흥미로운 팝콘 만드는 기계들이 영화관이나 공원에서 보이게 되었습니다.

23 마침내 가정용 전기 팝콘 기계가 1925년에 발명되었습니다.

24 믿기 힘들겠지만, 팝콘 기계는 그 수요가 많았고, 심지어 학교 동아리에서 중학생들에 의해서도 제작되었습니다.

25 당신은 어떤 팝콘을 좋아하나요? 달콤한, 매운, 향신료를 친 팝콘?

26 다음 번에 팝콘을 즐길 때에는 당신이 아메리카 원주민, 고대 중국인, 혹은 발명가라고 상상해 보세요.

27 한 그릇의 팝콘으로, 당신은 아메리카 원주민이 되어 예쁜 장식을 만들 수도 있고, 또는 고대 중국인이 되어 운세를 점쳐 볼 수도 있습니다.

28 혹은 더 좋게는, 발명가가 되어 당신이 가장 좋아하는 팝콘을 위해 새로운 팝콘 기계를 생각해 내는 것은 어떤가요?

※ 다음 우리말과 일치하도록 빈칸에 알맞은 말을 쓰시오.

1 Pop! Pop! Pop! _____ you _____ the _____ of _____ made popcorn?

2 It is _____ _____ the _____ _____ _____ _____ the world, and historians believe _____ people _____ _____ it for _____ _____ 5,000 years.

3 _____ _____ in Central America _____ corn was _____ _____, and it was in caves in New Mexico _____ the first popcorn was found.

4 Native Americans _____ _____ loved eating corn _____ _____ enjoyed the game of _____ _____.

5 Corn seeds _____ _____ _____ hot stones over a fire.

6 Then they _____ and _____ _____ white flowers.

7 The game was _____ _____ and _____ the _____ snacks.

8 Native Americans _____ popcorn _____ _____ as well.

9 Their teenage girls _____ popped corn _____ _____ _____.

10 The Aztecs _____ corn _____ for the _____ of the god of rain.

11 They _____ popcorn _____ _____ _____ _____ and _____.

12 They believed _____ they would _____ _____ by popping _____ when they wore _____ _____ _____ _____ _____.

13 _____ _____ _____ Native Americans, many _____ people around the world _____ this _____ snack.

14 The Chinese, _____ _____ _____ people in Sumatra and India, made popcorn _____ _____ Columbus _____ in the _____ _____.

1 펑! 펑! 펑! 당신은 갓 만들어진 팝콘의 냄새를 좋아하지 않나요?

2 그것은 전 세계에서 가장 인기 있는 간식 중 하나이고, 역사가 들은 사람들이 5,000년 이상 그것을 즐겨 왔다고 믿고 있습니다.

3 옥수수가 본래 재배된 곳은 중앙 아메리카였고, 최초의 팝콘 이 발견된 곳은 뉴멕시코의 동굴 안이었습니다.

4 아메리카 원주민들은 옥수수 먹는 것을 좋아했을 뿐만 아니라 옥수수를 튀기는 게임도 즐겼습니다.

5 옥수수 씨는 불 위의 뜨거운 돌들 위로 던져졌습니다.

6 그 다음 그것들은 펑 소리를 내며 튀겨졌고 하얀 꽃 모양으로 피어났습니다.

7 그 게임은 그 꽃 모양의 간식을 잡아서 즐기는 것이었습니다.

8 아메리카 원주민들은 팝콘을 장식을 위해서도 사용했습니다.

9 그들의 십 대 소녀들은 튀겨진 옥수수를 옷을 장식하는 데 사용했습니다.

10 아즈텍족 사람들은 비의 신 조각상을 위해 옥수수 장식품을 만들었습니다.

11 그들은 팝콘을 좋은 건강과 호의의 상징으로 생각했습니다.

12 그들은 튀겨진 옥수수로 만든 장식들을 달면 불쑥 나타나는 정령에 의해 보호받을 것이라고 믿었습니다.

13 아메리카 원주민 외에도, 전 세계의 많은 다른 사람들이 이 맛있는 간식을 즐겼습니다.

14 수마트라인과 인도인뿐 아니라 중국인들도 콜럼버스가 서인도 제도에 도착하기 훨씬 이전부터 팝콘을 만들었습니다.

15 In ancient China, people popped corn _____ _____ _____ for the _____ _____ and their _____ future _____.

16 In the Song Dynasty, Chinese people _____ large pot-shaped popping _____ _____ _____ corn, and these machines _____ still _____ _____ street poppers today.

17 _____ _____ Americans _____ tried _____ _____ _____ popping corn _____ the _____ century.

18 Some _____ corn seeds _____ hot ashes, _____, and then _____ _____ the popped _____ _____.

19 Others _____ corn _____ fat or butter and _____ in a pan.

20 They thought popping corn _____ and _____.

21 A more _____ way was _____ popcorn _____ an open fire in a wire box _____ a long _____ _____.

22 The fanciest popcorn popper _____ _____ _____ Charles Cretors in 1893, and before long _____ _____ of interesting poppers _____ _____ in movie theaters and parks.

23 _____, an electric popcorn popper for the home _____ _____ in 1925.

24 _____ it or _____, poppers were _____ and were even _____ _____ middle school students in school clubs.

25 _____ do you _____ your popcorn? Sweet, hot, or spicy?

26 Next time you enjoy popcorn, _____ _____ as a _____ _____, an ancient Chinese person, or an _____.

27 _____ a _____ of popcorn, you _____ _____ a Native American and make _____ _____ or be _____ _____ person and tell _____.

28 Or better still, _____ _____ _____ be an inventor and _____ _____ _____ a new popper for your favorite popcorn?

15 고대 중국에서, 사람들은 다음 해와 그들의 딸들의 장래의 혼사를 점치기 위해 옥수수를 펑 소리를 내며 튀겼습니다.

16 송나라 왕조에서, 중국 사람들은 옥수수를 튀기기 위해 커다란 항아리 모양의 팝콘 튀기는 기계를 발명하였고, 이 기계는 오늘날에도 길거리에서 팝콘 만드는 이들에 의해 사용뇌고 있습니다.

17 19세기 동안 옥수수를 튀기는 흥미로운 방법들을 시도해 본 것은 바로 미국인들이었습니다.

18 이들 중 일부는 뜨거운 잿더미 위로 옥수수 씨를 던지고, 뒤섞은 다음, 펑 터져 나온 옥수수 알갱이들을 집어냈습니다.

19 다른 이들은 옥수수를 기름이나 버터와 섞고 이를 납작한 냄비에 요리하였습니다.

20 그들은 옥수수를 튀기는 것을 멋지고 재미있다고 생각했습니다.

21 보다 인기 있는 방법은 팝콘을 긴 나무 손잡이가 있는 철사 상자 안에 넣어 덮개가 없는 불에서 요리하는 방법이었습니다.

22 가장 멋진 팝콘 튀기는 기계는 1893년 Charles Cretors에 의해 발명되었는데, 오래지 않아 많은 종류의 흥미로운 팝콘 만드는 기계들이 영화관이나 공원에서 보이게 되었습니다.

23 마침내 가정용 전기 팝콘 기계가 1925년에 발명되었습니다.

24 믿기 힘들겠지만, 팝콘 기계는 그 수요가 많았고, 심지어 학교 동아리에서 중학생들에 의해서도 제작되었습니다.

25 당신은 어떤 팝콘을 좋아하나요? 달콤한, 매운, 향료를 친 팝콘?

26 다음 번에 팝콘을 즐길 때에는 당신이 아메리카 원주민, 고대 중국인, 혹은 발명가라고 상상해 보세요.

27 한 그릇의 팝콘으로, 당신은 아메리카 원주민이 되어 예쁜 장식을 만들 수도 있고, 또는 고대 중국인이 되어 운세를 점쳐 볼 수도 있습니다.

28 혹은 더 좋게는, 발명가가 되어 당신이 가장 좋아하는 팝콘을 위해 새로운 팝콘 기계를 생각해 내는 것은 어떤가요?

※ 다음 문장을 우리말로 쓰시오.

1 Pop! Pop! Pop! Don't you love the smell of freshly made popcorn?

➡ _____

2 It is one of the most popular snacks around the world, and historians believe that people have enjoyed it for more than 5,000 years.

➡ _____

_____

3 It was in Central America that corn was originally grown, and it was in caves in New Mexico that the first popcorn was found.

➡ _____

4 Native Americans not only loved eating corn but also enjoyed the game of popping corn.

➡ _____

5 Corn seeds were thrown on hot stones over a fire.

➡ _____

6 Then they popped and bloomed into white flowers.

➡ _____

7 The game was to catch and enjoy the flowery snacks.

➡ _____

8 Native Americans used popcorn for decoration as well.

➡ _____

9 Their teenage girls used popped corn to decorate clothes.

➡ _____

10 The Aztecs made corn decorations for the statues of the god of rain.

➡ _____

11 They thought popcorn a symbol of good health and goodwill.

➡ _____

12 They believed that they would be protected by popping spirits when they wore decorations made with popped corn.

➡ _____

13 In addition to Native Americans, many other people around the world enjoyed this tasty snack.

➡ _____

14 The Chinese, as well as people in Sumatra and India, made popcorn long before Columbus arrived in the West Indies.

➡ _____

15 In ancient China, people popped corn to tell fortunes for the coming year and their daughters' future marriage.

➡ _____

16 In the Song Dynasty, Chinese people invented large pot-shaped popping machines to pop corn, and these machines are still used by street poppers today.

➡ _____

_____

17 It was Americans that tried interesting ways of popping corn during the nineteenth century.

➡ _____

18 Some threw corn seeds onto hot ashes, stirred, and then picked out the popped corn pieces.

➡ _____

19 Others mixed corn with fat or butter and cooked it in a pan.

➡ _____

20 They thought popping corn wonderful and exciting.

➡ _____

21 A more popular way was cooking popcorn over an open fire in a wire box with a long wooden handle.

➡ _____

22 The fanciest popcorn popper was invented by Charles Cretors in 1893, and before long many types of interesting poppers were seen in movie theaters and parks.

➡ _____

23 Finally, an electric popcorn popper for the home was invented in 1925.

➡ _____

24 Believe it or not, poppers were in high demand and were even made by middle school students in school clubs.

➡ _____

25 How do you like your popcorn? Sweet, hot, or spicy?

➡ _____

26 Next time you enjoy popcorn, imagine yourself as a Native American, an ancient Chinese person, or an inventor.

➡ _____

27 With a bowl of popcorn, you can be a Native American and make pretty decorations or be an ancient Chinese person and tell fortunes.

➡ _____

_____

28 Or better still, why don't you be an inventor and come up with a new popper for your favorite popcorn?

➡ _____

※ 다음 괄호 안의 단어들을 우리말에 맞도록 바르게 배열하시오.

1 (Pop! / Pop! / Pop! // you / don't / love / smell / the / of / made / popcorn? / freshly)
➡ _____

2 (is / it / of / one / most / the / snacks / popular / the / around / world, / and / believe / historians / people / that / enjoyed / have / for / it / than / more / years. / 5,000)
➡ _____

3 (was / it / Central / in / America / corn / that / originally / was / grown, / it / and / in / was / caves / New / in / Mexico / that / first / the / was / found. / popcorn)
➡ _____

4 (Americans / Native / only / not / eating / loved / but / corn / also / the / enjoyed / game / popping / of / corn.)
➡ _____

5 (seeds / corn / thrown / were / hot / on / stones / a / over / fire.)
➡ _____

6 (they / then / bloomed / and / popped / white / into / flowers.)
➡ _____

7 (game / the / to / was / catch / enjoy / and / the / snacks. / flowery)
➡ _____

8 (Americans / Native / popcorn / used / decoration / for / well. / as)
➡ _____

9 (teenage / their / used / girls / corn / popped / decorate / to / clothes.)
➡ _____

10 (Aztecs / the / corn / made / for / decorations / the / of / statues / the / of / rain. / god)
➡ _____

11 (thought / they / a / popcorn / symbol / good / of / health / goodwill. / and)
➡ _____

12 (believed / they / that / would / they / be / by / protected / spirits / popping / they / when / decorations / wore / with / made / corn. / popped)
➡ _____

13 (addition / in / Native / to / Americans, / other / many / around / people / world / the / this / enjoyed / snack. / tasty)
➡ _____

14 (Chinese, / the / well / as / people / as / Sumatra / in / India, / and / popcorn / made / before / long / arrived / Columbus / the / in / Indies. / West)
➡ _____

1 펑! 펑! 펑! 당신은 갓 만들어진 팝콘의 냄새를 좋아하지 않나요?

2 그것은 전 세계에서 가장 인기 있는 간식 중 하나이고, 역사가들이 사람들이 5,000년 이상 그것을 즐겨 왔다고 믿고 있습니다.

3 옥수수가 본래 재배된 곳은 중앙 아메리카였고, 최초의 팝콘이 발견된 곳은 뉴멕시코의 동굴 안이었습니다.

4 아메리카 원주민들은 옥수수 먹는 것을 좋아했을 뿐만 아니라 옥수수를 튀기는 게임도 즐겼습니다.

5 옥수수 씨는 불 위의 뜨거운 돌들 위로 던져졌습니다.

6 그 다음 그것들은 펑 소리를 내며 튀겨졌고 하얀 꽃 모양으로 피어났습니다.

7 그 게임은 그 꽃 모양의 간식을 잡아서 즐기는 것이었습니다.

8 아메리카 원주민들은 팝콘을 장식을 위해서도 사용했습니다.

9 그들의 십 대 소녀들은 튀겨진 옥수수를 옷을 장식하는 데 사용했습니다.

10 아즈텍족 사람들은 비의 신 조각상을 위해 옥수수 장식품을 만들었습니다.

11 그들은 팝콘을 좋은 건강과 호의의 상징으로 생각했습니다.

12 그들은 튀겨진 옥수수로 만든 장식들을 달면 불쑥 나타나는 정령에 의해 보호받을 것이라고 믿었습니다.

13 아메리카 원주민 외에도, 전 세계의 많은 다른 사람들이 이 맛있는 간식을 즐겼습니다.

14 수마트라인과 인도인뿐 아니라 중국인들도 콜럼버스가 서인도 제도에 도착하기 훨씬 이전부터 팝콘을 만들었습니다.

15 (ancient / in / China, / popped / people / to / corn / fortunes / tell / the / for / year / coming / and / daughters' / their / marriage. / future)

➡ _____

16 (the / in / Dynasty, / Song / people / Chinese / large / invented / pot-shaped /machines / corn / to / pop / popping / and / machines / these / still / are / by / used / poppers / street / today.)

➡ _____

➡ _____

17 (was / it / that Americans / tired / ways / interesting / popping / of / during / corn / nineteeth / the / century.)

➡ _____

18 (threw / some / corn / into / seeds / ashes, / hot / and / stirred / then / out / picked / popped / the / pieces. / corn)

➡ _____

19 (mixed / others / with / corn / or / fat / and / butter / it / cooked / in / pan. / a)

➡ _____

20 (thought / they / corn / popping / wonderful / exciting. / and)

➡ _____

21 (more / a / way / popular / cooking / was / over / popcorn / an / fire / open / in / wire / a / box / a / with / wooden / handle. / long)

➡ _____

22 (fanciest / the / popcorn / was / popper / by / invented / Cretors / Charles / 1893, / in / and / long / before / many / of / types / poppers / interesting / seen / were / in / theaters / movie / parks. / and)

➡ _____

➡ _____

23 (an / finally, / popcorn / electric / popper / the / for / home / invented / was / 1925. / in)

➡ _____

24 (it / believe / not, / or / were / poppers / high / in / demand / were / and / even / by / made / school / middle / students / school / in / clubs.)

➡ _____

25 (do / how / like / you / popcorn? / your // hot, / sweet, / spicy? / or)

➡ _____

26 (time / next / enjoy / popcorn, / you / imagine / as / yourself / a / American, / Native / ancient / an / person, / Chinese / or / inventor. / an)

➡ _____

27 (a / with / of / bowl / popcorn, / can / you / a / be / American / Native / and / pretty / make / decorations / be / or / an / Chinese / ancient / person / tell / and / fortunes.)

➡ _____

➡ _____

28 (better / or / why / still, / don't / be / you / inventor / an / and / up / come / a / with / new / for / popper / favorite / your / popcoen?)

➡ _____

➡ _____

15 고대 중국에서, 사람들은 다음 해와 그들의 딸들의 장래의 혼사를 점치기 위해 옥수수를 펑 소리를 내며 튀겼습니다.

16 송나라 왕조에서, 중국 사람들은 옥수수를 튀기기 위해 커다란 항아리 모양의 팝콘 튀기는 기계를 발명하였고, 이 기계는 오늘날에도 길거리에서 팝콘 만드는 이들에 의해 사용되고 있습니다.

17 19세기 동안 옥수수를 튀기는 흥미로운 방법들을 시도해 본 것은 바로 미국인들이었습니다.

18 이들 중 일부는 뜨거운 잿더미 위로 옥수수 씨를 던지고, 뒤섞은 다음, 펑 터져 나온 옥수수 알갱이들을 집어냈습니다.

19 다른 이들은 옥수수를 기름이나 버터와 섞고 이를 납작한 냄비에 요리하였습니다.

20 그들은 옥수수를 튀기는 것을 멋지고 재미있다고 생각했습니다.

21 보다 인기 있는 방법은 팝콘을 긴 나무 손잡이가 있는 철사 상자 안에 넣어 덮개가 없는 불에서 요리하는 방법이었습니다.

22 가장 멋진 팝콘 튀기는 기계는 1893년 Charles Cretors에 의해 발명되었는데, 오래지 않아 많은 종류의 흥미로운 팝콘 만드는 기계들이 영화관이나 공원에서 보이게 되었습니다.

23 마침내 가정용 전기 팝콘 기계가 1925년에 발명되었습니다.

24 믿기 힘들겠지만, 팝콘 기계는 그 수요가 많았고, 심지어 학교 동아리에서 중학생들에 의해서도 제작되었습니다.

25 당신은 어떤 팝콘을 좋아하나요? 달콤한, 매운, 향신료를 친 팝콘?

26 다음 번에 팝콘을 즐길 때에는 당신이 아메리카 원주민, 고대 중국인, 혹은 발명가라고 상상해 보세요.

27 한 그릇의 팝콘으로, 당신은 아메리카 원주민이 되어 예쁜 장식을 만들 수도 있고, 또는 고대 중국인이 되어 운세를 점쳐 볼 수도 있습니다.

28 혹은 더 좋게는, 발명가가 되어 당신이 가장 좋아하는 팝콘을 위해 새로운 팝콘 기계를 생각해 내는 것은 어떤가요?

※ 다음 우리말을 영어로 쓰시오.

1 펑! 펑! 펑! 당신은 갓 만들어진 팝콘의 냄새를 좋아하지 않나요?

➡ _____

2 그것은 전 세계에서 가장 인기 있는 간식 중 하나이고, 역사가들은 사람들이 5,000년 이상 그것을 즐겨 왔다고 믿고 있습니다.

➡ _____

_____

3 옥수수가 본래 재배된 곳은 중앙아메리카였고, 최초의 팝콘이 발견된 곳은 뉴멕시코의 동굴 안이었습니다.

➡ _____

_____

4 아메리카 원주민들은 옥수수 먹는 것을 좋아했을 뿐만 아니라 옥수수를 튀기는 게임도 즐겼습니다.

➡ _____

5 옥수수 씨는 불 위의 뜨거운 돌들 위로 던져졌습니다.

➡ _____

6 그 다음 그것들은 펑 소리를 내며 튀겨졌고 하얀 꽃 모양으로 피어났습니다.

➡ _____

7 그 게임은 그 꽃 모양의 간식을 잡아서 즐기는 것이었습니다.

➡ _____

8 아메리카 원주민들은 팝콘을 장식을 위해서도 사용했습니다.

➡ _____

9 그들의 십 대 소녀들은 튀겨진 옥수수를 옷을 장식하는 데 사용했습니다.

➡ _____

10 아즈텍족 사람들은 비의 신 조각상을 위해 옥수수 장식품을 만들었습니다.

➡ _____

11 그들은 팝콘을 좋은 건강과 호의의 상징으로 생각했습니다.

➡ _____

12 그들은 튀겨진 옥수수로 만든 장식들을 달면 불쑥 나타나는 정령에 의해 보호받을 것이라고 믿었습니다.

➡ _____

13 아메리카 원주민 외에도, 전 세계의 많은 다른 사람들이 이 맛있는 간식을 즐겼습니다.

➡ _____

14 수마트라인과 인도인뿐 아니라 중국인들도 콜럼버스가 서인도 제도에 도착하기 훨씬 이전부터 팝콘을 만들었습니다.

➡ _____

_____

15 고대 중국에서, 사람들은 다음 해와 그들의 딸들의 장래의 혼사를 점치기 위해 옥수수를 펑 소리를 내며 튀겼습니다.

➡ _____

_____

16 송나라 왕조에서, 중국 사람들은 옥수수를 튀기기 위해 커다란 항아리 모양의 팝콘 튀기는 기계를 발명하였고, 이 기계는 오늘날에도 길거리에서 팝콘 만드는 이들에 의해 사용되고 있습니다.

➡ _____

_____

17 19세기 동안 옥수수를 튀기는 흥미로운 방법들을 시도해 본 것은 바로 미국인들이었습니다.

➡ _____

18 이들 중 일부는 뜨거운 잿더미 위로 옥수수 씨를 던지고, 뒤섞은 다음, 펑 터져 나온 옥수수 알갱이들을 집어냈습니다.

➡ _____

19 다른 이들은 옥수수를 기름이나 버터와 섞고 이를 납작한 냄비에 요리하였습니다.

➡ _____

20 그들은 옥수수를 튀기는 것을 멋지고 재미있다고 생각했습니다.

➡ _____

21 보다 인기 있는 방법은 팝콘을 긴 나무 손잡이가 있는 철사 상자 안에 넣어 덮개가 없는 불에서 요리하는 방법이었습니다.

➡ _____

22 가장 멋진 팝콘 튀기는 기계는 1893년 Charles Cretors에 의해 발명되었는데, 오래지 않아 많은 종류의 흥미로운 팝콘 만드는 기계들이 영화관이나 공원에서 보이게 되었습니다.

➡ _____

_____

23 마침내 가정용 전기 팝콘 기계가 1925년에 발명되었습니다.

➡ _____

24 믿기 힘들겠지만, 팝콘 기계는 그 수요가 많았고, 심지어 학교 동아리에서 중학생들에 의해서도 제작되었습니다.

➡ _____

_____

25 당신은 어떤 팝콘을 좋아하나요? 달콤한, 매운, 향신료를 친 팝콘?

➡ _____

26 다음 번에 팝콘을 즐길 때에는 당신이 아메리카 원주민, 고대 중국인, 혹은 발명가라고 상상해 보세요.

➡ _____

27 한 그릇의 팝콘으로, 당신은 아메리카 원주민이 되어 예쁜 장식을 만들 수도 있고, 또는 고대 중국인이 되어 운세를 점쳐 볼 수도 있습니다.

➡ _____

_____

28 혹은 더 좋게는, 발명가가 되어 당신이 가장 좋아하는 팝콘을 위해 새로운 팝콘 기계를 생각해 내는 것은 어떤가요?

➡ _____

※ 다음 우리말과 일치하도록 빈칸에 알맞은 말을 쓰시오.

Write & Speak 2 B

1. A: _____ do you _____ my hamburger?

2. B: I _____ _____ it. _____ _____!

3. A: Thanks. I'm _____ you _____.

1. A: 내 햄버거 어때?
2. B: 너무 좋아. 정말 맛있다!
3. A: 고마워. 네가 마음에 든다니 기쁘다.

Real Life Task Step 3

1. On our _____ _____ _____, we have ice cream and apple juice.

2. _____ the Tuesday menu, we _____ _____ and _____ _____.

3. _____ _____, we enjoy _____ _____ and _____.

4. On Thursday, we _____ _____ _____ and milk.

5. And _____ _____, we _____ _____ _____ and mango juice.

1. 우리의 월요일 간식 메뉴에는 아이스 크림과 사과 주스가 있다.
2. 화요일 메뉴에는 바나나와 오렌지 주스가 있다.
3. 수요일에는 당근 케이크와 초콜릿 우유를 즐긴다.
4. 목요일에는 감자 칩과 우유가 있다.
5. 그리고 금요일에는 사과 조각과 망고 주스를 즐긴다.

Before I Read

1. _____ corn seeds _____ hot ashes.

2. _____ corn _____ _____ and _____ _____ in a pan.

3. _____ corn _____ an open fire _____ _____ _____ _____.

4. _____ corn in _____ _____ _____.

1. 옥수수 씨를 뜨거운 재에 뿌린다.
2. 옥수수와 지방을 섞어서 팬에 요리한다.
3. 철사 상자 안에 넣어 덮개가 없는 불에서 옥수수를 요리한다.
4. 팝콘 튀기는 기계에서 옥수수를 튀긴다.

※ 다음 우리말을 영어로 쓰시오.

Write & Speak 2 B

1. A: 내 햄버거 어때?

➡ _____

2. B: 너무 좋아. 정말 맛있다!

➡ _____

3. A: 고마워. 네가 마음에 든다니 기쁘다.

➡ _____

Real Life Task Step 3

1. 우리의 월요일 간식 메뉴에는 아이스크림과 사과 주스가 있다.

➡ _____

2. 화요일 메뉴에는 바나나와 오렌지 주스가 있다.

➡ _____

3. 수요일에는 당근 케이크와 초콜릿 우유를 즐긴다.

➡ _____

4. 목요일에는 감자 칩과 우유가 있다.

➡ _____

5. 그리고 금요일에는 사과 조각과 망고 주스를 즐긴다.

➡ _____

Before I Read

1. 옥수수 씨를 뜨거운 재에 뿌린다.

➡ _____

2. 옥수수와 지방을 섞어서 팬에 요리한다.

➡ _____

3. 철사 상자 안에 넣어 덮개가 없는 불에서 옥수수를 요리한다.

➡ _____

4. 팝콘 튀기는 기계에서 옥수수를 튀긴다.

➡ _____

※ 다음 영어를 우리말로 쓰시오.

01	receipt	
02	brand-new	
03	suffer	
04	recommend	
05	flash sale	
06	grab	
07	helpful	
08	attack	
09	booth	
10	hurt	
11	incredibly	
12	instead	
13	treasure	
14	taste	
15	knee	
16	limited edition	
17	high-end	
18	lively	
19	pocket money	
20	floor	
21	slippery	

22	include	
23	collection	
24	empty-handed	
25	trend	
26	featuring	
27	consumer	
28	presentation	
29	celebrity	
30	steal	
31	product	
32	traditional	
33	rest stop	
34	appreciation	
35	take off	
36	carry around	
37	due to	
38	watch out for	
39	cut down	
40	look around	
41	be willing to	
42	put on	
43	sign out	

※ 다음 우리말을 영어로 쓰시오.

01	포함하다	_____	22	영수증	_____

01 포함하다 _____

02 점포 _____

03 수집품 _____

04 소비자 _____

05 바닥, 층 _____

06 움켜쥐다 _____

07 도움이 되는, 유익한 _____

08 감상 _____

09 미끄러운 _____

10 공격하다 _____

11 명품의, 고급의 _____

12 믿을 수 없을 정도로 _____

13 휴게소 _____

14 대신에 _____

15 반짝 세일 _____

16 겪다 _____

17 한정판 _____

18 보물 _____

19 생생한, 활발한 _____

20 유명한 사람 _____

21 상품 _____

22 영수증 _____

23 빈손으로 _____

24 특징으로 하는 _____

25 추천하다 _____

26 수영복 _____

27 발표 _____

28 반품하다 _____

29 유행 _____

30 훔치다; 도루, 공짜 _____

31 맛보다 _____

32 전통적인 _____

33 완전히 새로운 _____

34 판매 게시물 _____

35 떠들다 _____

36 둘러보다 _____

37 이륙하다 _____

38 진정하다 _____

39 ~ 때문에 _____

40 포기하다 _____

41 ~을 계속하다, ~을 고수하다 _____

42 줄이다 _____

43 들고 다니다 _____

※ 다음 영영풀이에 알맞은 단어를 <보기>에서 골라 쓴 후, 우리말 뜻을 쓰시오.

1 _____ : new and not yet used: _____

2 _____ : rise into the air from the ground: _____

3 _____ : a famous living person: _____

4 _____ : the joint that bends in the middle of your leg: _____

5 _____ : someone who buys and uses products:: _____

6 _____ : to say or write something again or more than once: _____

7 _____ : to tell somebody that something is good or useful: _____

8 _____ : pleasure you feel when you realize something is good: _____

9 _____ : a group of valuable things such as gold, silver, jewels: _____

10 _____ : to deliberately use violence to hurt a person or damage a place: _____

11 _____ : to bring, give, put, or send something back to someone or something:

_____

12 _____ : to make someone or something part of a larger group: _____

13 _____ : a piece of paper that shows that goods or services have been paid for:

_____

14 _____ : more expensive and of better quality than other products of the same

type: _____

15 _____ : difficult to hold or to stand or move on, because it is smooth, wet

or polished: _____

16 _____ : an activity in which someone shows, describes, or explains something to

a group of people: _____

high-end	receipt	repeat	knee
consumer	slippery	appreciation	brand-new
recommend	take off	return	include
presentation	celebrity	attack	treasure

※ 다음 우리말과 일치하도록 빈칸에 알맞은 말을 쓰시오.

해석

Listen & Speak 1 A-1

G: They are _____ cute. Let's _____ _____ _____ them.

M: OK. But _____ _____, and do not _____ them.

G: _____ not?

M: _____ they _____ _____ you.

소녀: 동물들이 너무 귀여워요. 우리 더 가까이 가요.
남자: 그래. 하지만 조심해, 만지면 안돼.
소녀: 왜 안 돼요?
남자: 동물들이 너를 공격할 수도 있으니까.

Listen & Speak 1 A-2

B: Ouch!

W: _____ you _____ _____, Jinsu?

B: No, I'm not. I _____ my _____.

W: The _____ is always _____ here. _____ _____ _____ _____ _____.

소년: 아야!
여자: 진수야 괜찮니?
소년: 아니요. 무릎을 다쳤어요.
여자: 여기는 바닥이 항상 미끄러워. 뛰지 않도록 명심해.

Listen & Speak 1 A-3

B: Excuse me. _____ is the _____?

W: It's _____ _____. But you _____ _____ it now.

B: Oh. Why _____?

W: We're _____ _____ soon. _____ _____ you _____ in your seat when the seat _____ _____ is _____.

소년: 실례합니다. 화장실이 어디인가요?
여자: 저쪽이에요. 하지만 지금은 화장실을 사용할 수 없어요.
소년: 오. 왜 안 되나요?
여자: 비행기가 곧 이륙합니다. 안전벨트 표시등이 켜지면 자리에 앉아 계셔야 합니다.

Listen & Speak 1 B

A: Now, we're _____ to the _____ stop. Any _____?

B: Yes. _____ I go to the snack stands?

A: Of course, but _____ _____ you don't _____ too much money.

B: OK. Thanks.

A: 이제 우리는 휴게소에 갑니다. 질문 있나요?
B: 네. 간식 파는 곳에 가도 되나요?
A: 물론이에요, 하지만 돈을 너무 많이 쓰지 않도록 하세요.
B: 네. 감사합니다.

Listen & Speak 2 A-1

G: I _____ my room and _____ some old T-shirts.

B: _____ are you _____ _____ do _____ them? Are you _____ _____ _____ them _____?

G: No. I will _____ an eco bag _____ _____ them.

B: That's a good idea!

소녀: 방 청소를 하다가 오래된 티셔츠 몇 벌을 찾았어.
소년: 그 옷들을 어떻게 할 거야? 그 옷들을 버릴 생각이니?
소녀: 아니. 그 옷들로 에코백을 만들 거야.
소년: 그거 좋은 생각이다!

Listen & Speak 2 A-2

B: What _____ you _____?

G: I'm _____ _____ the _____ for my new watch.

소년: 너 뭐 하고 있니?
소녀: 새로 산 시계 영수증 찾고 있어.

B: Why? Are you _____ _____ _____ it?

G: Yes. It suddenly _____ _____.

Listen & Speak 2 B

A: _____ _____ are you _____ _____?

B: I'm _____ to the _____ _____.

A: Are you _____ _____ _____ a movie?

B: No, I'm not. I'm _____ of playing _____ dogs.

Conversation

Seho: Oh! It's almost _____ time. Hurry _____!

Semi(Seho's sister): _____ down, Seho. We've _____ everything.

Seho: No. I need to visit Sneaker Ground. They're _____ a sale there.

Semi: What? Are you _____ of _____ sneakers?

Seho: Yes. I can _____ _____ sneakers _____ 70% _____. It's a _____.

Semi: Well, it was just a week ago _____ you _____ blue sneakers there. Have you _____ _____ them _____?

Seho: No. They don't _____ any of my pants.

Semi: You see? _____ _____ you don't _____ the same mistake.

Seho: I see _____ you mean, but it's _____ _____ never. I can't _____ _____.

Semi: You are _____.

Real Life Task Stpe 1

B: What do you do first when you _____ your _____ _____? I always _____ 30 percent of my pocket money. How do I do this? I _____ _____ my _____ _____ ice cream and soft drinks. Why _____ you give it a _____ and get RICH? _____ _____ you _____ _____ _____ in the middle.

Real Life Task Stpe 2

A: _____ did you _____ the _____?

B: It was very _____. I need to do something to save money.

A: Are you _____ of _____ _____ your _____?

B: Yes, I am. I'll spend _____ _____ _____.

A: Good for you, but _____ _____ you don't _____ up your style.

※ 다음 우리말에 맞도록 대화를 영어로 쓰시오.

Listen & Speak 1 A-1

G: _____

M: _____

G: _____

M: _____

소녀: 동물들이 너무 귀여워요. 우리 더 가까이 가요.
남자: 그래. 하지만 조심해. 만지면 안돼.
소녀: 왜 안 돼요?
남자: 동물들이 너를 공격할 수도 있으니까.

Listen & Speak 1 A-2

B: _____

W: _____

B: _____

W: _____

소년: 아야!
여자: 진수야 괜찮니?
소년: 아니요. 무릎을 다쳤어요.
여자: 여기는 바닥이 항상 미끄러워. 뛰지 않도록 명심해.

Listen & Speak 1 A-3

B: _____

W: _____

B: _____

W: _____

_____

소년: 실례합니다. 화장실이 어디인가요?
여자: 저쪽이에요. 하지만 지금은 화장실을 사용할 수 없어요.
소년: 오. 왜 안 되나요?
여자: 비행기가 곧 이륙합니다. 안전벨트 표시등이 켜지면 자리에 앉아 계셔야 합니다.

Listen & Speak 1 B

A: _____

B: _____

A: _____

B: _____

A: 이제 우리는 휴게소에 갑니다. 질문 있나요?
B: 네. 간식 파는 곳에 가도 되나요?
A: 물론이에요. 하지만 돈을 너무 많이 쓰지 않도록 하세요.
B: 네. 감사합니다.

Listen & Speak 2 A-1

G: _____

B: _____

G: _____

B: _____

소녀: 방 청소를 하다가 오래된 티셔츠 몇 벌을 찾았어.
소년: 그 옷들을 어떻게 할 거야? 그 옷들을 버릴 생각이니?
소녀: 아니. 그 옷들로 에코백을 만들 거야.
소년: 그거 좋은 생각이다!

Listen & Speak 2 A-2

B: _____

G: _____

소년: 너 뭐 하고 있니?
소녀: 새로 산 시계 영수증 찾고 있어.

B: _____

G: _____

소년: 왜? 시계를 반품시키려고 하는 거야?
소녀: 응. 시계가 갑자기 작동하지 않아.

Listen & Speak 2 B

A: _____

B: _____

A: _____

B: _____

A: 몇 층을 가시나요?
B: 저는 3층에 갑니다.
A: 영화 보려고 하시나요?
B: 아니요. 개들과 놀려구요.

Conversation

Seho: _____

Semi(Seho's sister): _____

Seho: _____

Semi: _____

Seho: _____

Semi: _____

_____

Seho: _____

Semi: _____

Seho: _____

Semi: _____

세호: 앗! 문 닫을 시간이 거의 다 됐네. 서둘러!
세미(세호 누나): 진정해, 세호야. 우리 다 샀어.
세호: 아니야. Sneaker Ground에 가야 돼. 거기 지금 세일 중이거든.
세미: 뭐? 너 운동화 살 생각이니?
세호: 응. 명품 운동화를 70% 할인에 살 수 있어. 공짜나 다름없어.
세미: 글쎄, 네가 거기에서 파란 운동화 산 것이 고작 일주일 전이야. 그거 신어나 봤어?
세호: 아니. 그 운동화는 내가 가진 바지 중 어떤 것과도 어울리지 않아.
세미: 알겠지? 똑같은 실수를 저지르지 않도록 명심해.
세호: 누나 뜻이 뭔지는 알겠는데, 이런 기회는 다시 오지 않아. 놓칠 수 없어.
세미: 너 정말 못 말리겠네.

Real Life Task Stpe 1

B: _____

_____

_____

_____

소년: 여러분은 용돈을 받으면 먼저 무엇을 하시나요? 저는 항상 용돈의 30퍼센트를 저축합니다. 어떻게 이렇게 하냐고요? 저는 아이스크림과 청량음료의 소비를 줄입니다. 여러분도 한번 시도해 보고 부자가 되는 것은 어떨까요? 중간에 포기하지 않도록 명심하세요.

Real Life Task Stpe 2

A: _____

B: _____

A: _____

B: _____

A: _____

A: 발표 어땠어?
B: 도움이 많이 되었어. 나는 돈을 절약하기 위해서 무언가를 해야 할 것 같아.
A: 돈 쓰는 걸 줄이겠다는 거니?
B: 응. 옷 사는 데 돈을 덜 써야겠어.
A: 잘됐다, 그래도 네 스타일은 포기하지 않도록 해.

※ 다음 우리말과 일치하도록 빈칸에 알맞은 것을 골라 쓰시오.

What Makes You Shop?

1 What _____ you _____? Do you buy only _____ you really _____?

A. what   B. shop   C. need   D. makes

2 Read _____ and think about your _____ _____.

A. habits   B. on   C. shopping

3 **Mina:** _____ _____ that!

A. at   B. look

Somin: Wow! N-girls _____ _____ a _____ jacket.

A. wearing   B. are   C. brand-new

Mina: It _____ very _____. I have _____ have _____ just like it.

A. to   B. cute   C. one   D. looks

Somin: _____, _____.

A. too   B. me

4 Many teens like to do _____ their _____ _____ _____.

A. celebrities   B. what   C. do   D. favorite

5 They are more _____ willing _____ _____ what the stars _____.

A. buy   B. to   C. use   D. than

6 They want to _____ _____ their _____.

A. like   B. look   C. heroes

7 They think _____ brands will _____ them _____, happy, and _____.

A. cool   B. celebrity   C. popular   D. make

8 **Somin:** _____ you _____ me, Inho?

A. help   B. can

Inho: Sure. _____ _____?

A. up   B. what's

Somin: There's going to be an oline _____ _____ on new sneakers. Please _____ me _____ a pair.

A. flash   B. grab   C. help   D. sale

Inho: Okay, I'll click _____ _____.

A. crazy   B. like

9 When a product sells _____ hot cakes, some people often feel _____ they won't be able to get it _____ they are not fast _____.

A. if   B. enough   C. that   D. like

무엇이 여러분을 쇼핑하게 합니까?

1 무엇이 여러분을 쇼핑하게 합니까? 여러분은 정말로 필요한 것만을 삽니까?

2 읽어 가며 여러분의 쇼핑 습관에 대해 생각해 보십시오.

3 미나: 저것 좀 봐!

소민: 와! N-girls가 신상품 재킷을 입고 있네.

미나: 정말 귀여워 보여. 나도 그것과 꼭 같은 것을 하나 가지고 있어야만 되겠어.

소민: 나도 그래.

4 많은 십대들은 좋아하는 유명인이 하는 것을 하기 좋아합니다.

5 그들은 스타들이 사용하는 것을 기꺼이 사고자 합니다.

6 그들은 그들의 영웅처럼 보이기를 원합니다.

7 그들은 유명인 브랜드가 그들을 멋지고 행복하며 인기 있게 만들 것이라고 생각합니다.

8 소민: 나 도와줄 수 있어, 인호야?

인호: 물론이지. 무슨 일이야?

소민: 새로운 운동화의 온라인 반짝 판매가 있을 예정이야. 부탁인데, 내가 한 켤레를 손에 넣도록 도와줘.

인호: 알겠어. 내가 열심히 클릭할게.

9 한 상품이 불티나게 팔릴 때, 어떤 사람들은 그들이 충분히 재빠르지 않으면 그것을 얻을 수 없을 것이라고 흔히 느낍니다.

10 They _____ from FOMO, Fear of Missing Out, _____ they see sales signs _____ _____ *Limited Edition* and *Flash Sale*.

    A. when   B. as   C. suffer   D. such

11 The signs _____ them _____ that it is the last _____ to _____ the cool products.

    A. believe   B. grab   C. make   D. chance

12 Then, getting quick-selling goods _____ _____ _____ winning a game _____ spending money.

    A. than   B. becomes   C. like   D. more

13 **Inho:** _____ a _____ !

    A. pick   B. what

    Mina: Did you _____ _____, Inho?

    A. it   B. get

    Inho: Yeah, _____. This _____ my _____.

    A. completes   B. finally   C. collection

    Mina: _____ _____ you!

    A. for   B. good

14 _____ popular things is one of the _____ _____ among young _____.

    A. trends   B. consumers   C. collecting   D. hottest

15 The most popular _____ _____ character stickers, baseball card _____, and goods _____ pop stars.

    A. featuring   B. include   C. collections   D. sets

16 Teen consumers enjoy _____ more and more of these, _____ the idea _____ *more is better* _____ them happy.

    A. because   B. getting   C. of   D. makes

17 What _____ brands have you _____? What quick-selling goods have you _____? What character stickers have you _____?

    A. collected   B. bought   C. grabbed   D. celebrity

10 그들은 '한정판'이나 '반짝 판매'와 같은 판매 게시물을 보면, FOMO(놓치는 것에 대한 두려움)를 겪습니다.

11 그 게시물들은 그들로 하여금 그것이 그 멋진 상품들을 손에 넣을 마지막 기회라고 믿게 만듭니다.

12 그러면, 빨리 팔리는 물건을 사는 것은 돈을 쓰는 것이라기보다는 게임에서 이기는 것과 같아집니다.

13 인호: 정말 잘 골랐네!

미나: 너 그거 손에 넣었어, 인호야?

인호: 응, 마침내. 이것이 내 수집품을 완성하네.

미나: 잘됐네!

14 인기 있는 것들을 모으는 것은 젊은 소비자들 사이에서 가장 인기 있는 유행 중 하나입니다.

15 가장 인기 있는 수집품으로 캐릭터 스티커, 야구 카드 세트, 팝 스타를 특징으로 삼는 상품 등이 있습니다.

16 십대 소비자들은 이것들을 점점 더 많이 가지는 것을 즐기는데, '많을수록 좋다'라는 생각이 그들을 행복하게 만들어 주기 때문입니다.

17 어떤 유명인 상표를 구입해 보셨습니까? 어떤 빨리 팔리는 상품을 손에 넣어 보셨습니까? 어떤 캐릭터 스티커를 수집해 보셨습니까?

18 Are you happy with _____ you have _____, _____, and _____?

    A. bought   B. what   C. collected   D. grabbed

19 If you are happy _____ _____, that's _____ _____.

    A. them   B. right   C. with   D. all

20 If you _____, _____, you should try _____ _____ a smarter shopper.

    A. be   B. however   C. aren't   D. to

21 Here _____ three shopping tips _____ _____ _____.

    A. by   B. to   C. are   D. live

22 TIP 01. _____ _____ A LIST.

    A. TO   B. STICK

23 Make a shopping list and _____ it _____. Run _____ a store and get _____ you need.

    A. into   B. around   C. what   D. carry

24 If you can't find _____ on the list, walk out _____. You will feel _____ _____.

    A. lihgt   B. anything   C. empty-handed D. incredibly

25 TIP 02. _____ _____ FOR A DAY.

    A. OFF   B. COOL

26 When you shop online, don't click "Buy Now." _____, hit "_____ To Cart" and _____ _____.

    A. sign   B. instead   C. add   D. out

27 After 24 hours of _____ _____, come back and see _____ you _____ want it.

    A. off   B. still   C. if   D. cooling

28 TIP 03. FIND _____ _____.

    A. TREASURES   B. OLD

29 Whenever you want to buy something _____, go _____ your closet and see _____ you have. Find old treasures and enjoy a new _____ for them.

    A. through   B. appreciation   C. what   D. new

18 여러분이 구입하고 손에 넣고 수집한 것에 만족하십니까?

19 여러분들이 그것들에 만족한다면, 괜찮습니다.

20 그러나 여러분이 그것들에 만족하지 않는다면, 여러분은 더 똑똑한 구매자가 되려고 노력해야 합니다.

21 여기 생활 속에서 지켜야 할 세 가지 구매 팁이 있습니다.

22 조언 01 목록을 고수하세요.

23 쇼핑 목록을 작성하고 휴대하세요. 상점 안으로 달려가서 필요한 것을 얻으세요.

24 목록에 있는 것을 찾을 수 없다면, 빈손으로 걸어 나오세요. 믿을 수 없을 정도로 경쾌한 기분을 느끼게 될 거예요.

25 조언 02 하루 동안 진정해 보세요.

26 온라인 쇼핑을 할 때 "바로 구입"을 클릭하지 마세요. 대신, "장바구니에 추가"를 누르고 로그아웃 하세요.

27 24시간 동안 진정한 이후에, 돌아와서 여전히 그것을 원하는지 확인해 보세요.

28 조언 03 오래된 보물들을 찾으세요.

29 새로운 물건을 사고 싶을 때마다 옷장을 살펴보고 갖고 있는 물건을 확인해 보세요. 오래된 보물들을 찾고 그것들을 새롭게 감상하며 즐기세요.

※ 다음 우리말과 일치하도록 빈칸에 알맞은 말을 쓰시오.

What Makes You Shop?

1 What _____ you _____? Do you buy only _____ _____ _____?

2 Read _____ and think about your _____ _____.

3 Mina: _____ _____ that!

Somin: Wow! N-girls _____ _____ a _____ jacket.

Mina: It _____ very _____. I have _____ _____ _____ just _____ it.

Somin: Me, _____.

4 Many teens like to do _____ _____ _____ _____.

5 They are _____ _____ willing _____ _____ _____ the stars _____.

6 They want to _____ _____ their _____.

7 They think _____ _____ will _____ _____ _____ _____, _____, and _____.

8 Somin: _____ you _____ me, Inho?

Inho: Sure. _____ _____?

Somin: There's going to be an _____ _____ _____ on new sneakers. Please _____ me _____ _____ _____.

Inho: Okay, I'll click _____ _____.

9 When a product _____ _____ _____ _____, some people often feel _____ they won't _____ _____ _____ get it _____ they are _____ _____ _____.

10 They _____ _____ FOMO, Fear of Missing Out, _____ they see sales signs _____ _____ *Limited Edition* and *Flash Sale.*

11 The signs _____ them _____ that it is the _____ _____ _____ _____ the _____ _____.

12 Then, getting quick-selling goods _____ _____ winning a game _____ _____ money.

무엇이 여러분을 쇼핑하게 합니까?

1 무엇이 여러분을 쇼핑하게 합니까? 여러분은 정말로 필요한 것만을 삽니까?

2 읽어 가며 여러분의 쇼핑 습관에 대해 생각해 보십시오.

3 미나: 저것 좀 봐!
소민: 와! N-girls가 신상품 재킷을 입고 있네.
미나: 정말 귀여워 보여. 나도 그것과 꼭 같은 것을 하나 가지고 있어야만 되겠어.
소민: 나도 그래.

4 많은 십대들은 좋아하는 유명인이 하는 것을 하기 좋아합니다.

5 그들은 스타들이 사용하는 것을 기꺼이 사고자 합니다.

6 그들은 그들의 영웅처럼 보이기를 원합니다.

7 그들은 유명인 브랜드가 그들을 멋지고 행복하며 인기 있게 만들 것이라고 생각합니다.

8 소민: 나 도와줄 수 있어, 인호야?
인호: 물론이지. 무슨 일이야?
소민: 새로운 운동화의 온라인 반짝 판매가 있을 예정이야. 부탁인데, 내가 한 켤레를 손에 넣도록 도와줘.
인호: 알겠어. 내가 열심히 클릭할게.

9 한 상품이 불티나게 팔릴 때, 어떤 사람들은 그들이 충분히 재빠르지 않으면 그것을 얻을 수 없을 것이라고 흔히 느낍니다.

10 그들은 '한정판'이나 '반짝 판매'와 같은 판매 게시물을 보면, FOMO(놓치는 것에 대한 두려움)를 겪습니다.

11 그 게시물들은 그들로 하여금 그것이 그 멋진 상품들을 손에 넣을 마지막 기회라고 믿게 만듭니다.

12 그러면, 빨리 팔리는 물건을 사는 것은 돈을 쓰는 것이라기보다는 게임에서 이기는 것과 같아집니다.

13 **Inho:** What _____ _____!

Mina: Did you get _____, Inho?

Inho: Yeah, _____. This _____ my _____.

Mina: Good _____ you!

14 _____ popular things _____ one of the _____ _____ _____ young _____.

15 The _____ _____ _____ _____ character stickers, baseball card sets, and goods _____ pop stars.

16 Teen consumers enjoy _____ more and more of these, _____ the idea _____ *more is better* makes them happy.

17 What _____ brands _____ you _____? What quick-selling goods _____ you _____? What character stickers _____ you _____?

18 Are you happy with _____ you _____ _____, _____, and _____?

19 If you are happy _____ _____, that's _____ _____.

20 If you _____, _____, you should try _____ _____ a _____ _____.

21 Here _____ three shopping tips _____ _____ _____.

22 TIP 01. _____ _____ A LIST.

23 Make a _____ _____ and carry _____ around. _____ _____ a store and get _____ _____ _____.

24 If you can't find _____ _____ _____ _____ _____, walk out _____. You will _____ _____ _____ _____.

25 TIP 02. _____ _____ FOR A DAY.

26 When you shop _____, don't click "Buy Now." _____, hit "_____ To Cart" and _____ _____.

27 After 24 hours of _____ _____, _____ _____ and see _____ you _____ _____ _____.

28 TIP 03. FIND _____ _____.

29 _____ you want to buy _____ _____, _____ _____ your closet and see _____ you have. Find _____ _____ and enjoy _____ _____ _____ _____ _____.

13 인호: 정말 잘 골랐네!
미나: 너 그거 손에 넣었어, 인호야?
인호: 응, 마침내. 이것이 내 수집품을 완성하네.
미나: 잘됐네!

14 인기 있는 것들을 모으는 것은 젊은 소비자들 사이에서 가장 인기 있는 유행 중 하나입니다.

15 가장 인기 있는 수집품으로 캐릭터 스티커, 야구 카드 세트, 팝 스타를 특징으로 삼는 상품 등이 있습니다.

16 십대 소비자들은 이것들을 점점 더 많이 가지는 것을 즐기는데, '많을수록 좋다'라는 생각이 그들을 행복하게 만들어 주기 때문입니다.

17 어떤 유명인 상표를 구입해 보셨습니까? 어떤 빨리 팔리는 상품을 손에 넣어 보셨습니까? 어떤 캐릭터 스티커를 수집해 보셨습니까?

18 여러분이 구입하고 손에 넣고 수집한 것에 만족하십니까?

19 여러분들이 그것들에 만족한다면, 괜찮습니다.

20 그러나 여러분이 그것들에 만족하지 않는다면, 여러분은 더 똑똑한 구매자가 되려고 노력해야 합니다.

21 여기 생활 속에서 지켜야 할 세 가지 구매 팁이 있습니다.

22 조언 01 목록을 고수하세요.

23 쇼핑 목록을 작성하고 휴대하세요. 상점 안으로 달려가서 필요한 것을 얻으세요.

24 목록에 있는 것을 찾을 수 없다면, 빈손으로 걸어 나오세요. 믿을 수 없을 정도로 경쾌한 기분을 느끼게 될 거예요.

25 조언 02 하루 동안 진정해 보세요.

26 온라인 쇼핑을 할 때 "바로 구입"을 클릭하지 마세요. 대신, "장바구니에 추가"를 누르고 로그아웃 하세요.

27 24시간 동안 진정한 이후에, 돌아와서 여전히 그것을 원하는지 확인해 보세요.

28 조언 03 오래된 보물들을 찾으세요.

29 새로운 물건을 사고 싶을 때마다 옷장을 살펴보고 갖고 있는 물건을 확인해 보세요. 오래된 보물들을 찾고 그것들을 새롭게 감상하며 즐기세요.

※ 다음 문장을 우리말로 쓰시오.

What Makes You Shop?

1 What makes you shop? Do you buy only what you really need?

➡ _____

2 Read on and think about your shopping habits.

➡ _____

3 Mina: Look at that! / Somin: Wow! N-girls are wearing a brand-new jacket.

Mina: It looks very cute. I have to have one just like it. / Somin: Me, too.

➡ _____

_____

4 Many teens like to do what their favorite celebrities do.

➡ _____

5 They are more than willing to buy what the stars use.

➡ _____

6 They want to look like their heroes.

➡ _____

7 They think celebrity brands will make them cool, happy, and popular.

➡ _____

8 Somin: Can you help me, Inho? / Inho: Sure. What's up?

Somin: There's going to be an online flash sale on new sneakers. Please help me grab a pair. / Inho: Okay, I'll click like crazy.

➡ _____

_____

9 When a product sells like hot cakes, some people often feel that they won't be able to get it if they are not fast enough.

➡ _____

_____

10 They suffer from FOMO, Fear of Missing Out, when they see sales signs such as *Limited Edition* and *Flash Sale*.

➡ _____

11 The signs make them believe that it is the last chance to grab the cool products.

➡ _____

12 Then, getting quick-selling goods becomes more like winning a game than spending money.

➡ _____

13 Inho: What a pick! / Mina: Did you get it, Inho?

Inho: Yeah, finally. This completes my collection. / Mina: Good for you!

➡ _____

_____

14 Collecting popular things is one of the hottest trends among young consumers.

➡ _____

15 The most popular collections include character stickers, baseball card sets, and goods featuring pop stars.

➡ _____

16 Teen consumers enjoy getting more and more of these, because the idea of more is better makes them happy.

➡ _____

17 What celebrity brands have you bought? What quick-selling goods have you grabbed?

What character stickers have you collected?

➡ _____

_____

18 Are you happy with what you have bought, grabbed, and collected?

➡ _____

19 If you are happy with them, that's all right.

➡ _____

20 If you aren't, however, you should try to be a smarter shopper.

➡ _____

21 Here are three shopping tips to live by.

➡ _____

22 TIP 01. STICK TO A LIST.

➡ _____

23 Make a shopping list and carry it around. Run into a store and get what you need.

➡ _____

24 If you can't find anything on the list, walk out empty-handed. You will feel incredibly light.

➡ _____

25 TIP 02. COOL OFF FOR A DAY.

➡ _____

26 When you shop online, don't click "Buy Now." Instead, hit "Add To Cart" and sign out.

➡ _____

27 After 24 hours of cooling off, come back and see if you still want it.

➡ _____

28 TIP 03. FIND OLD TREASURES.

➡ _____

29 Whenever you want to buy something new, go through your closet and see what you have.

Find old treasures and enjoy a new appreciation for them.

➡ _____

_____

※ 다음 괄호 안의 단어들을 우리말에 맞도록 바르게 배열하시오.

What Makes You Shop?

1 (makes / what / shop? / you // you / do / only / buy / you / what / need? / really)

➡ _____

2 (on / read / and / about / think / shopping / habits. / your)

➡ _____

3 (Mina: / at / look / that! // Somin: / wow! / are / N-girls / wearing / are / brand-new / a / jacket. // Mina / looks / it / cute. / very // I / to / have / one / have / like / it. / just // Somin: / too. / me,)

➡ _____

_____

4 (teens / many / to / like / do / their / what / celebrities / do. / favorite)

➡ _____

5 (are / they / than / more / to / willing / what / buy / use. / stars / the)

➡ _____

6 (want / they / look / to / their / like / heroes.)

➡ _____

7 (think / they / brands / celebrity / make / will / cool, / them / and / happy, / popular.)

➡ _____

8 (Somin: / you / can / me, / help / Inho? // Inho: / sure. // up? / what's // Somin: / going / there's / be / to / an / flash / online / on / sale / sneakers. / new // help / please / grab / me / pair. / a // Inho: / I'll / okay, / like / click / crazy.)

➡ _____

_____

_____

9 (a / when / sells / product / hot / like / cakes, / people / some / feel / often / that / won't / they / able / be / get / to / if / it / are / they / fast / not / enough.)

➡ _____

_____

무엇이 여러분을 쇼핑하게 합니까?

1 무엇이 여러분을 쇼핑하게 합니까? 여러분은 정말로 필요한 것만을 삽니까?

2 읽어 가며 여러분의 쇼핑 습관에 대해 생각해 보십시오.

3 미나: 저것 좀 봐!

소민: 와! N-girls가 신상품 재킷을 입고 있네.

미나: 정말 귀여워 보여. 나도 그것과 꼭 같은 것을 하나 가지고 있어야만 되겠어.

소민: 나도 그래.

4 많은 십대들은 좋아하는 유명인이 하는 것을 하기 좋아합니다.

5 그들은 스타들이 사용하는 것을 기꺼이 사고자 합니다.

6 그들은 그들의 영웅처럼 보이기를 원합니다.

7 그들은 유명인 브랜드가 그들을 멋지고 행복하며 인기 있게 만들 것이라고 생각합니다.

8 소민: 나 도와줄 수 있어, 인호야?

인호: 물론이지. 무슨 일이야?

소민: 새로운 운동화의 온라인 반짝 판매가 있을 예정이야. 부탁인데, 내가 한 켤레를 손에 넣도록 도와줘.

인호: 알겠어. 내가 열심히 클릭할게.

9 한 상품이 불티나게 팔릴 때, 어떤 사람들은 그들이 충분히 재빠르지 않으면 그것을 얻을 수 없을 것이라고 흔히 느낍니다.

10 (suffer / they / FOMO, / from / of / Fear / Out, / Missing / they / when / sales / see / signs / as / such *Edition / Limited /* and / *Sale. / Flash*)

➡ _____

_____

11 (signs / the / them / make / that / believe / is / it / last / the / to / chance / grab / the / products. / cool)

➡ _____

_____

12 (getting / then, / goods / quick-selling / becomes / like / more / a / winning / than / game / money. / spending)

➡ _____

_____

13 (Inho: / a / what / pick! // Mina: / you / did / it, / get / Inho? // Inho: / finally. / yeah, / completes / this / collection. / my // Mina: / for / good / you!)

➡ _____

_____

14 (popular / collecting / is / things / of / one / hottest / the / among / trends / consumers. / young)

➡ _____

_____

15 (most / the / collections / popular / include / stickers, / character / card / baseball / sets, / goods / and / pop / featuring / stars.)

➡ _____

_____

16 (consumers / teen / getting / enjoy / more / and / of / more / these, / the / because / idea / more / of / better / is / them / happy. / makes)

➡ _____

_____

17 (celebrity / what / have / brands / bought? / you // quick-selling / what / have / goods / grabbed? / you // character / what / stickers / you / have / collected?)

➡ _____

_____

10 그들은 '한정판'이나 '반짝 판매'와 같은 판매 게시물을 보면, FOMO(놓치는 것에 대한 두려움)를 겪습니다.

11 그 게시물들은 그들로 하여금 그것이 그 멋진 상품들을 손에 넣을 마지막 기회라고 믿게 만듭니다.

12 그러면, 빨리 팔리는 물건을 사는 것은 돈을 쓰는 것이라기보다는 게임에서 이기는 것과 같아집니다.

13 인호: 정말 잘 골랐네!

미나: 너 그거 손에 넣었어, 인호야?

인호: 응, 마침내. 이것이 내 수집품을 완성하네.

미나: 잘됐네!

14 인기 있는 것들을 모으는 것은 젊은 소비자들 사이에서 가장 인기 있는 유행 중 하나입니다.

15 가장 인기 있는 수집품으로 캐릭터 스티커, 야구 카드 세트, 팝 스타를 특징으로 삼는 상품 등이 있습니다.

16 십대 소비자들은 이것들을 점점 더 많이 가지는 것을 즐기는데, '많을수록 좋다'라는 생각이 그들을 행복하게 만들어 주기 때문입니다.

17 어떤 유명인 상표를 구입해 보셨습니까? 어떤 빨리 팔리는 상품을 손에 넣어 보셨습니까? 어떤 캐릭터 스티커를 수집해 보셨습니까?

18 (you / are / with / happy / you / what / bought, / have / and / grabbed, / collected?)

➡ _____

19 (you / if / happy / are / them, / with / all / that's / right.)

➡ _____

20 (you / if / aren't, / you / however, / should / to / try / a / be / shopper. / smarter)

➡ _____

21 (are / here / shopping / three / to / tips / by. / live)

➡ _____

22 (01. / TIP / TO / STICK / LIST. / A)

➡ _____

23 (a / make / shopping / and / list / it / carry / around. // into / run / store / a / and / what / get / need. / you)

➡ _____
_____

24 (you / if / find / can't / on / anything / list, / the / out / walk / empty-handed. // will / you / incredibly / feel / light.)

➡ _____
_____

25 (02. / TIP / OFF / COOL / FOR / DAY. / A)

➡ _____

26 (you / when / online, / shop / click / don't / Now." / "Buy // hit / instead, / TO / "Add / Cart" / and / out. / sign)

➡ _____
_____

27 (24 / after / of / hours / off, / cooling / back / come / and / if / see / still / you / it. / want)

➡ _____

28 (03. / TIP / OLD / FIND / TREASURES.)

➡ _____

29 (you / whenever / to / want / something / buy / new, / through / go / closet / your / see / and / what / have. / you // old / find / and / treasures / a / enjoy / new / for / appreciation / them.)

➡ _____
_____
_____

---

18 여러분이 구입하고 손에 넣고 수집한 것에 만족하십니까?

19 여러분들이 그것들에 만족한다면, 괜찮습니다.

20 그러나 여러분이 그것들에 만족하지 않는다면, 여러분은 더 똑똑한 구매자가 되려고 노력해야 합니다.

21 여기 생활 속에서 지켜야 할 세 가지 구매 팁이 있습니다.

22 조언 01 목록을 고수하세요.

23 쇼핑 목록을 작성하고 휴대하세요. 상점 안으로 달려가서 필요한 것을 얻으세요.

24 목록에 있는 것을 찾을 수 없다면, 빈손으로 걸어 나오세요. 믿을 수 없을 정도로 경쾌한 기분을 느끼게 될 거예요.

25 조언 02 하루 동안 진정해 보세요.

26 온라인 쇼핑을 할 때 "바로 구입"을 클릭하지 마세요. 대신, "장바구니에 추가"를 누르고 로그아웃 하세요.

27 24시간 동안 진정한 이후에, 돌아와서 여전히 그것을 원하는지 확인해 보세요.

28 조언 03 오래된 보물들을 찾으세요.

29 새로운 물건을 사고 싶을 때마다 옷장을 살펴보고 갖고 있는 물건을 확인해 보세요. 오래된 보물들을 찾고 그것들을 새롭게 감상하며 즐기세요.

※ **다음 우리말을 영어로 쓰시오.**

What Makes You Shop?

1 무엇이 여러분을 쇼핑하게 합니까? 여러분은 정말로 필요한 것만을 삽니까?

➡ _____

2 읽어 가며 여러분의 쇼핑 습관에 대해 생각해 보십시오.

➡ _____

3 미나: 저것 좀 봐! / 소민: 와! N-girls가 신상품 재킷을 입고 있네.

미나: 정말 귀여워 보여. 나도 그것과 꼭 같은 것을 하나 가지고 있어야만 되겠어. / 소민: 나도 그래.

➡ _____

4 많은 십대들은 좋아하는 유명인이 하는 것을 하기 좋아합니다.

➡ _____

5 그들은 스타들이 사용하는 것을 기꺼이 사고자 합니다.

➡ _____

6 그들은 그들의 영웅처럼 보이기를 원합니다.

➡ _____

7 그들은 유명인 브랜드가 그들을 멋지고 행복하며 인기 있게 만들 것이라고 생각합니다.

➡ _____

8 소민: 나 도와줄 수 있어, 인호야? / 인호: 물론이지. 무슨 일이야?

소민: 새로운 운동화의 온라인 반짝 판매가 있을 예정이야. 부탁인데, 내가 한 켤레를 손에 넣도록 도와줘. / 인호: 알겠어. 내가 열심히 클릭할게.

➡ _____

_____

_____

9 한 상품이 불티나게 팔릴 때, 어떤 사람들은 그들이 충분히 재빠르지 않으면 그것을 얻을 수 없을 것이라고 흔히 느낍니다.

➡ _____

_____

10 그들은 '한정판'이나 '반짝 판매'와 같은 판매 게시물을 보면, FOMO(놓치는 것에 대한 두려움)를 겪습니다.

➡ _____

_____

11 그 게시물들은 그들로 하여금 그것이 그 멋진 상품들을 손에 넣을 마지막 기회라고 믿게 만듭니다.

➡ _____

12 그러면, 빨리 팔리는 물건을 사는 것은 돈을 쓰는 것이라기보다는 게임에서 이기는 것과 같아집니다.

➡ _____

13 인호: 정말 잘 골랐네! / 미나: 너 그거 손에 넣었어, 인호야?
인호: 응, 마침내. 이것이 내 수집품을 완성하네. / 미나: 잘됐네!

➡ _____

_____

14 인기 있는 것들을 모으는 것은 젊은 소비자들 사이에서 가장 인기 있는 유행 중 하나입니다.

➡ _____

15 가장 인기 있는 수집품으로 캐릭터 스티커, 야구 카드 세트, 팝 스타를 특징으로 삼는 상품 등이 있습니다.

➡ _____

16 십대 소비자들은 이것들을 점점 더 많이 가지는 것을 즐기는데, '많을수록 좋다'라는 생각이 그들을
행복하게 만들어 주기 때문입니다.

➡ _____

17 어떤 유명인 상표를 구입해 보셨습니까? 어떤 빨리 팔리는 상품을 손에 넣어 보셨습니까? 어떤 캐릭터
스티커를 수집해 보셨습니까?

➡ _____

_____

18 여러분이 구입하고 손에 넣고 수집한 것에 만족하십니까?

➡ _____

19 여러분들이 그것들에 만족한다면, 괜찮습니다.

➡ _____

20 그러나 여러분이 그것들에 만족하지 않는다면, 여러분은 더 똑똑한 구매자가 되려고 노력해야 합니다.

➡ _____

21 여기 생활 속에서 지켜야 할 세 가지 구매 팁이 있습니다.

➡ _____

22 조언 01 목록을 고수하세요.

➡ _____

23 쇼핑 목록을 작성하고 휴대하세요. 상점 안으로 달려가서 필요한 것을 얻으세요.

➡ _____

24 목록에 있는 것을 찾을 수 없다면, 빈손으로 걸어 나오세요. 믿을 수 없을 정도로 경쾌한 기분을 느끼게 될 거예요.

➡ _____

25 조언 02 하루 동안 진정해 보세요.

➡ _____

26 온라인 쇼핑을 할 때 "바로 구입"을 클릭하지 마세요. 대신, "장바구니에 추가"를 누르고 로그아웃 하세요.

➡ _____

27 24시간 동안 진정한 이후에, 돌아와서 여전히 그것을 원하는지 확인해 보세요.

➡ _____

28 조언 03 오래된 보물들을 찾으세요.

➡ _____

29 새로운 물건을 사고 싶을 때마다 옷장을 살펴보고 갖고 있는 물건을 확인해 보세요. 오래된 보물들을
찾고 그것들을 새롭게 감상하며 즐기세요.

➡ _____

_____

※ 다음 우리말과 일치하도록 빈칸에 알맞은 말을 쓰시오.

Listen & Speak 2 B

1. A: _____ _____ are you _____ _____?

2. B: I'm going to the _____ _____.

3. A: _____ you _____ of having pizza?

4. B: No, I'm not. I'm _____ _____ _____ _____.

1. A: 몇 층을 가시나요?
2. B: 저는 2층에 갑니다.
3. A: 피자를 먹으려고 하시나요?
4. B: 아니요. 팝콘을 먹으려고요.

Real Life Task Step 3

1. We are _____ _____ _____ _____ our spending _____ _____ money.

2. Nara will _____ _____ _____ _____.

3. Seho will _____ _____ _____ and _____.

4. Jina will come to school _____ _____, _____ _____ _____.

1. 우리는 돈을 절약하기 위해서 지출을 줄이려고 합니다.
2. 나라는 옷을 덜 살 것입니다.
3. 세호는 간식과 음료를 덜 살 것입니다.
4. 지나는 버스가 아닌 자전거를 타고 등교할 것입니다.

Before I Read

1. _____ _____

2. _____ _____ FOR SMART _____.

3. 50% _____ ON _____ _____ FOR THIS _____ _____.

4. GRAB THESE _____ _____ BEFORE THEY _____ _____.

1. 반짝 세일
2. 똑똑한 소비자들을 위한 특별한 할인.
3. 유명인 브랜드를 이번 주말에만 50% 할인된 가격으로.
4. 다 팔리기 전에 이 새 상품들을 가져가세요.

※ 다음 우리말을 영어로 쓰시오.

Listen & Speak 2 B

1. A: 몇 층을 가시나요?

➡ _____

2. B: 저는 2층에 갑니다.

➡ _____

3. A: 피자를 먹으려고 하시나요?

➡ _____

4. B: 아니요. 팝콘을 먹으려고요.

➡ _____

Real Life Task Step 3

1. 우리는 돈을 절약하기 위해서 지출을 줄이려고 합니다.

➡ _____

2. 나라는 옷을 덜 살 것입니다.

➡ _____

3. 세호는 간식과 음료를 덜 살 것입니다.

➡ _____

4. 지나는 버스가 아닌 자전거를 타고 등교할 것입니다.

➡ _____

Before I Read

1. 반짝 세일

➡ _____

2. 똑똑한 소비자들을 위한 특별한 할인.

➡ _____

3. 유명인 브랜드를 이번 주말에만 50% 할인된 가격으로.

➡ _____

4. 다 팔리기 전에 이 새 상품들을 가져가세요.

➡ _____

MEMO

영어 기출 문제집

적중100

적중100

1학기

정답 및 해설

능률 | 양현권

중 3

영어 기출 문제집

정답 및 해설

적중100

1학기

능률 | 양현권

중 3

적중100

Lesson 1

How Are You Getting Along?

시험대비 실력평가   p.08

01 ③   02 (g)et (a)long   03 ①   04 ②
05 (p)ermission   06 ⑤   07 ①

01 주어진 단어는 반의어 관계이다. difficulty 어려움 ease 쉬움 noisy 시끄러운 silent 조용한

02 "~와 사이좋게 지내다"의 의미로 "get along with"가 되어야 한다.

03 put up with: ~을 참다

04 소년이 무서운 이야기라고 하는 것과는 달리 슬픈 이야기라고 하는 것은 자신의 의견을 나타내는 것이다.

05 문맥상 나의 언니가 허가 없이 나의 방에 들어온다는 의미가 되어야 한다.

06 ① 친구를 사귀다 make friends ② 아마도 possibly ③ ~ 학년 생 graders ④ 응답 replies ⑤ 괴롭히다 bother

07 명사 'cook'은 '요리사'라는 뜻이고 동사로 쓰였을 때 '요리하다'의 뜻이다.

서술형 시험대비   p.09

01 (1) get   (2) share   (3) lose, temper
     (4) put up with
02 (l)aughter
03 (s)uggests
04 golden
05 (1) luck   (2) word   (3) stick by   (4) wake up
06 (A) out   (B) big   (C) privacy   (D) only

01 (1) 함께 모이다 = get together (2) 같이 쓰다 = share (3) 화를 내다 = lose one's temper (4) put up with ~을 참다, 견디다

02 '사람이 웃는 소리'는 'laughter 웃음'이다.

03 'recommend 추천하다'와 비슷한 말은 'suggest 제안하다'이다.

04 '멋진, 금으로 만든'이라는 뜻으로 명사 child를 수식하는 형용사가 되어야 한다.

05 (1) 행운 = good luck (2) 단어 = word (3) ~의 곁을 지키다 = stick by (4) 깨우다 = wake up

06 (A) 외식하러 가다 = go out to eat (B) 대가족 = a big family (C) 사생활 = privacy (D) 외동 = an only child

Conversation

핵심 Check   p.10~11

1 ②   2 ⑤

01 '내 생각에 그것은 슬픈 이야기이다.'의 의미를 나타내는 표현이다. ②는 '나는 그것이 슬픈 이야기인지 궁금하다.'의 뜻이다.

02 만족 여부를 묻는 질문에 어울리지 않는 것은 "⑤ 가격은 얼마였니?"이다.

교과서 대화문 익히기

Check(√) True or False   p.12

1 F   2 T   3 T   4 F

교과서 확인학습   p.14~15

Listen & Speak 1 A-1

Have, read / story, scary / opinion, sad / could

Listen & Speak 1 A-2

seen, movie / have, best / seem, like / How, possibly, view, wonderful

Listen & Speak 1 A-3

painting strange / think / after taking, look, beautiful / don't, agree

Listen & Speak 1 B

third graders, important / say that, What should / opinion, make, friends / right, important

Listen & Speak 2 A-1

hear, cream, opened / Sure, already / Have, was / great / How / high, happy

Listen & Speak 2 A-2

There, here / here, since, ordered / service, slow, happy / those, over, being served / Didn't, earlier / fair

Conversation B

go out, eat / food, family, too / How / seven, grandparents, brothers / don't, privacy / get what, good, have, lonely, only, what

Real Life Task Step 1

happy, different, asked, whom, More, feel, with, number, with, friends, Interestingly, asked, alone

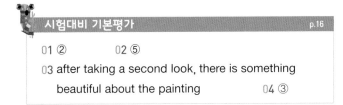

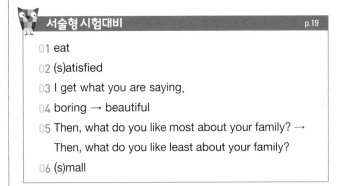

시험대비 기본평가 p.16

01 ②   02 ⑤

03 after taking a second look, there is something beautiful about the painting   04 ③

01 소년이 무서운 이야기라고 한 것과는 대조적으로 소녀가 슬픈 이야기라고 하는 것은 자신의 의견을 나타내는 것이다.

02 (C) 아이스크림이 만족스러웠는지 묻는 말에 대답하고 (B) 가격에 대하여 질문을 하자 (A) 가격이 비싸서 불만이라는 대답을 한다.

03 다시 보니 = after taking a second look, ~가 있다 = there is ~, 아름다운 것 = something beautiful

04 소년은 처음에 그림이 이상하다고 말하고, 나중에는 그림에 뭔가 아름다운 것이 있다고 했다.

시험대비 실력평가 p.17~18

01 ⑤   02 How can you possibly say that?

03 ⑤   04 ②

05 I think it's also important to read a lot of books.

06 ③   07 Yes, I did. → Yes, I have.   08 ⑤

09 ④   10 ②   11 ③   12 ③

13 What should family members do to have a happy family?

01 그 영화가 자신이 본 최고의 영화라는 말에 대한 반응으로 적절한 것은 '너는 그 영화를 좋아하는 것 같다.'가 적절하다.

02 '어떻게 ~할 수 있니?'는 'How can you ~?'이다.

03 빈칸에는 자신의 의견을 밝히는 표현이 적절하다.

04 ②는 상대의 말에 동의하는 말로 '동의한다.'는 의미이다.

05 '~라고 생각하다' = I think ~, ~하는 것도 중요하다 = It's also important to~

06 소녀는 친구를 많이 사귀려는 소년의 생각에 동의하는 입장이므로 친구를 많이 사귈 것이다.

07 현재완료의 질문에 대한 대답은 do, does, did가 아니라 have, has로 대답하여야 한다.

08 'Sure.' 'Have you?'를 보면 소년은 그 상점에 다녀온 것을 알 수 있다.

09 가격이 너무 높다고 불평하고 있으므로 만족스럽지 않다는 내용이

적절하다.

10 음식을 주문한지 30분이 지났고 만족스럽지 않다는 반응을 보여주는 것으로 보아서 서비스가 좋지는 않다는 의미가 적절하다.

11 'They are being served now.'의 They는 제시 문장의 'those people over there'를 지칭한다.

12 30분 이상 기다리고, 나중에 온 사람이 먼저 서비스를 받는 것을 보고 식당에 대한 불만족을 표시하고 있다. 음식의 맛에 대한 언급은 없다.

13 가족 구성원들이 무엇을 해야 하니? = What should family members do 행복한 가정을 위하여 = to have a happy family

서술형 시험대비 p.19

01 eat

02 (s)atisfied

03 I get what you are saying.

04 boring → beautiful

05 Then, what do you like most about your family? → Then, what do you like least about your family?

06 (s)mall

01 go out to eat = 외식하다(= eat out)

02 만족스럽지 못한 것을 나타낼 때 "I am not satisfied with~." 라고 할 수 있다.

03 나는 알겠다. = I get, 네가 무슨 말을 하는지 = what you are saying

04 소녀가 소년에게 '내 의견에 동의할 필요가 없다.'고 하는 것으로 보아 소년은 다시 보았을 때 '아름다운 어떤 것'이 있다고 했다.

05 이어지는 내용이 불만족스러운 감정을 나타내는 것으로 보아 most가 아니라 least가 되는 것이 적절하다.

06 "I'm not happy about its size."로 보아 크기가 작아서 불만이라고 생각할 수 있다.

교과서

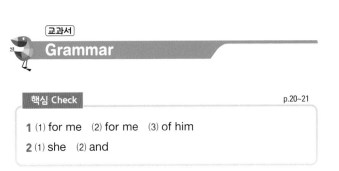

Grammar

핵심 Check p.20~21

1 (1) for me   (2) for me   (3) of him

2 (1) she   (2) and

01 ①

02 I have a brother, who is a doctor.   03 ③

04 ⑤

01 ②, ③, ⑤ difficult, easy 등의 형용사 뒤에 to부정사의 의미상 주어는 'for+목적격"이고, ①, ④ 사람의 성격, 성질, 품성을 나타내는 형용사 뒤에 쓰일 경우 「of+목적격」의 형태로 쓰인다.

02 계속적 용법을 나타내는 관계대명사 who를 사용하여 영작한다.

03 ①, ②, ④, ⑤ dangerous, boring, difficult, easy는 사람의 성격, 성질, 품성을 나타내는 형용사가 아니므로 「for+목적격」의 형태로 의미상 주어를 나타낸다. ③ silly는 사람의 성격, 성질, 품성을 나타내는 형용사로 의미상 주어의 형태는 「of+목적격」이 알맞다.

04 ① that → who ② which → who ③ that → which ④ what → that[which]

01 ③   02 ⑤   03 for him to   04 ①

05 ④   06 ⑤   07 ②

08 (1) ⓐ → I respect Mother Theresa, who devoted her life to others.

    (2) ⓑ → We'll go to The Ken's Market, which sells fresh food.

    (3) ⓓ → Jessica sent the letter to Mike, which made him happy.

    (4) ⓖ → I don't know where my bag has gone, which was put on the table a few hours ago.

09 ③   10 ②

11 (1) Here is some water, which is fresh.

    (2) I know the girl, who[whom] Tom danced with last night.   12 ④

13 of him to lend me   14 ⑤   15 ③

16 My brother, who is a pilot, lives in Busan.

01 ③: rude는 사람의 성격을 나타내는 형용사로 의미상 주어의 형태는 「of+목적격」 ①, ②, ④, ⑤ hard, necessary, safe, important는 「for+목적격」의 형태로 의미상 주어를 나타낸다.

02 (A), (C), (D)는 사람의 성격을 나타내는 형용사가 아니므로 'for+목적격'의 형태 (B) careless는 사람의 성격, 성질, 품성을 나타내는 형용사이므로 of me의 형태 (E) 문장의 주어이므로 to부정사로 쓰는 것이 알맞다.

03 가주어 it으로 시작하는 문장의 의미상 주어를 쓰고, 진주어는 to부정사가 되도록 한다.

04 계속적 용법(비제한적 용법)의 관계대명사로 that은 쓰지 않는

다.

05 (A) 선행사 an uncle에 이어지는 계속적 용법 관계대명사 who가 들어가는 것이 알맞다. (2) kind 뒤에는 의미상 주어를 of로 나타낸다.

06 a bedroom을 수식하는 계속적 용법의 관계대명사 which, two sons를 수식하는 계속적 용법의 관계대명사 who가 알맞다.

07 ② 목적격 관계대명사는 생략 가능하지만 ①, ⑤ 주격관계대명사는 생략할 수 없다. ③ 계속적 용법의 주격관계대명사로 생략할 수 없다. ④ 관계대명사 what은 생략할 수 없다.

08 ⓐ 선행사 Mother Theresa는 관계대명사 who ⓑ 선행사 The Ken's Market는 which를 쓰고, ⓓ 관계대명사 that은 계속적 용법으로 사용할 수 없고, ⓖ 선행사 my bag을 수식하는 계속적 용법의 관계대명사 자리로 주격 관계대명사인 which로 바꿔준다.

09 ① 관계사절의 목적어인 them을 삭제 ② 계속적 용법은 that은 사용 불가 ④ 사람이 선행사일 때는 who ⑤ 주어는 Emma and Charlie로 복수이므로 동사도 is가 아닌 are로 바꿔줘야 한다.

10 ① 계속적 용법의 관계대명사 which는 '접속사+대명사'로 바꾸어 쓸 수 있는데 이때 의미에 따라 접속사는 and, but, for, though 등 다양하게 올 수 있다. ① I don't know the man though he lives next door. ③ and she → and they ④ but → for ⑤ Leonardo da Vinci가 the Mona Lisa를 그린 주체이므로 수동태가 아닌 능동태가 되어야 한다.

11 (1) 접속사+대명사 부분을 관계대명사로 고칠 수 있으므로 and it은 which (2) 전치사의 목적어 her를 목적격 관계대명사 whom 또는 who로 바꾸어 쓴다.

12 사람의 성격을 나타내는 ④는 of, 나머지는 for를 쓴다.

13 사람의 감정을 나타내는 경우 to부정사의 의미상의 주어는 'of+목적격'으로 쓴다.

14 ① 계속적 용법에서는 that을 쓸 수 없다. ② 선행사가 사람이므로 who ③ he를 who로 바꾼다. ④ what은 선행사가 없을 때 사용한다.

16 계속적 용법의 관계대명사 who를 이용하고, "I have a brother, who is a pilot and lives in Busan."이라고 할 수도 있다.

01 of him to help me with my homework

02 (1) for us to move this chair

    (2) of you to open the window

03 easy, to learn English

04 (1) I said nothing, which made Tom angry.

    (2) Brain, who is from the South, hates cold

weather.

05 (1) who

   (2) which

06 for me

07 (1) I read a story about Helen Keller, who overcame her physical difficulties.

   (2) We'll go to The Hope Mart, which sells fresh food.

   (3) Everyone likes our kind and gentle teacher, who teaches English to us.

   (4) I took a swimming lesson from Mr. Jonson, who made me enjoy swimming.

08 (1) It is important for the meeting to be a success

   (2) It is impossible for us to finish the job in time.

   (3) *The Sherlock Holmes* stories were written by Arthur Conan Doyle, who was born in Edinburgh.

   (4) Samuel Johnson, who died in 1784, is buried in Westminster Abbey.

09 (1) for   (2) for us   (3) for her to learn

10 (1) This is my best friend, Rachel, who lives next door to me.

   (2) David moved to his new apartment, which is very close to the park.

---

01 kind는 사람의 성격을 나타내는 형용사이므로 의미상 주어를 of him의 형태로 써야 한다. It이 가주어이므로 to help me with my homework가 진주어로 쓰인다.

02 (1) difficult 다음에는 의미상 주어 for us가 필요하다. (2) careless는 사람의 성격을 나타내는 형용사이므로 의미상의 주어를 of you의 형태로 써야 한다.

03 가주어 it, 진주어 to부정사가 쓰인 문장으로 It is 뒤에 형용사인 easy를, to부정사의 의미상의 주어인 for Karl 뒤에 to부정사구를 쓴다.

04 (1) '나는 아무 말도 안했다'를 선행사로 하는 관계대명사 which를 사용하여 계속적 용법을 나타낸다. (2) Brian을 선행사로 하는 계속적 용법의 관계대명사 who를 사용하여 문장을 써준다.

05 선행사인 tsunami는 사물을 나타내므로 관계대명사 who를 which로 바꿔준다.

06 to부정사의 의미상의 주어는 'for+목적격'으로 to부정사 바로 앞에 쓴다.

07 (1) Helen Keller, (2) The Hope Mart (3) teacher (4) Mr. Jonson을 선행사로 하는 계속적 용법의 관계대명사를 써준다.

08 (1), (2) to부정사의 의미상의 주어는 'for+목적격'을 써서 'for the meeting' 'for us"가 되어야 한다. (3), (4) that은 비제한

적 용법(계속적 용법)의 관계대명사로 쓰일 수 없다.

09 to부정사의 의미상의 주어는 'for+목적격'으로 to부정사 앞에 쓴다.

10 (1) Rachel을 선행사로 하는 관계대명사 who를 이용하여 계속적 용법, (2) his new apartment를 선행사로 하는 관계대명사 which를 사용하여 계속적 용법으로 나타낸다.

교과서 Reading

확인문제   p.28

1 F   2 T   3 T   4 F

확인문제   p.29

1 T   2 F   3 F   4 T   5 F

교과서 확인학습 A   p.30~31

01 may have different meanings

02 How, doing, their replies

03 ask, whether, get along with, more often than not, whether

04 For one thing, bother

05 comes into, without, permission, to wake up

06 asks, to walk, tells me to clean

07 getting on my nerves

08 end up loving, at my worst, to do so

09 share, who is, older

10 When, her mood, changing

11 would lose, over nothing, read, watch

12 difficult for me to

13 my turn to be, getting better

14 Whenever, tries to support

15 understand, better than, because, what it feels like

16 get to know, feel greater love

17 who entered, is the golden child

18 a perfect son, student at

19 Needless to say, such a shining brother

20 poor at, that, am great at

21 no eye for, whenever, hard time choosing

22 pleased, thanks, for, appreciates

23 for me to live with, believe in, own trade

24 their own difficulties

25 find special meanings

26 would, tell

27 is made of, years, grows, passing of time

1 The word *family* may have different meanings to different people.

2 We asked our readers, "How are you doing with your family?" Here are some of their replies.

3 I often ask myself whether I get along with my family members, and more often than not, I'm not sure whether I really do.

4 For one thing, they bother me all the time.

5 My sister comes into my room without my permission and shouts at me to wake up on Sunday mornings.

6 Next, Mom asks me to walk the dog, and then Dad tells me to clean my room.

7 They keep getting on my nerves until I get angry at them.

8 But I always end up loving them because they have been with me at my worst, still stick by me now, and will continue to do so in the future.

9 I share a room with my sister, who is two years older than me.

10 When she became a teenager, her mood started changing every minute.

11 She would lose her temper over nothing one moment and happily read a book or watch a film the next.

12 It was difficult for me to put up with her.

13 Now it's my turn to be a teenager. My sister is still one, but she is getting better.

14 Whenever I lose my temper, she tries to support me.

15 I also understand her better than before because now I know what it feels like to be a teenager.

16 As we get to know each other better, we feel greater love toward each other.

17 My older brother, who entered university this year, is the golden child.

18 He is a perfect son at home and a perfect student at school.

19 Needless to say, it is really stressful to have such a shining brother.

20 Well, in fact, he is not perfect and is poor at one thing that I am great at.

21 He has no eye for fashion, and I always help him whenever he has a hard time choosing clothes for a date.

22 I feel pleased when he thanks me for my help and appreciates my fashion sense.

23 It is not always difficult for me to live with the perfect brother, and I believe in "every man for his own trade."

24 Kamala, Rachel, and Minsu all have their own difficulties in their family life.

25 At the same time, they love their families and find special meanings in them.

26 What story would you tell us about your family?

27 A family / is made of love and tears, / laughter and years. / It grows stronger with the passing of time.

01 ③

02 different meanings to different people

03 ④   04 ⑤   05 stick by

06 Her father tells her to clean her room.   07 ④

08 It's because she knows what it feels like to be a teenager.

09 ③   10 ④   11 ②   12 ⑤

13 He feels pleased.   14 ④   15 ⑤

16 walk the dog, stick by you   17 ④

18 ②   19 ⑤

20 Her sister tries to support Rachel.   21 ④

22 ③   23 ④   24 ⑤

25 Minsu helps his brother whenever he has a hard time choosing clothes for a date.

01 가족들과 어떻게 지내는지 묻는 말에 대한 답변이라고 하였으므로 ③번이 가장 적절하다.

02 가족은 각각의 사람들에게 서로 다른 의미를 가질 수 있다고 하였다.

03 내용으로 보아 가족들이 Kamala를 귀찮게 하는 것임을 알 수 있다.

04 Kamala는 결국 가족들을 사랑하게 된다고 하였다.

05 '누군가에게 충성스럽고 어려운 시기에도 그들을 계속해서 지지하다'는 stick by(~을 떠나지 않다, ~의 곁을 지키다)이다.

06 Kamala의 아버지는 그녀에게 그녀의 방을 치우라고 말한다고 하였다.

07 ④번이 이끄는 문장에서 one이 가리키는 것은 주어진 문장의 a

teenager이다.

08 Rachel은 10대가 되는 것이 어떤 것인지를 알기 때문에 전보다 그녀의 언니를 더 잘 이해하게 되었다고 하였다.

09 Whenever는 '~할 때마다'라는 의미로 every time과 같은 의미이다.

10 Rachel이 몇 살인지는 나와 있지 않다.

11 형이 데이트를 위한 옷을 고르는 데 어려움을 겪을 때 돕는다고 하였으므로 fashion이 가장 적절하다.

12 패션 감각이 없는 민수의 형이 데이트를 위한 옷을 고를 때 어려움을 겪으면 민수가 돕는다고 하였다. 민수는 그의 형에게는 없는 자신만의 특별한 능력을 가지고 있다.

13 형이 자신의 도움에 감사해 할 때 민수는 기쁘다고 하였다.

14 (A) 주어가 some of their replies이므로 are (B) '~인지 아닌지'라는 의미가 되어야 하므로 whether (C) end up Ving: 결국 V하게 되다

15 Kamala의 허락 없이 그녀의 언니는 그녀의 방으로 들어온다고 하였다.

16 Kamala의 어머니는 그녀에게 개를 산책시키라고 요청한다. Kamala는 글의 후반부에 그녀의 가족이 계속 자신 곁에 있을 것이라고 하였으므로 stick by you를 쓸 수 있다.

17 가족들이 자신을 성가시게 한다고 하였으므로 'until I get angry at them'이라고 쓰는 것이 적절하다.

18 언니의 기분이 매분마다 바뀜 - [B] 매분마다 바뀌는 기분 설명 - [A] Rachel은 이것을 참기 힘들었지만 이제 그녀 자신이 10대가 되고 언니가 그녀를 지지해 줌 - [C] Rachel은 언니를 더 잘 이해하게 됨.

19 Rachel의 언니는 아직도 10대라고 하였다.

20 Rachel이 화를 낼 때마다 그녀의 언니가 그녀를 지지해 주려고 노력한다고 하였다.

21 위 글의 내용에 따르면 10대가 되는 것의 증상은 잦은 기분 변화이다. symptom: 증상

22 형에 대한 설명을 한 후 완벽한 형을 가진 것이 스트레스라는 말이 이어지고 있으므로 '말할 필요도 없이(Needless to say)'가 가장 적절하다. ④ 말하자면 ⑤ 우선

23 (B)에는 전치사 at이 들어간다. ① turn down: 거절하다 ② consist of: ~으로 구성되다 ③ be responsible for: ~에 책임이 있다 ④ be surprised at: ~에 놀라다 ⑤ from time to time: 때때로, 가끔

24 패션에 대한 안목이 없다는 말이다. 따라서 ⑤번이 가장 적절하다.

25 민수는 형이 데이트를 위한 옷을 고르는 것을 어려워할 때마다 형을 돕는다고 하였다.

01 their families

02 A family is made of love and tears, laughter and years.

03 replies

04 get along with my family members

05 She often asks herself if she gets along with her family members.

06 Her family members have been with her at her worst.

07 a teenager

08 Her mood started changing every minute.

09 They feel greater love toward each other.

10 have become a teenage, lose your temper

11 It's because he is a perfect son at home and a perfect student at school.

12 It is really stressful to have such a shining brother.

13 an eye for fashion

14 Well, in fact, he is not perfect and is poor at one thing that I am great at.

01 Kamala, Rachel, 민수 각자의 가족을 지칭하는 말이다.

02 가족은 사랑과 눈물, 웃음과 세월로 만들어진다고 하였다.

03 누군가에게 대답하거나 편지 혹은 질문에 답할 때 당신이 말하거나 쓰는 어떤 것은 '대답(reply)'이다.

04 자신의 가족들과 잘 지내는 것을 의미한다.

05 그녀는 스스로에게 자신이 가족들과 잘 지내는지를 자신에게 종종 묻는다고 하였다.

06 그녀의 가족은 그녀가 가장 어려울 때 함께 있었다고 하였다.

07 10대를 가리키는 말이다.

08 10대가 되자 Rachel의 언니의 기분이 매분마다 바뀌었다고 하였다.

09 그들은 서로를 알아가게 되면서, 서로를 향해 더 큰 사랑을 느낀다고 하였다.

10 해석: 안녕, Rachel. 이제 네가 10대가 되었구나. 네가 화를 낼 때마다 나는 너를 이해하려고 애쓸 거야.

11 민수의 형은 집에서는 완벽한 아들이고 학교에서는 완벽한 학생이기 때문이다.

12 그렇게 눈부신 형이 있다는 것은 정말 골치 아픈 일이라고 하였다.

13 형과는 다르게, 민수는 패션에 대한 안목이 있다.

14 be great at: ~을 잘하다 관계대명사 that은 전치사 at의 목적어로 쓰인 것이므로 전치사를 생략해서는 안 된다.

01 ⑤	02 they get on my nerves	03 ①
04 ①	05 ④	06 ⑤ 07 opinion
08 ③	09 Yes, I did. → Yes, I have.	10 ①
11 ③	12 ⑤	13 ③ 14 ①
15 ②	16 ③	17 ③ 18 ⑤
19 ⑤	20 ④	

21 He is a perfect son at home and a perfect student at school.

22 He has no eye for fashion.   23 ④

24 ④   25 ③   26 ⑤

27 She comes into Kamala's room without her permission and shouts at her to wake up on Sunday mornings.

28 who   29 ⑤

01 "get+형용사"의 형태가 되어서 보어를 가지는 get은 "~하게 되다"의 의미이다.

03 "혼자 있거나 이야기할 사람이 없어서 불행한"은 '외로운 = lonely'에 해당한다. only 유일한, lunar 음력의, least 가장 적은 possibly 아마도

04 앞에서 자신이 본 최고의 영화라고 했으므로 영화에 대한 긍정적인 언급이 적절하다.

05 (C) 'Have you ~?'에 대한 대답은 have로 해야 하고 (A) 책 내용에 대해 다른 의견을 제시한 다음 (B) 그럴 수도 있다고 인정하는 내용이 이어지는 것이 자연스럽다.

06 대화의 내용으로 보아 빈칸에는 상대의 말에 동의하는 표현이 적절하다. ⑤ '너는 왜 그렇게 생각하니?'의 의미로 이유를 묻는 말이다.

07 '특정한 주제에 대한 생각, 신념'은 '의견, 견해'이다.

08 'We are ~ graders.'를 보면 두 사람이 같은 학년인 것을 알 수 있고, 소녀는 소년의 의견에 대해 동의하고 있다.

09 현재완료로 물었으므로 have를 써서 대답해야 한다.

10 주어진 문장은 현재완료의 경험이다. ① 경험 ② 완료 ③ 계속 ④ 결과 ⑤ 계속

11 먹어 본 아이스크림에 대한 평가가 나오기 전에 들어가는 것이 적절하다.

12 상점이 새로 개업한 것은 나와 있지만 언제 문을 여는지에 대한 언급은 없다.

13 사물을 선행사로 하는 관계대명사의 계속적 용법은 which를 사용한다.

14 ① generous는 사람의 성격을 나타내는 형용사로 의미상 주어의 형태는 「of+목적격」 ②~⑤ difficult, okay, impossible, important는 사람의 성격을 나타내는 형용사가 아니므로 「for+목적격」의 형태로 의미상 주어를 나타낸다.

15 ② that은 계속적 용법으로 사용될 수 없으므로 which로 바꾼다.

16 "too ~ to 너무 ~해서 ~할 수 없다"의 구문에 to부정사의 의미상의 주어 "for+목적격"을 사용하였다.

17 ①, ②, ④ 주격 관계대명사와 ⑤ 계속적 용법의 관계대명사는 생략하지 않는다.

18 주어진 문장은 "It is easy for them to study English."로 네 번째 오는 단어는 for이다.

19 ⑤ 앞 문장 전체를 선행사로 하는 계속적 용법의 관계대명사 which가 정답이다.

20 형은 완벽한 아들임 - [C] 눈부신 형이 있다는 것은 골치 아픈 일이지만, 형도 내가 잘하는 일에는 형편이 없음 - [B] 형은 패션을 보는 눈이 없어서 내가 형을 도와줌 - [A] 형이 나의 도움을 고마워함.

21 형은 집에서는 완벽한 아들이고 학교에서는 완벽한 학생이라고 하였으므로 the golden child라고 했음을 알 수 있다.

22 민수의 형은 패션을 보는 눈이 없다고 하였다.

23 데이트에 입고 갈 옷을 고르는 걸 어려워하는 사람은 민수의 형이다.

24 '~인지 아닌지'를 묻고, 확신하지 못한다는 의미가 가장 자연스럽다. 따라서 whether가 적절하다.

25 요일 앞에는 전치사 on이 쓰인다. get on one's nerve: ~의 신경을 건드리다

26 Kamala는 언니가 허락 없이 방에 들어와서 소리친다고 하였으므로 ⑤번은 위 글에서 찾아볼 수 없다.

27 Kamala의 언니는 일요일 아침에 그녀의 허락도 없이 방으로 들어와 일어나라고 소리친다고 하였다.

28 사람을 선행사로 취하면서 계속적 용법으로 쓰일 수 있는 것은 관계대명사 who이다.

29 나라의 남편과 아이들 셋이 있으므로 가족이 모두 다섯이다.

01 ④	02 ④	03 ②	04 ①
05 ①	06 ①	07 ②	08 ⑤
09 ②	10 ④	11 Well, it could be.	
12 ③	13 ②	14 ③	15 ④
16 ④			

17 Rachel shares her room with her sister.

18 ⑤   19 ③   20 getting   21 ②

22 Kamala is not sure whether she really gets along with her family members.

23 ④

01 언니가 기분이 매 순간 변했다는 설명으로 보아 '화내다 = lose one's temper'가 적절하다 attitude 태도

02 ① 사이좋게 지내다 = get along with ② ~ 없이 = without

③ 함께 쓰다 = share ④ 입학했다 entered ⑤ ~로 이루어져
있다 = be made of

03 "약간 걱정되거나 화나게 하거나 신경 쓰이게 만들다"는 "괴롭히
다, 귀찮게 굴다 = bother"에 해당한다.

04 주어진 단어는 동의어 관계이다. bother 괴롭히다, 귀찮게 굴
다 irritate 짜증나게 하다 difficulty 어려움 trouble 어려움
present 선물 reply 응답 order 주문 permission 허가

05 질문이 '가족에 대해 가장 안 좋은 점'이므로 가족생활에서 만족
스럽지 못한 의견을 나타내는 말이 적절하다.

06 (A) 민수에게 영화에 대하여 질문한 대답이 나와야 하고 (C) 남
호가 부정적인 의견을 말하는 것에 대하여 (B) 나라가 어떻게
그렇게 말할 수 있느냐고 말하는 순서가 자연스러운 배열이다.

07 이어서 가족 구성원을 소개하고 있는 것으로 보아 자기 가족이
대가족이라고 한 것에 대한 보충 설명이 될 수 있는 내용이 적절
하다.

08 선행사를 포함하고 있는 관계대명사 what이 되어야 한다.

09 ② 세호의 가족이 어떤 식당에 갔는지는 알 수 없다.

10 이어지는 내용으로 보아 서로 다른 의견을 표현할 때 어울리는 말
이 들어가는 것이 자연스럽다.

11 약한 가능성의 의미로 could를 사용하여 'it could be a sad
story.'를 줄여서 'it could be'라고 하였다.

12 ① what과 ② that은 계속적 용법으로 사용할 수 없고 ④ 관계
대명사가 수식하는 것이 앞 문장 전체이므로 who는 which로
고친다. ⑤ which는 앞 문장 전체를 수식하는 계속적 용법으로
사용되었기 때문에 앞에 콤마를 붙여야 한다.

13 계속적 용법의 관계대명사로 쓸 수 있는 which가 들어가는 ②
가 정답이다.

14 사람의 성격을 나타내는 형용사 다음에 부정사의 의미상 주어는
'of 목적격'이다.

15 이어지는 글의 내용으로 보아 기분이 매분마다 바뀌기 시작했다는
말이 들어가는 것이 적절하다.

16 빈칸 (B)에는 to부정사의 의미상의 주어를 완성하는 전치사 for
가 들어간다. 모두 for가 쓰이지만 사람의 성질을 나타내는 형용
사 unwise 뒤에는 of가 쓰인다.

17 Rachel이 방을 함께 쓰는 사람은 그녀의 언니이다.

18 (C)는 '차례'라는 의미의 명사로 쓰였다. ① (예상치 못한 방향
으로의) 전환 ② 돌기, 돌리기 ③ (차량의) 방향 전환, 회전 ④
(~한 상태로) 변하다 ⑤ 차례

19 (A) wake up: 깨우다 (C) end up ~ing: 결국 ~하게 되다

20 keep Ving: 계속해서 V하다

21 자신이 힘들 때 가족들이 자신을 지지해 준다는 의미이다.

22 Kamala는 자신이 가족과 잘 지내는지 확신하지 못한다고 하
였다.

23 Kamala는 결국 가족들을 사랑하게 된다고 하였으므로 ④번이
가장 적절하다.

01 Didn't we come in later? → Didn't we come in
   earlier?
02 slow
03 happily
04 (1) (e)nd up loving (2) (p)assing (3) (a)ppreciates
05 (1) I can't find my phone, which happens all the
   time.
   (2) Tom got up late this morning, which made him
   miss the bus.
06 was silly of him to believe such a strange rumor
07 get angry
08 It's because her mom and dad keep asking her
   about her school work.
09 She advises Amie to try to let it go and do her
   work.
10 She would lose her temper over nothing one
   moment and happily read a book or watch a film
   the next.
11 It was difficult for me to put up with her.
12 She tries to support her whenever Rachel loses
   her temper.

01 문맥상 우리가 먼저 왔는데 다른 사람의 음식이 먼저 제공되는
것이 부당하다는 것이 되어야 하므로 later가 아니라 earlier라
고 해야 한다.

02 "The service is so slow. I'm not happy about it."을 보면
소년은 서비스가 느려서 불만이라는 것을 알 수 있다.

03 동사 read를 수식하는 부사가 되어야 한다.

04 (1) 결국 ~하게 되다 = end up -ing (2) 시간의 흐름 = the
passing of time (3) 진가를 인정하다 = appreciate

05 주어진 보기는 계속적 용법의 관계대명사를 이용하고 있다.

06 사람의 성격을 나타내는 silly 다음에는 to부정사의 의미상의 주
어로 'of+목적격'으로 나타낸다.

07 lose one's temper: 화를 내다

08 Amie가 그녀의 엄마와 아빠가 계속 학업에 대해 묻기 때문에 신
경을 거슬르게 한다고 하였다.

09 Ms. Know-It-All은 Amie에게 그냥 내버려두고 자신의 일을
하라고 조언하였다.

10 어느 순간 갑자기 아무것도 아닌 일에 화를 내다가 바로 다음 순
간 즐겁게 책을 읽거나 영화를 보곤 했던 일을 의미한다.

11 가주어 it과 to부정사의 의미상 주어(for+목적격)를 활용하여 문장을 쓸 수 있다.

12 Rachel이 화를 낼 때마다 언니는 그녀를 지지해 주려고 노력한다고 하였다.

|모범답안|

01 build confidence / develop responsibility / learn about a new culture

02 (1) who has always tried hard to teach me English
   (2) who often tells me interesting stories
   (3) who sometimes tells me a joke to wake me up

03 wife, has a warm and loving heart / two kids, are healthy and smart / are the funniest people in the world

01 (1) walk (2) angry (3) at my worst (4) get together
02 ① 03 stressful
04 It's been 30 minutes before we ordered. → It's been 30 minutes since we ordered.
05 ⑤ 06 ④ 07 ②
08 cheap → high 또는 expensive
09 ④ 10 ④ 11 ③ 12 ③
13 ④ 14 ① 15 which was
16 ③
17 It is considerate of you to help me to finish the work.
18 who 19 ⑤ 20 ③
21 She is getting better. 22 ④ 23 ④
24 such a good fashion sense / had a hard time
25 ③

01 (1) 산책시키다 walk (2) 화내다 get angry (3) at my worst 내가 가장 힘들 때 (4) 모이다 get together

02 형이 완벽하지 않아서 한 가지 서투른 점이 있다는 것으로 보아 패션을 보는 안목이 없다는 설명이 되도록 하는 것이 적절하다. have no eye for ~= ~에 대한 안목이 없다

03 be동사의 보어로 stress의 형용사형인 stressful이 되어야 한다.

04 현재완료와 함께 쓰여서 '~한 이래로'의 의미를 나타내는 since가 적절하다.

05 식당에서 음식을 주문하고 기다리는 중에 나중에 온 사람들이 먼저 음식을 받는 것을 보고 보여주는 반응은 '불공평하다'는 것이어야 한다.

06 식당에서 음식을 주문한지 30분이 지난 것은 나와 있지만 주문한 음식의 종류에 대한 언급은 없다.

07 2000명에게 질문을 했고, 절반 이상이 가족, 두 번째로 많은 숫자인 800명 이하가 친구와 있을 때 행복하다고 했다. 약 260명은 혼자 있을 때 행복하다고 했고, 질문은 "With whom are you feel happiest?"이었다.

08 'I was not happy about it.'이라고 하는 것으로 보아 가격이 높아서 불만족스러웠다는 것을 알 수 있다.

09 ①, ③ 소녀는 아직 아이스크림 가게를 가보지 못했다. ② 소년은 그 가게에 다녀왔고 ⑤ 소녀는 아이스크림 가게에 대해서 잘 알지 못한다.

10 긍정적인 의미로 동의한다는 의미의 표현이 적절하다.

11 제시된 문장의 질문 상대가 Minsu이기 때문에 Minsu의 대답 앞에 놓아야 한다.

12 Namho는 Minsu와 반대의 의견을 가지고 있는 것으로 보아 동의한다고 할 수 없다.

13 제시된 문장의 it은 가주어이다. ①, ②, ⑤의 it은 비인칭 주어이고 ③의 it은 인칭대명사이다.

14 ①번에는 관계대명사 who가 들어가고, 나머지에는 모두 which가 들어간다.

15 계속적 용법의 관계대명사 which를 이용하여 영작한다.

16 ⓐ that은 계속적 용법으로 사용될 수 없으므로 which로 고친다. ⓑ who가 수식하는 선행사 a son이 단수이므로 동사도 단수형 lives로 고친다.

17 사람의 성격을 나타내는 형용사 considerate 다음에는 의미상 주어 of you를 쓴다.

18 '접속사+대명사'를 관계대명사의 계속적 용법으로 쓸 수 있다. 사람이 선행사이므로 who를 쓰는 것이 적절하다.

19 글의 흐름상 Rachel 역시 이상한 감정 변화를 겪는다는 의미가 가장 적절하다.

20 Rachel의 언니는 Rachel이 화를 낼 때마다 그녀를 지지해 주려고 노력한다고 하였다.

21 Rachel의 언니는 점점 나아지고 있다고 하였다.

22 형도 완벽하지는 않고 민수에게도 나름의 잘하는 일이 있다는 내용이므로 '굼벵이도 구르는 재주가 있다'는 것이 가장 적절하다. ① 유유상종 ② 집 같은 곳은 없다 (집이 제일 편하다) ③ 뛰기 전에 봐라(신중하게 행동해라) ⑤ 부전자전

23 내가 잘하는 일에 형이 형편없는 것은 패션을 보는 눈이며, 형을 도와주면 형이 고마워한다는 내용이 이어지는 것이 자연스럽다. 따라서 ④번이 적절하다.

24 'such+a+형용사+명사'의 어순에 유의하여 답한다. have a hard time Ving: V하느라 어려움을 겪다

25 golden child: 누구나 좋아하는 사람

Foods from Around the World

시험대비 실력평가   p.60

01 ②	02 ①	03 ②	04 ①
05 arrive	06 ②	07 ②	

01 주어진 단어는 동의어 관계이다. finally: 마침내, eventually: 결국, base: 기초, foundation: 기초

02 "아메리카 원주민 이외에도"라는 뜻으로 "In addition to"가 적절하다.

03 (1) 인기 있는 = popular (2) 믿기 힘들겠지만 = believe it or not (3) "꽃 모양의 = flowery (4) 호의 = goodwill (5) 훨씬 이전 = long before

04 "be made from ~"은 "~로 만들어지다", "come up with"는 "~을 생각해 내다"의 뜻이다.

05 "당신이 가려는 장소에 다다르다"는 arrive(도착하다)이다.

06 the base of this sweet cake에서 base는 기본 재료라는 뜻이다.

07 ② "이 규칙은 아이들뿐만 아니라 부모에게도 적용이 된다."라는 의미의 문장이다. "~뿐만 아니라"의 의미로는 as well as가 적절하다.

서술형 시험대비   p.61

01 inventive
02 arrive
03 (1) freshly (2) seeds (3) as well (4) forward to
04 (d)elicious
05 (s)tatue, (n)oodle, (o)rigin (1) origin (2) noodles
   (3) statue
06 good
07 (1) not only (2) it or not (3) demand (4) ancient

01 "토마스 에디슨은 창의적인 재능이 있었다." 명사를 수식하는 형용사 "inventive"가 적절하다.

02 주어진 단어는 반의어 관계이다. ancient: 고대의, modern: 현대의, arrive: 도착하다, depart: 떠나다

03 (1) 당신은 갓 만들어진 팝콘의 냄새를 좋아하지 않나요? freshly: 갓, 새로이 (2) 옥수수 씨는 불 위의 뜨거워진 돌들 위로 던져졌습니다. seed: 씨앗 (3) 아메리카 원주민들은 또한 장식을

위해 팝콘을 사용했다. as well: 또한, 역시 (4) 저는 신년 전야제 파티를 손꼽아 기다리고 있어요. look forward to: ~을 손꼽아 기다리다

04 tasty: 맛있는(= delicious)

05 단단한 재료로 만든 사람이나 동물의 형상"은 statue(조각상), "밀가루, 물, 달걀의 반죽으로 만든 음식의 긴 가락"은 noodle(국수), "무엇이 존재하기 시작한 장소나 상황"은 origin(기원)이다.

06 be good at: ~을 잘하다

07 (1) ~ 뿐만 아니라 …도 = not only ~ but also (2) 믿건 말건 = believe it or not (3) 수요가 높은 = in high demand (4) 고대의 = ancient

교과서 Conversation

핵심 Check   p.62~63

1 ① 2 ①

01 "How do you like ~?"는 만족 여부를 묻는 말로, "Are you satisfied with ~?"라고 할 수 있다.

02 피자에 만족하는지 묻는 질문에 이어서 피자를 좋아한다는 대답을 듣고 칭찬에 답하는 의미로 "It's nice of you to say so."라고 할 수 있다.

교과서 대화문 익히기

Check(√) True or False   p.64

1 F 2 T 3 T 4 T

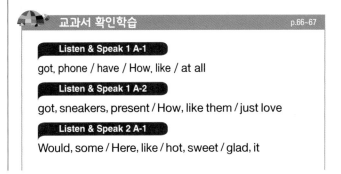

교과서 확인학습   p.66~67

Listen & Speak 1 A-1
got, phone / have / How, like / at all

Listen & Speak 1 A-2
got, sneakers, present / How, like them / just love

Listen & Speak 2 A-1
Would, some / Here, like / hot, sweet / glad, it

Listen & Speak 2 A-2

make, by yourself / looks, wonderful / happy, like

Listen & Speak 2 A-3

How, face / pleased, love

Conversation

Would, like, chocolate / Sure, had, ages / lot, good at / Thanks, glad, By, way, once called, really / enjoyed, emperor, once, the / thanks

Real Life Task Step 1

How, like, What, have, like, cool, Why don't, answer, looking forward, getting

Real Life Task Step 2

What, have, snack / have, apple, like / sounds, like / glad

Check My Progress 1

got, backpack / present / How nice / color / favorite

Check My Progress 2

bake, these, yourself / look, wonderful / try / do / happy

시험대비 기본평가 p.68

01 ④   02 ②
03 Would you like some soup?   04 ③

01 "그것이 마음에 드니?"에 해당하는 만족을 묻는 표현이 적절하다.

02 (B) 선물을 받았다고 말하고 (A) 그것이 마음에 드는지 만족 여부를 묻고 (C) 그것에 만족한다는 대답을 하는 순서가 자연스럽다.

03 상대방에게 음식을 권할 때는 'Would you like (some)+음식?'으로 말할 수 있다. 유사한 표현으로 'Please try some+음식'으로도 말할 수 있다. try 대신에 have를 써도 같은 뜻이다.

04 소년이 수프를 권하고, 그것을 맛본 소녀가 만족해 한다는 내용이다.

시험대비 실력평가 p.69~70

01 ②   02 Because its color is blue.
03 ⑤   04 ⑤   05 ④   06 ③
07 ②   08 I'm glad you like it.   09 ②
10 ③   11 ④   12 ③

01 생일 선물로 backpack을 받았다는 말을 듣고 만족하는지 여부를 묻는 말이 적절하다.

---

02 소년은 배낭의 색깔을 마음에 들어 한다.

03 소년이 그 선물이 처음에 마음에 들지 않았는지 여부는 나와 있지 않다.

04 상대방의 칭찬에 대하여 감사하는 표현이 적절하다.

05 'Would you like+음식?'은 '~ 좀 먹어 보실래요?'라는 뜻의 음식을 권유하는 표현으로 'Would you like to try+음식?'으로도 쓸 수 있다.

06 소년이 직접 만든 케이크를 맛본 소녀가 만족스러움을 나타내고 소년이 칭찬에 대하여 감사하는 내용이다.

07 "How do you like it?"은 만족하는지 여부를 묻는 말로 "Are you happy with it?"에 해당한다.

08 칭찬해 준 사람에게 고맙다고 말하는 표현으로 "I'm glad you like it."을 쓴다.

09 과거에 초콜릿이 신들의 음료라고 불리게 된 것은 초콜릿이 어떻게 사용되기 시작했는지 그 유래와 관련이 있다.

10 Jinho가 구운 쿠키를 Minji에게 권하는 표현이 들어가는 것이 적절하다.

11 상대방이 권하는 음식에 대하여 만족한다는 대답을 하는 것으로 ⓓ가 적절한 위치이다.

12 "How do you like it?"이라고 만족 여부를 묻는 사람은 Minji가 아니고 Jinho이다.

서술형 시험대비 p.71

01 You are very good at making hot chocolate.
02 ordinary people → emperor
03 How nice of her!
04 isn't it
05 answer the questions
06 (s)atisfied

01 "~을 잘하다"는 "be good at"을 사용한다.

02 이어지는 대화에서 "gods' drink"라고 하는 것으로 보아 chocolate이 높은 지위의 사람들에 의해서 사용되었다고 생각할 수 있다.

03 How로 시작하는 감탄문을 쓴다.

04 Your favorite color는 it으로 받는다.

05 이 안내 방송은 학교 점심에 대한 아이디어를 요청하는 방송으로 방송을 듣고 난 후에는 홈페이지를 방문하여 질문에 대답하는 것이다.

06 상대방에게 만족을 묻는 표현은 "How do you like it?" 또는 "Are you satisfied with it?"이다.

Grammar

핵심 Check   p.72~73

1 (1) was Mary that played   (2) It was, that
  (3) in the park

2 (1) exciting   (2) kind   (3) to edit

3 (1) People consider Newton a genius.

01 It is와 that을 사용하여 강조 구문을 만들 때는 강조하려는 내
   용을 it is와 that 사이에 두고, 나머지는 that 뒤에 그대로 쓴다.

02 목적격보어가 될 수 있는 것은 명사, 형용사, to부정사 등이다. 부
   사는 목적격보어로 쓰지 않는다.

03 "주어+동사+목적어+목적격보어"의 구조가 되도록 한다. 목적어
   는 Newton, 목적격보어는 a genius이다.

시험대비 기본평가   p.74

01 ④   02 ②   03 ①
04 it's on May 20 that the school festival will start

01 "think+목적어+형용사/명사"의 구조로 목적격보어가 있는 문
   장이 되어야 한다. 부사 well은 목적격보어가 될 수 없다.

02 ②의 It is ~ that은 가주어-진주어 구문이고, 나머지는 모두 강
   조 구문으로 사용되었다.

03 "think/make+목적어+목적격보어(형용사)"의 구조가 되어야
   한다. 부사는 목적격보어로 쓰이지 않는다. fame 명성

04 질문에서 시간을 나타내는 부분이 게시판의 내용과 다르므로, 시
   간을 나타내는 부사구인 on May 20을 강조하는 문장으로 영작
   한다.

시험대비 실력평가   p.75~77

01 ②   02 ①, ③   03 wonderfully → wonderful
04 ④   05 ⑤   06 ③   07 that
08 ②, ④   09 ③   10 ②   11 ①, ②
12 ②   13 ③   14 ①   15 ⑤
16 ①, ③   17 ②   18 ③

19 People think Nam June Paik a world famous
   video artist.

01 "주어+동사+목적어+목적격보어" 구문에서 목적격보어로 부
   사를 쓸 수 없다. 또 목적어가 능동이면 현재분사를, 목적어가
   수동이면 과거분사를 목적격보어로 쓴다. ① beautifully →
   beautiful ③ sadly → sad ④ kindly → kind ⑤ exciting
   → excited

02 강조하고자 하는 Tom을 It과 that 사이에 써서 강조하는데, 사람
   을 강조할 때는 that 대신 who를 쓸 수 있다.

03 "think+목적어+목적격보어(형용사)" 구조로 "~을 …하다고
   생각하다"의 의미이다.

04 주어진 문장과 ④의 that은 강조 구문의 that이다. ①, ③ 목
   적어 역할을 하는 접속사 that ② 지시형용사 that ⑤ 형용사
   easy를 수식하는 지시부사 that이다.

05 "It ~ that" 강조구문에서 사람을 강조할 때는 that이나 who, 사
   물은 that이나 which, 장소는 where를 쓴다.

06 "think/make/keep+목적어+목적격보어(형용사)" 구조이다.
   ① → keep the classroom clean ② → think the city very
   quiet ④ → made my mother angry ⑤ → makes me
   happy

07 주어진 문장들은 모두 "It ~ that 강조 구문"으로 빈칸에는 that이
   들어가야 한다.

08 ② It was in this park that I met him last year. ④ It
   was in 2014 that we met him for the first time.이 올바
   르게 영작한 표현이다.

09 ③은 "주어+동사+간접목적어+직접목적어"이고, 나머지는 모
   두 "주어+동사+목적어+목적격보어"의 구조이다.

10 "주어+동사+목적어+목적격보어"의 구조이다. ① very well →
   very good ③ sadly → sad ④ crying → cry ⑤ interested
   → interesting

11 목적어인 Nara를 강조하는 표현으로 It과 that 사이에 Nara를 써
   주고 that 이하의 문장에서 목적어인 Nara는 생략시킨다. that은
   Nara가 사람이기 때문에 whom으로 바꿔 쓸 수 있다.

12 "주어+동사+목적어+목적격보어"의 구조로 목적격보어는 a
   great writer이다.

13 '시험 결과'를 강조하는 문장으로 It과 that 사이에 the test
   result를 넣어 영작한 문장이 정답이다.

14 ② 시제가 과거이므로 does는 did로, ③ whom은 which나
   that으로, ④ when은 that으로, ⑤ where는 that으로 고쳐야
   한다.

15 "주어+동사+목적어+목적격보어"의 구조로 ⑤ smartly는 형용
   사 smart가 되어야 한다.

16 ① It was Jack whom I met yesterday.와 같이 주어를 넣어
   서 문장을 써줘야 올바르다. ③ 목적어인 the song이 강조되고
   있는 문장이므로 that절의 목적어인 it은 삭제해야 한다.

17 "think+목적어+목적격보어(명사구)", "make+목적어+목적보
   어(동사원형)"의 구조이다.

18 ③의 that은 동사 know의 목적어를 이끄는 접속사로 사용되었
   고, 나머지는 모두 "It ~ that 강조 구문"의 that이다.

19 "주어+동사+목적어+목적격보어"의 구조가 되도록 한다.

13

01 Kevin called me Angel.

02 I consider Paris beautiful.

03 to be honest

04 thought popcorn a symbol of good health and goodwill

05 My friends call me a couch potato.

06 It was in the park that I lost my wallet.

07 (1) the boy band that will visit our school in May

(2) in the park that the third graders take pictures

(3) on April 30 that the midterm exams will start

08 (1) It was John that[who] slept all day long.

(2) It was this novel that[which] Jane wrote in 2015.

09 (1) I think old movies boring.

(2) We believe baseball games (to be) exciting.

10 beautiful flowers that made

11 (1) think this work too difficult

(2) think a rainbow a symbol of hope

12 (1) was Robert that[who] broke the window

(2) was at the Jay's shop that I bought this sweater

13 It was the graduation ceremony that was held last Friday.

02 주어진 문장은 모두 "주어+동사+목적어+목적격보어"의 구조가 되도록 하여야 한다.

03 want의 목적격보어는 to부정사가 되도록 한다.

04 "~을 …라고 생각하다"는 "think+목적어+목적격보어(명사)"의 구조이다.

05 "~을 …라고 부르다"는 "call+목적어+목적격보어(명사)"의 구조이다.

06 주어진 대답에서 장소 부사구 in the park를 It was와 that 사이에 써서 강조구문을 만든다.

07 (1) 주어인 The boy band가, (2) 장소의 부사구인 in the park가, (3) 때의 부사구인 on April 30가 강조되는 문장이다.

08 (1) 주어인 John을 강조하기 위해 It과 that 사이에 넣어 강조하고, (2) 목적어인 this novel을 강조하기 위해 It과 that 사이에 넣어 강조시킨다.

09 "~을 …하다고 생각하다 / 믿다"는 "think+목적어+목적격보어(형용사)의 구조이다.

10 beautiful flowers를 It과 that 사이에 넣어 강조하는 문장으로 완성한다.

11 "~을 …라고 생각하다"의 의미를 "think+목적어+목적격보어(명사, 형용사)"의 구조로 나타낸다.

12 (1) 강조하려는 Robert를 It was와 that 사이에 넣어 강조한다. (2) 강조하려는 at the Jay's shop을 It was와 that 사이에

넣어 강조한다.

13 주어인 the graduation ceremony를 It was와 that 사이에 넣어서 강조한다.

Reading

1 F 2 T 3 F 4 T

1 F 2 T 3 F

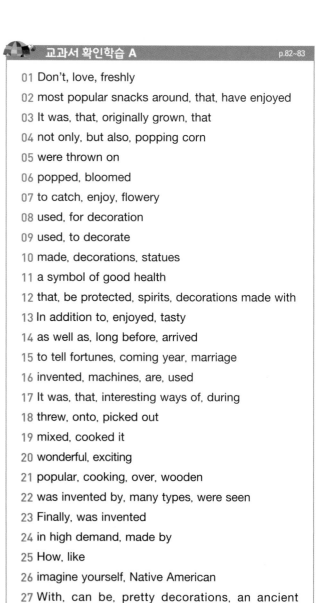

01 Don't, love, freshly

02 most popular snacks around, that, have enjoyed

03 It was, that, originally grown, that

04 not only, but also, popping corn

05 were thrown on

06 popped, bloomed

07 to catch, enjoy, flowery

08 used, for decoration

09 used, to decorate

10 made, decorations, statues

11 a symbol of good health

12 that, be protected, spirits, decorations made with

13 In addition to, enjoyed, tasty

14 as well as, long before, arrived

15 to tell fortunes, coming year, marriage

16 invented, machines, are, used

17 It was, that, interesting ways of, during

18 threw, onto, picked out

19 mixed, cooked it

20 wonderful, exciting

21 popular, cooking, over, wooden

22 was invented by, many types, were seen

23 Finally, was invented

24 in high demand, made by

25 How, like

26 imagine yourself, Native American

27 With, can be, pretty decorations, an ancient Chinese, fortunes

28 why don't you, come up with

1 Pop! Pop! Pop! Don't you love the smell of freshly made popcorn?

2 It is one of the most popular snacks around the world, and historians believe that people have enjoyed it for more than 5,000 years.

3 It was in Central America that corn was originally grown, and it was in caves in New Mexico that the first popcorn was found.

4 Native Americans not only loved eating corn but also enjoyed the game of popping corn.

5 Corn seeds were thrown on hot stones over a fire.

6 Then they popped and bloomed into white flowers.

7 The game was to catch and enjoy the flowery snacks.

8 Native Americans used popcorn for decoration as well.

9 Their teenage girls used popped corn to decorate clothes.

10 The Aztecs made corn decorations for the statues of the god of rain.

11 They thought popcorn a symbol of good health and goodwill.

12 They believed that they would be protected by popping spirits when they wore decorations made with popped corn.

13 In addition to Native Americans, many other people around the world enjoyed this tasty snack.

14 The Chinese, as well as people in Sumatra and India, made popcorn long before Columbus arrived in the West Indies.

15 In ancient China, people popped corn to tell fortunes for the coming year and their daughters' future marriage.

16 In the Song Dynasty, Chinese people invented large pot-shaped popping machines to pop corn, and these machines are still used by street poppers today.

17 It was Americans that tried interesting ways of popping corn during the nineteenth century.

18 Some threw corn seeds onto hot ashes, stirred, and then picked out the popped corn pieces.

19 Others mixed corn with fat or butter and cooked it in a pan..

20 They thought popping corn wonderful and exciting.

21 A more popular way was cooking popcorn over an open fire in a wire box with a long wooden handle.

22 The fanciest popcorn popper was invented by Charles Cretors in 1893, and before long many types of interesting poppers were seen in movie theaters and parks.

23 Finally, an electric popcorn popper for the home was invented in 1925.

24 Believe it or not, poppers were in high demand and were even made by middle school students in school clubs.

25 How do you like your popcorn? Sweet, hot, or spicy?

26 Next time you enjoy popcorn, imagine yourself as a Native American, an ancient Chinese person, or an inventor.

27 With a bowl of popcorn, you can be a Native American and make pretty decorations or be an ancient Chinese person and tell fortunes.

28 Or better still, why don't you be an inventor and come up with a new popper for your favorite popcorn?

01 popcorn   02 ④   03 ③   04 ③

05 The Aztecs made corn decorations for the statues of the god of rain.

06 statue   07 popcorn   08 ④

09 They were invented in China in the Song Dynasty.

10 ②   11 was invented   12 ③

13 They made poppers in school clubs.   14 ④

15 I can make pretty decorations.   16 ⑤

17 It was found in caves in New Mexico.

18 [C]-[B]-[A]   19 ⑤   20 flowers

21 ⑤   22 It looked like a pot.   23 ⑤

24 threw away → picked out   25 ②

01 팝콘을 가리키는 말이다.

02 최초의 팝콘이 언제 발견되었는지는 나와 있지 않다.

03 주어진 문장은 아메리카 원주민들이 팝콘을 장식을 위해서도 사용했다는 의미이다. 따라서 튀겨진 옥수수로 옷을 장식했다는 문장 앞인 ③번이 적절하다.

04 아메리카 원주민들이 오직 옥수수 먹기를 즐겼다는 말은 없고, 옥수수 씨는 불 위의 뜨거운 돌들 위에서 튀겨졌다. 아메리카 원주민 소녀들은 튀겨진 옥수수를 옷을 장식하는 데 사용했으며,

아즈텍족 사람들은 팝콘 장식을 한 것이 아니라 비의 신 조각상에 옥수수 장식을 했다. 아즈텍족 사람들은 불쑥 나타나는 정령을 보호한 것이 아니라, 정령의 보호를 받은 것이라고 믿었다.

05 아즈텍족 사람들은 비의 신 조각상을 위해 옥수수 장식품을 만들었다.

06 '돌이나 금속으로 만들어진 사람 혹은 동물의 큰 조각'은 '조각상(statue)'이다.

07 글의 내용으로 보아 (A)는 팝콘을 의미한다.

08 '점치기 위해서'라는 의미의 to부정사가 쓰이는 것이 적절하다.

09 팝콘 튀기는 기계는 중국의 송나라 왕조 때 발명되었다.

10 이어지는 글의 내용은 '옥수수를 튀기는 흥미로운 방법'이다. 따라서 ②번이 가장 적절하다.

11 Charles Cretors에 의해 팝콘 기계가 발명된 것으로 수동태(be동사+과거분사)를 쓴다.

12 철사 상자에는 긴 나무 손잡이가 있었다고 하였다.

13 중학교 학생들은 학교 동아리에서 팝콘 기계를 만들었다고 하였다.

14 빈칸 (A)에는 전치사 with가 들어간다. come up with: ~을 생각해 내다 ① pay attention to: ~에 주의를 기울이다 ② take care of: ~을 돌보다 ③ listen to: ~을 듣다 ④ deal with: ~을 다루다, 처리하다 ⑤ work out: 운동하다

15 한 그릇의 팝콘으로 아메리카 원주민이 되어 예쁜 장식을 만들 수 있다고 하였다.

16 모두 팝콘을 의미하지만 ⑤번은 It ~ that 강조구문의 It이다.

17 최초의 팝콘이 발견된 곳은 뉴멕시코의 동굴 안이었다.

18 [C] 뜨거운 돌들 위에 던져진 옥수수가 하얀 꽃 모양으로 피어나고 - [B] 이 꽃 모양의 간식을 잡아서 즐기는 것이 아메리카 원주민들이 즐긴 게임이고 이외에도 장식을 위해 팝콘을 사용했다고 언급하고, - [A] 장식으로 사용한 예가 이어지는 것이 자연스러운 흐름이다.

19 아즈텍족 사람들이 생계를 위하여 무엇을 했는지는 위 글을 읽고 알 수 없다.

20 해석: 불 위의 뜨거워진 돌들 위로 던져진 옥수수 씨는 꽃 같은 모양으로 변했다.

21 고대 중국에서, 사람들은 다음 해와 딸들의 장래 혼사를 점치기 위해 옥수수를 펑 소리를 내며 튀겼다고 하였다.

22 송나라 왕조에서 발명한 팝콘 튀기는 기계는 항아리 모양이라고 하였다.

23 Charles Cretors가 언제 태어났는지는 위 글을 읽고 답할 수 없다.

24 펑 터져 나온 옥수수 알갱이들을 버린 것이 아니라 집어냈다고 하였다.

25 in high demand는 '수요가 많은'이라는 의미이다.

---

01 freshly made popcorn

02 People have enjoyed popcorn for more than 5,000 years.

03 Corn was originally grown in Central America.

04 the game of popping corn, eating corn

05 They popped and bloomed into white flowers.

06 They used popped corn in order to decorate clothes.

07 It was corn decorations that the Aztecs made for the statues of the god of rain.

08 They popped corn to tell fortunes for the coming year and their daughters' future marriage.

09 long after → long before, since ancient times → since the Song Dynasty

10 Americans tried interesting ways of popping corn during the nineteenth century.

11 They stirred and picked out the popped corn pieces.

12 It had a long wooden handle.

13 It was Charles Cretors that invented the fanciest popcorn popper.

14 1925

---

01 '만들어진'이라고 하였으므로 make(만들다)의 과거분사로 popcorn을 수식하도록 만든다. freshly: 갓 ~한

02 사람들은 5천년 이상 팝콘을 즐겨왔다고 하였다.

03 옥수수가 본래 재배된 곳은 중앙 아메리카였다.

04 not only A but also B = B as well as A: A 뿐만 아니라 B도

05 뜨거운 돌들 위로 던져진 옥수수 씨는 펑 소리를 내며 튀겨지고 하얀 꽃 모양으로 피어났다고 하였다.

06 10대 소녀들은 튀겨진 옥수수를 옷을 장식하는 데 사용했다고 하였다.

07 아즈텍족 사람들이 비의 신의 조각상을 위해 만든 것은 옥수수 장식품이었다.

08 중국인들은 다음 해와 그들의 딸들의 장래 혼사를 점치기 위해 옥수수를 펑 소리를 내며 튀겼다.

09 콜럼버스가 서인도 제도에 도착하기 훨씬 이전에 중국인들은 팝콘을 만들었고, 커다란 항아리 모양의 팝콘 튀기는 기계는 송나라 왕조 때 발명된 것이다.

10 19세기 동안 옥수수를 튀기는 흥미로운 방법들을 시도해 본 것은 미국인들이었다.

11 뜨거운 잿더미 위로 옥수수 씨를 던진 후 뒤섞은 다음 펑 터져 나온 옥수수 알갱이들을 집어냈다.

12 철사 상자는 긴 나무 손잡이가 있다고 하였다.

13 가장 멋진 팝콘 튀기는 기계를 발명한 사람은 Charles Cretors 였다.

14 1925년이 되어서야 비로소 사람들은 마침내 가정용 전기 팝콘 기계를 사용할 수 있었다. not until A that B: A하고 나서야 비로소 B하다

01 ③	02 ②	03 ⑤	04 (r)oot
05 ③	06 ⑤	07 ②	08 ④

09 ⑤   **10** By the way, did you know that chocolate was once called the "drink of the gods?"

11 ②   **12** ③

13 We think Jang Yeong-sil a great scientist during the Chosun Dynasty.   **14** ②, ④

15 ①	16 ④	17 ④	18 ⑤

19 It is Hana that speaks French very well.

20 ①, ③	21 ④	22 ②

23 decorations

24 Native Americans threw corn seeds on hot stones over a fire.

25 ②	26 ④	27 ④	28 ⑤

29 ⑤   **30** the fanciest popcorn popper was invented by Charles Cretors in 1893

01 "특정 가문이 한 나라를 재배한 시기"는 dynasty(왕조)이다.

02 be mixed with: ~와 섞이다, be served with: ~와 함께 제 공되다.

03 ① take care of: 돌보다 ② look up to: 존경하다 ③ get used to: 익숙해지다 ④ pay attention to: 주의를 기울이다 ⑤ look forward to: 기대하다

04 origin (기원)과 동의어는 root (근원)이다.

05 "How do you like it?"은 만족하는지를 묻는 말이다.

06 "Yes, I have."에 이어지는 설명을 보면 새로 가진 가방에 대하 여 물어보는 것을 알 수 있다. "have got"은 "가지다"의 의미이 다.

07 "소년이 어떻게 backpack을 가지게 되었는가?"에 대한 대답은 "어머니의 생일 선물"이라는 말에서 알 수 있다.

08 소년은 backpack의 색상이 마음에 든다고 했고, 이어지 는 소녀의 말(Your favorite color is blue, isn't it?)에서 backpack이 파란색임을 알 수 있다.

09 "너 핫 초콜릿을 만드는 재주가 정말 좋구나."의 의미로 상대방을 칭찬하는 말이 적절하다.

10 그런데 = by the way, 한때 ~라고 불렸다 = was once called

12 (B) 무엇을 읽고 있는지 묻는 말에 대답하고, (C) 그것이 마음

에 드는지 묻고, (A) 만족감을 표시하는 순서가 자연스럽다.

13 "~을 …라고 생각하다"는 "think+목적어+목적격보어"의 구조 로 나타낸다. 목적어는 Jang Yeong-sil, 목적격보어는 a great scientist이다.

14 ② 목적격보어는 형용사 sad가 되어야 한다. ④ she는 목적격 her로 써야 한다.

15 ①번은 It이 가주어이고 that 이하가 진주어인 구문이고, 나머 지는 모두 "It ~ that" 강조 구문이다.

16 ④ in December를 It과 that 사이에 쓴다.

17 ① telling → to tell ② 동사 broke 앞에 주어 필요 ③ to use → use ⑤ to clean → clean

18 동사 want는 목적격보어로 to부정사가 쓰인다.

19 It과 that 사이에 강조할 어구인 Hana를 넣어준다.

20 주어진 문장과 ①, ③의 that은 강조 구문의 that이다. ② 진주 어로 사용된 that ④ "so ~ that" 구문으로 사용된 that ⑤ 접속 사로 사용된 that

21 빈칸 뒤에 이어지는 내용에서 팝콘으로 옷을 장식 했다고 했으 므로 ④번이 가장 적절하다.

22 ②번에 이어지고 있는 the flowery snacks는 주어진 문장의 '튀겨지고 하얀 꽃 모양으로 피어난' 팝콘을 가리키는 말이다.

23 '더 매력적으로 보이기 위해 어떠한 것에 추가되는 특징'은 '장식 (decoration)'이다.

24 아메리카 원주민들은 옥수수 씨를 불 위의 뜨거운 돌들 위로 던 졌다.

25 세계에서 가장 인기 있는 간식이 무엇인지는 위 글을 읽고 답할 수 없다. 팝콘은 전 세계에서 가장 인기 있는 간식 중 하나일 뿐, 이것이 가장 인기 있는 간식이라는 의미가 아니다.

26 밑줄 친 (A)는 to부정사의 부사적 용법 중 '~하기 위해서'라는 의미의 '목적'을 나타내는 용도로 쓰이고 있다. ① to부정사의 명사적 용법(진주어) ② 명사적 용법 (진주어) ③ 명사적 용법 (목적어) ④ 부사적 용법 중 목적 ⑤ 부사적 용법 중 감정의 원 인

27 고대 중국인들은 팝콘을 사용하여 운을 점쳤다고 하였다.

28 "가정용 전기 팝콘 기계가 발명되었다"는 수동의 의미이고 주어 가 an electric popcorn popper로 단수이므로 was invented 가 적절하다.

29 중학교 학생들은 학교 동아리에서 팝콘 기계를 만들었다고 하였 다.

30 Charles Cretors가 1893년 가장 멋진 팝콘 튀기는 기계를 발 명하고 오래지 않아 많은 종류의 흥미로운 팝콘 만드는 기계들이 나왔다.

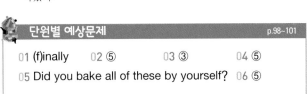

01 (f)inally	02 ⑤	03 ③	04 ⑤

05 Did you bake all of these by yourself?   **06** ⑤

07 ③　　　08 ④　　　09 ①　　　10 ①

11 It was for 20 hours that he worked without rest.

12 ②, ④　　　13 ①

14 was Hana that I met yesterday　　　15 ③

16 ③　　　17 ③　　　18 stir

19 A more popular way was cooking popcorn over an open fire in a wire box with a long wooden handle.　20 ④　　　21 ②

22 With a bowl of popcorn, we can be an ancient Chinese person and tell fortunes.

01 주어진 단어는 동의어 관계이다. freshly 갓 ~한, 새롭게 – newly 새롭게 finally 마침내, 결국 – eventually 결국

02 be interested in; ~에 관심이 있다 come up with: ~을 생각해 내다

03 "머지않아, 오래되지 않아서"는 before long이다.

04 (1) 저는 신년 전야제 파티를 손꼽아 기다리고 있어요. look forward to: 기대하다 (2) 중국인들은 콜럼버스가 서인도 제도에 도착하기 훨씬 이전에 팝콘을 만들었습니다. long before 훨씬 이전에 (3) 그는 어려운 수학 문제 푸는 것을 잘한다. be good at 잘하다 (4) 매일 아침 직장에 정각에 도착해야 함을 명심하라. arrive: 도착하다 (5) 중국 사람들은 옥수수를 튀기기 위해 커다란 항아리 모양의 팝콘 튀기는 기계를 발명하였다. invented: 발명했다

05 ~을 네가 직접 구웠니? = Did you bake ~ by yourself?

06 음식을 권하는 의미로 "Would you like to try ~?" 또는 "Would you like ~?"가 적절하다.

07 "I just love this."를 보면 소녀는 케이크가 만족스럽게 여기는 것을 알 수 있다.

08 (C) 상대방의 질문에 대한 대답을 하고 (A) 재료가 무엇인지를 질문하고, (B) 무엇으로 만들어졌는지 설명하는 순서가 자연스럽다.

09 ① It ~ that 강조 구문인데, the boat는 propose를 한 장소이므로 장소 부사구 on the boat를 써서 It was on the boat that he proposed to Mary.로 해야 어법상 적절하다.

10 주어진 문장과 선택지 ②~⑤는 강조 구문이고, ①번 문장에서는 날씨를 나타내는 비인칭 주어 It 다음에 so ~ that(~해서 …하다) 구문이 이어지고 있다.

11 for 20 hours를 It과 that 사이에 써서 강조 구문을 만든다.

12 ①, ⑤ 목적격보어로 형용사가 적절하다. ① greatly → great, ⑤ sadly→sad. ③ 사역동사(make)가 쓰였으므로 목적격보어로 동사원형이 적절하다. felt→feel.

13 ⓐ consider의 목적격보어로 형용사 kind가 적절하다. ⓑ think의 목적격보어로 a good teacher가 적절하다.

14 목적어 Hana를 It과 that 사이에 넣어 강조 구문을 만든다.

15 위 글은 팝콘의 역사를 간략하게 소개하고 있다. 따라서 ③번이 가장 적절하다.

16 모두 팝콘을 지칭하지만 ③번은 It ~ that 강조 구문의 It이다.

17 in high demand: 수요가 많은

18 '수저 같은 것을 사용하여 용기 안에서 어떤 것을 섞다'는 stir(젓다, 섞다)이다.

19 보다 인기 있는 방법은 팝콘을 긴 나무 손잡이가 있는 철사 상자 안에 넣어 덮개가 없는 불 위에서 요리하는 방법이었다.

20 17세기가 아닌 19세기 동안에 옥수수를 튀기는 흥미로운 방법들이 많이 있었다.

21 명령문의 생략된 주어인 you와 목적어가 같으므로 목적어로 재귀대명사 yourself를 쓰는 것이 적절하다.

22 한 그릇의 팝콘으로 고대 중국인이 되어 운세를 점쳐 볼 수 있다고 하였다.

서술형 실전문제
p.102~103

01 (c)ome (u)p (w)ith
02 marriage
03 How do you like my idea?
04 (p)leased
05 We consider Mozart a great musician.
06 (1) It was some food that Hana bought on her way home.
　(2) It was on her way home that Hana bought some food.
07 It was interesting ways of enjoying popcorn that Native Americans tried.
08 people in China / Americans
09 It was in New Mexico that the snack was first found
10 They thought popping corn wonderful and exciting.
11 After 1893, popcorn poppers started to be seen in movie theaters and parks.
12 An electric popcorn popper for the home was invented in 1925.

01 '~을 생각해 내다'는 'come up with'이다.

02 주어진 단어는 동사-명사의 관계이다. invent(발명하다)-invention(발명), marry(결혼하다)-marriage(결혼)

03 "~는 어떠니?"라고 만족하는지 묻는 것은 How do you like ~?이다.

04 "I'm glad you love/like ~."는 "I'm pleased/happy you

18 정답 및 해설

05 "~을 ~라고 여기다"는 "consider+목적어+목적격보어"이다.

06 It ~ that 강조 구문을 사용하여 강조할 때는, 강조하려는 어구를 It과 that 사이에 넣어 영작한다.

07 아메리카 원주민들이 시도한 것은 팝콘을 즐기기 위한 흥미로운 방법이라고 하였다.

08 not only A but also B = B as well as A: A 뿐만 아니라 B도

09 강조 구문을 사용하기 전 문장을 써 보면 'The snack was first found in New Mexico'이다. 따라서 강조 구문 사이에 in New Mexico라고 쓰는 것이 적절하다.

10 "think+목적어+목적격보어"의 구조로 된 문장이다. '옥수수를 튀기는 것'이 목적어이므로 popping corn이라고 쓰고 목적격보어가 '멋지고 재미있는'이므로 'wonderful and exciting'이라고 쓴다.

11 Charles Cretors가 가장 멋진 팝콘 튀기는 기계를 발명한 해는 1893년이었고, 오래지 않아 많은 종류의 흥미로운 팝콘 만드는 기계들이 영화관이나 공원에서 보이게 되었다.

12 가정용 전기 팝콘 기계는 1925년에 발명되었다.

창의사고력 서술형 문제
p.104

|모범답안|

01 (1) It was Jake that threw a stone at my dog in the park yesterday.

(2) It was a stone that Jake threw at my dog in the park yesterday.

(3) It was in the park that Jake threw a stone at my dog yesterday.

(4) It was yesterday that Jake threw a stone at my dog in the park.

02 The pretzel, for more than 1,600 years / in Italy, people in Germany, tried interesting ways of enjoying it / in Germany, Americans as well as people in Europe have enjoyed making it

단원별 모의고사
p.105~108

01 ④   02 (1) (b)owl (2) (c)ave (3) (d)ynasty
   (4) (g)oodwill   03 marriage
04 ②   05 ②, ④   06 ④   07 ③
08 (A) Would you like some hot chocolate
   (B) I'm glad you like it.
09 ⑤   10 ⑤   11 ②   12 ③
13 We're looking forward to getting your answers.
14 ⑤   15 ③   16 ④

17 (1) at the bus stop that Hana met Nara
   (2) in 1492 that Columbus discovered America
18 (A) popping   (B) popped   19 ③
20 Native Americans loved eating corn.
   They enjoyed the game of popping corn.
   They used popcorn for decoration.
21 It was the Aztecs that made corn decorations for the statues of the god of rain.   22 ④
23 ④
24 They were invented in the Song Dynasty.
25 ④

01 ancient(고대의) – modern(현대의) goodwill(친선, 호의) – hostility(적개심)

02 (1) "위가 열린 넓고 둥근 그릇"은 bowl(우묵한 그릇, 사발) (2) "절벽 옆구리에 나 있는 자연적인 구멍"은 cave(동굴) (3) "한 가문이 나라를 지배한 시기"는 dynasty(왕조) (4) "사람들을 향한 친절한 감정"은 goodwill(친선, 호의)을 나타낸다.

03 marry의 명사형 marriage가 되어야 한다.

04 만족하는지를 물어볼 때는 "How do you like ~?을 쓰고 형용사와 함께 감탄문을 만들 때는 "How+형용사(+주어+동사)!"를 쓴다.

05 음식을 권할 때는 "Would you like to try ~?," "Would you like ~?," "Please try some ~." 등으로 나타낸다.

06 상대방이 만족하는지 묻는 말은 "How do you like it?"이다.

07 민지는 "It's so sweet. I just love it."이라고 하는 것으로 보아 cookie가 달콤해서 좋다는 의미로 말한다. "too sweet"는 지나치게 달아서 좋지 않다는 의미가 된다.

08 음식을 권하는 표현은 "Would you like+음식?"이다. 상대방이 만족할 때는 "I'm glad you like it."이라고 말한다.

09 주어진 문장은 초콜릿의 기원에 관한 설명을 듣고 보이는 반응으로 초콜릿의 기원에 대한 설명 다음에 이어지는 것이 적절하다.

10 Nara는 hot chocolate을 잘 만든다는 것을 알 수 있지만, 왜 만들었는지에 대한 언급은 없다.

11 (A) 만족하는지 물어볼 때는 "How do you like ~?", (B) 원하는 것이 무엇인지 물어볼 때는 "What would you like to have ~?", (C) 권하거나 제안할 때는 "Why don't you ~?"를 쓴다.

12 "Why don't you visit www.mslunch.ms.kr and answer the questions about your school lunch?"에서 이 방송을 들은 학생들이 무엇을 할지 알 수 있다.

13 "우리는 ~을 고대합니다.는 We're looking forward to, "여러분의 응답을 고대하다"는 look forward to getting your

answers이다.

14 ⑤는 It이 가주어, that절이 진주어이고, 나머지는 모두 It ~, that 강조 구문이다.

15 believe의 목적격보어는 형용사가 되어야 하므로 honest라고 해야 한다.

16 "~을 …라고 믿다"는 "believe+목적어+목적격보어"이다. believe의 목적격보어 (명사, 형용사) 앞에는 to be를 쓰거나 생략할 수 있다.

17 'It ~ that' 강조 구문에서 주어, 목적어, 부사구 등을 강조할 때, 강조하려는 표현을 It과 that 사이에 넣어서 문장을 쓴다.

18 (A)에는 '불쑥 나타나는 정령'이라는 능동의 의미로 현재분사 popping을 쓰는 것이 적절하며, (B)에는 '튀겨진 옥수수로 만들어진 장식'이라는 수동의 의미이므로 과거분사 popped가 적절하다.

19 주어진 문장의 the flowery snacks는 불 위의 뜨거워진 돌들 위에서 펑 소리를 내며 튀겨져 하얀 꽃 모양으로 피어난 팝콘을 의미하므로 ③번이 적절하다.

20 아메리카 원주민들은 옥수수를 먹는 것을 좋아했을 뿐만 아니라 옥수수씨를 튀기는 게임을 즐겼고, 튀겨진 옥수수를 옷을 장식하는 데 사용했다.

21 비의 신 조각상을 위해 옥수수 장식품을 만든 것은 아즈텍족 사람들이다.

22 팝콘은 아즈텍족 사람들에게는 건강과 선의의 상징이었다.

23 (A)는 '운'이라는 의미로 쓰였다. 따라서 ④번이 가장 적절하다.
① 가난 ② 부 ③ 재산 ⑤ 수단

24 커다란 항아리 모양의 팝콘 튀기는 기계는 송나라 왕조 때 발명되었다.

25 고대 중국인들이 옥수수를 튀긴 이유는 다음 해와 그들의 딸들의 장래 혼사를 점치기 위해서였다.

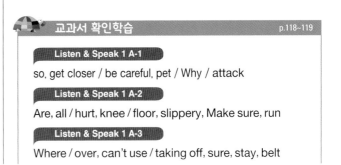

Lesson **3**

What Makes Us Shop?

시험대비 실력평가   p.112

01 ⑤   02 ④   03 ④   04 ③

05 ①   06 ③   07 ③

01 "버리다"의 의미로 "throw away", "진정하다"의 의미로 "cool off"가 적절하다.

02 주어진 단어는 동의어 관계이다. celebrity 유명한 사람 star 유명한 사람 collect 수집하다 – gather 모으다

03 (1) 유명 인사 = celebrities (2) 시도해 보다 = give it a try (3) 이륙하다 = take off (4) carry ~ around = ~을 들고 다니다 (5) featuring = 특징으로 삼는

04 "기꺼이 ~하려고 하다"의 의미에 해당하는 "be willing to"가 적절하다.

05 "instead"는 "대신, 대신에"의 의미이다.

06 "어떤 사람을 다치게 하거나 어떤 장소에 손상을 가하기 위하여 의도적으로 폭력을 사용하다"는 "attack 공격하다"에 해당한다.

07 ③ "get away from"은 "멀리하다"의 의미로 귀여운 것을 보았을 때 "가까이 가보다"의 의미에 해당하는 "get closer to"가 적절하다.

서술형 시험대비   p.113

01 incredibly

02 attack

03 (1) give (2) suffer (3) hot cakes (4) high-end

04 (a)llowance

05 (a)ttack, (b)rand-new, (c)elebrity

    (1) celebrity (2) attack (3) brand-new

06 down

07 (1) carry around (2) stick to (3) consumer

    (4) out for

01 "목록에 있는 것을 찾을 수 없다면, 빈손으로 걸어 나오세요. 믿을 수 없을 정도로 경쾌한 기분을 느끼게 될 거예요."라는 뜻으로 형용사 light를 수식하는 부사 incredibly가 적절하다.

02 주어진 단어는 반의어 관계이다. include 포함하다, exclude 제외하다, attack 공격하다, defend 방어하다

03 (1) give up 포기하다 (2) suffer from ~을 겪다 (3) sell like hot cakes 날개 돋친 듯이 팔리다 (4) high-end 명품의

04 "pocket money"는 "용돈"이라는 뜻으로 "allowance"에 해당한다.

05 "손상을 주기 위해 의도적으로 폭력을 사용하다"는 "attack 공격하다", "새것이고 아직 사용되지 않은"은 "brand-new 신상품", "살아 있는 유명한 사람"은 "celebrity 유명한 사람"에 해당한다.

06 "진정해! 다음에 잘하면 되잖아." calm down 진정하다, "그는 기록을 1시간 5분으로 단축했다" cut down 단축하다

07 (1) 들고 다니다 = carry around (2) 고수하다 = stick to (3) 소비자 = consumer (4) 주의하다 = look out for

교과서
Conversation

핵심 Check   p.114~115

1 Make sure you don't run. **2** ⑤

01 경고하는 의미로 make, don't, run을 포함한 표현은 "Make sure you don't run."이다.

02 ⑤는 "그것들을 버린다는 것은 무엇을 의미하니?"라는 의미로 상대가 "throwing them away"라는 표현을 사용하였을 때 그 구절의 의미가 무엇인지 묻는 말이고, 나머지는 모두 "그 옷들을 버릴 작정이니?"라는 의미로 상대의 의도를 묻는 말이다.

교과서 대화문 익히기

Check(√) True or False   p.116

1 F   2 T   3 F   4 F

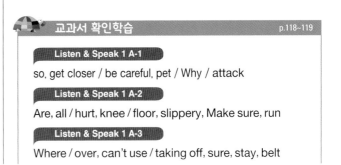

교과서 확인학습   p.118~119

Listen & Speak 1 A-1

so, get closer / be careful, pet / Why / attack

Listen & Speak 1 A-2

Are, all / hurt, knee / floor, slippery, Make sure, run

Listen & Speak 1 A-3

Where / over, can't use / taking off, sure, stay, belt

sign, on

Listen & Speak 1 B
getting, rest, questions / Can / make sure, spend

Listen & Speak 2 A-1
cleaned, found / What, with, thinking of throwing / make, out of

Listen & Speak 2 A-2
looking for, receipt / thinking of returning / stopped

Listen & Speak 2 B
Which floor / going / thinking of / thinking

Conversation
closing / Calm, got / having / thinking, getting / get, for, steal / that, bought, even put / match / Make sure, repeat / what, now or, out / impossible

Real Life Task Step 1
get, save, cut down, on, don't, try, sure, give up

Real Life Task Step 2
How / helpful / thinking, cutting / less / make sure, give

시험대비 기본평가 p.120

01 ④   02 ②
03 Make sure you stay in your seat   04 ④

01 "Because they may attack you."를 보면 동물들을 만지지 못하게 경고하는 표현이 들어갔음을 알 수 있다. ④는 '그것들을 만지는 것을 잊지 마.'라는 의미이다.

02 (B) 상대방의 비명을 듣고 괜찮은지 묻는다. (A) 무릎을 다쳤다고 한다. (C) 바닥이 미끄러우니 뛰지 않도록 경고를 한다.

03 "반드시 ~해라"는 경고의 의미는 "Make sure ~"이다.

04 "take off 이륙하다"를 보면 이 대화는 비행기에서 일어나는 것으로 안전벨트 표시등이 켜지면 자리에 앉아 있어야 하고 돌아다니면 안 된다.

시험대비 실력평가 p.121~122

01 ②   02 ⑤   03 ③   04 ⑤
05 ①   06 ③   07 ②   08 ①
09 ③   10 ⑤   11 ⑤   12 ③

01 간식을 사먹어도 된다는 말을 보면 버스가 휴게소에 도착하고 (getting to) 있음을 알 수 있다.

02 "make sure you don't ~"는 "~하지 않도록 주의해라"는 경고로 ⑤에 해당한다.

03 "Can I go to the snack stands?"라고 묻는 것으로 보아 간

식을 사먹을 것이라는 것을 알 수 있다.

04 (A) 버리다 = throw away (B) 재료를 나타내는 의미의 out of(~로)

05 "Are you thinking of ~?"는 "~할 생각이니?"의 의미로 상대의 의도를 묻는 말이다. "Are you going to ~?", "Are you considering ~?" 등으로 바꾸어 말할 수 있다.

06 소녀는 T-shirt로 an eco bag을 만들려고 하기 때문에 재활용하려고 하는 것을 알 수 있다.

07 새로 산 시계가 작동을 멈추어 영수증을 찾는 것으로 보아 반품(returning)하려고 한다고 생각할 수 있다.

08 이 대화를 통해서 알 수 있는 것은 작동을 멈춘 것 때문에 소녀가 영수증을 찾아서 새로 산 시계를 반품하려고 한다는 사실이다.

09 건물에서 "어느 층"이라고 할 때는 "Which floor"를 사용한다.

10 상대방이 피자를 먹을 것인지를 묻는 것에 대하여 팝콘을 먹을 생각이라고 하는 것으로 보아 앞의 질문에 대하여 부정적인 대답을 한 것을 알 수 있다.

11 "I'll buy fewer snacks and drinks."라고 대답하는 것으로 보아 소녀는 소비를 줄일 것이다. (줄이다 = cut down)

12 발표를 보고 "I'll buy fewer snacks and drinks."라고 한 것은 소년이다.

서술형 시험대비 p.123

01 ⓔ → can't miss out
02 it was just a week ago that you bought blue sneakers there
03 Make sure you don't repeat the same mistake.
04 it's now or never
05 I'll spend more on clothes. → I'll spend less on clothes.
06 Are you thinking of cut down your spending? → Are you thinking of cutting down your spending?
07 make sure you don't give up your style

01 "꼭 사고 싶다. 놓칠 수 없다"는 의미로 "I can't miss out."이 되어야 한다.

02 주어진 문장은 강조구문으로 it is/was와 that 사이에 강조할 내용을 쓰고 나머지는 that 뒤에 쓰는 구조로 what → that이어야 한다.

03 "~하지 않도록 명심하다"는 "Make sure you don't ~"이다.

04 "지금이 아니면 다른 기회가 없다."의 의미로 "이런 기회는 다시 오지 않아."라고 한 "it's now or never."에 해당한다.

05 소녀가 "make sure you don't give up your style"이라고 말하는 것을 보았을 때 소년은 옷을 사는 데 돈을 덜 쓰려고 하는 것을 알 수 있다.

06 전치사 of의 목적어는 명사 또는 동명사가 되어야 한다.

07 "~하지 않도록 해"라는 경고는 "Make sure you don't ~"이다.

교과서 Grammar

핵심 Check
p.124~125

1 (1) what   (2) What   (3) that

2 ②

3 (1) get   (2) go   (3) to clean

4 ④

02 ②의 what은 간접의문문의 의문대명사 what으로 "무엇"이라는 뜻이고, 나머지는 관계대명사 what으로 "~하는 것"이라는 뜻이다.

03 (1) 사역동사 make의 목적격보어로 원형부정사 get (2) 사역동사 let의 목적격보어로 원형부정사 go (3) 일반동사 ask의 목적격보어로 to부정사가 적절하다.

04 주어진 문장에 사용된 동사는 모두 사역동사로 목적격보어로 원형부정사가적절하다. ① went → go ② laughs→ laugh ③ taking → take ⑤ to decide → decide

시험대비 기본평가
p.74

01 ③   02 ①   03 ①   04 ①

01 what은 선행사가 없는 관계대명사로 명사절을 유도한다. 선행사 the robot이 있을 때는 관계대명사 which/that이 적절하다.

02 ⓐ 접속사 that이 들어가야 한다. ⓑ 관계대명사 동사 bought의 목적격 관계대명사 what이 적절하다. ⓒ the car를 선행사로 하는 관계대명사 which, that이 적절하다.

03 사역동사 make의 목적격보어는 원형부정사이다. ② watered → water ③ cleaned → clean ④ washed → wash ⑤ helping → help

04 동사 had가 사역동사로 쓰여서 목적격보어는 원형부정사 take가 되어야 한다.

시험대비 실력평가
p.75~77

01 ④	02 ⑤	03 ④	04 ②
05 ③	06 ③	07 ④	08 ③
09 ②	10 ②	11 ⑤	12 ④
13 ②	14 ②	15 ①	16 ④
17 ④	18 ②	19 ⑤	

01 ④ 동사 allow는 사역동사가 아닌 일반동사로 목적격보어는 to 부정사가 되어야 한다. go → to go

02 ⑤의 what은 "무엇"이라는 뜻으로 쓰인 의문대명사이고, 나머지는 모두 관계대명사 what이다.

03 ① 관계대명사 what이 적절하다. that → what ② the thing이 선행사이기 때문에 관계대명사 that이 적절하다. ③ 선행사 the book이 있을 때는 관계대명사 that이나 which이다. the book what → the book which/that ⑤ what은 접속사 that이 되어야 한다.

04 ⓑ "said"의 목적어가 필요한 구조이기 때문에 선행사를 포함하는 목적격 관계대명사 what이 적절하다. that → what ⓓ 동사 wrote의 목적어 역할을 하는 선행사를 포함한 관계대명사는 what이다. that → what

05 ③의 문장에서 사역동사 had의 목적어 his car는 fix하는 주체가 아니라 fix되는 수동적인 입장이므로 과거분사 fixed가 되어야 한다.

06 목적격보어로 원형부정사 do가 있는 것으로 보아 빈칸에는 사역동사 let, make, have 또는 help가 들어가는 것이 적절하다.

07 ④는 간접목적어, 직접목적어가 있는 수여동사이고 나머지는 원형부정사를 목적격보어로 가지는 사역동사이다.

08 (A) 사역동사 made의 목적격보어는 동사원형 believe이다. (B) 사역동사 had의 목적어는 deliver의 대상으로 수동의 의미를 나타내는 과거분사가 되어야 한다. (C) help의 목적격보어는 원형부정사와 to부정사가 모두 가능하다.

09 ① 문장의 주어가 되는 "That she told him"은 "What she told him"이다. ③ 선행사를 포함하는 관계대명사를 써서 "that he likes"는 "what he likes"가 되어야 한다. ④ "그가 말하는 것"은 "what he says"이다. ⑤ 선행사가 the song인 경우에는 관계대명사는 that이나 which이다.

10 "~에게 …하도록 시켰다"의 의미로 사역동사 make를 사용하여 "make+목적어+동사원형"의 구조가 되어야 한다.

11 ⑤는 선행사 the dog이 있으므로 관계대명사 which [that]이 적절하고 나머지는 모두 선행사를 포함한 관계대명사 what이 들어가야 한다.

12 (1) 동사 see의 목적어가 되면서 선행사를 포함하는 관계대명사는 what이다. (2) 동사 do의 목적어이면서 선행사를 포함하는

23

관계대명사는 what이다.

13 주어진 문장은 "목적어+원형부정사"의 구조를 가지는 사역동사 make이다. 사역동사로 쓰인 경우는 ㉮, ㉯에 사용된 make이다.

14 ① to use → use ③ to come → come ④ to wash → wash ⑤ working → work

15 [make+목적어+목적보어(동사원형)] '~가 …하게 하다' ②, ③ ~을 만들다 ④ make up one's mind 결심하다 ⑤ make it 약속하다, 가다

16 ④의 what은 의문대명사로 '무엇'의 의미를 가지며, 나머지는 모두 "~하는 것"이라는 의미의 관계대명사로 사용되었다.

17 ④는 everything을 선행사로 해서 수식하는 관계대명사 that이 들어간다. 나머지 빈칸에는 모두 what[What]이 들어간다.

18 ⓐ It is the last chocolate what I have now.에서는 관계대명사 what은 선행사를 취하지 않기 때문에 that으로 고쳐준다. ⓑ Every girl like to play with dolls.에서는 주어가 Every girl의 단수이므로 동사도 단수형태 likes로 고쳐준다. ⓒ Reading books is that he does in his free time.에서 that은 what으로 고쳐야 한다.

19 '~하는 것'이란 뜻의 선행사를 포함하는 관계대명사 what이 정답이다.

로 사용한다. 내가 필요한 것 = what I need 관계대명사 what이 주어 자리에 쓰이면 동사는 단수(is)로 일치시켜 준다.

04 "~하는 것"이라는 뜻으로 관계대명사 what을 포함한 명사절을 만들어 목적어 자리에 사용한다. 그가 말하는 것 = what he said

05 모자가 그를 늙어 보이게 하는 것으로 동사 make을 쓰면 목적격보어는 원형부정사를 쓰도록 한다.

06 주어진 동사를 사역동사 have의 과거 had로 바꾸면 목적격보어로 쓰이는 부정사 to look은 원형부정사 look이 되어야 한다.

07 "~에게 …하도록 시키다"를 사역동사 make를 써서 나타낼 때는 목적격보어로 원형부정사를 쓴다.

11 '~하는 것'이란 뜻으로 관계대명사 what이 포함된 명사절을 문장의 주어 자리에 사용한다. 관계대명사 what이 주어 자리에 쓰이면 동사는 단수(is)로 일치시켜 준다. "당신이 해야 할 것"은 "what you should do", "그것들 모두를 확인하는 것"은 "to check all of them"이다.

12 "어제 내가 산 것"은 "what I bought yesterday"이다.

13 "내가 ~하지 못하게 하다"는 사역동사 let을 사용하여 "didn't let me+동사원형"이다.

14 사역동사 have의 과거 had를 사용하면 목적격보어는 원형부정사 wash를 쓰도록 한다.

15 사역동사 made를 사용하면 목적격보어는 원형부정사 wash를 쓰도록 한다.

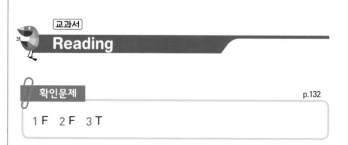

서술형 시험대비　　　　　　p.130~131

01 what Jisu told me is a lie
02 What I gave to Jessica
03 What I need is something to drink.
04 I couldn't understand what he said.
05 makes him look older
06 Mom had me look for her smartphone.
07 always makes me buy some milk
08 What she said
09 what you want
10 what they needed
11 What you should do is to check all of them.
12 This is what I bought yesterday.
13 didn't let me play
14 had Jane wash the dishes
15 made her son wash his hands

02 주어진 문장의 it은 앞 문장에서 말한 것을 나타낸다. it = what Jisu told me (Jisu가 나에게 말한 것)

02 It은 "'내가 Jessica에게 준 것'에 해당하는 "what I gave to Jessica"이다.

03 '~하는 것'이란 뜻으로 관계대명사 what을 포함한 명사절을 주어

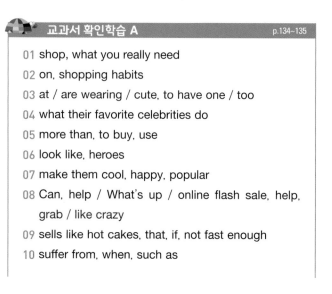

[교과서]
Reading

확인문제　　　　　　p.132

1 F　2 F　3 T

교과서 확인학습 A　　　　　　p.134~135

01 shop, what you really need
02 on, shopping habits
03 at / are wearing / cute, to have one / too
04 what their favorite celebrities do
05 more than, to buy, use
06 look like, heroes
07 make them cool, happy, popular
08 Can, help / What's up / online flash sale, help, grab / like crazy
09 sells like hot cakes, that, if, not fast enough
10 suffer from, when, such as

11 make, believe, chance to grab

12 becomes more like, than

13 a pick / it / finally, completes / for

14 Collecting, is, hottest trends, consumers

15 collections include, featuring

16 getting, because, of

17 have, bought, have, grabbed, have, collected

18 what, have bought, grabbed, collected

19 with them, all right

20 aren't, however, to be

21 are, to live by

22 STICK TO

23 shopping list, it, Run into, what

24 anything on the list, empty-handed, incredibly light

26 online, Instead, sign out

27 cooling off, if, still want it

28 OLD TREASURES

29 Whenever, something new, go through, what, a new appreciation for them

---

1 What makes you shop? Do you buy only what you really need?

2 Read on and think about your shopping habits.

3 Mina: Look at that! / Somin: Wow! N-girls are wearing a brand-new jacket.
Mina: It looks very cute. I have to have one just like it. / Somin: Me, too.

4 Many teens like to do what their favorite celebrities do.

5 They are more than willing to buy what the stars use.

6 They want to look like their heroes.

7 They think celebrity brands will make them cool, happy, and popular.

8 Somin: Can you help me, Inho? / Inho: Sure. What's up?
Somin: There's going to be an online flash sale on new sneakers. Please help me grab a pair. / Inho: Okay, I'll click like crazy.

9 When a product sells like hot cakes, some people often feel that they won't be able to get it if they are not fast enough.

10 They suffer from FOMO, Fear of Missing Out, when they see sales signs such as *Limited*

Edition and *Flash Sale*.

11 The signs make them believe that it is the last chance to grab the cool products.

12 Then, getting quick-selling goods becomes more like winning a game than spending money.

13 Inho: What a pick! / Mina: Did you get it, Inho?
Inho: Yeah, finally. This completes my collection. / Mina: Good for you!

14 Collecting popular things is one of the hottest trends among young consumers.

15 The most popular collections include character stickers, baseball card sets, and goods featuring pop stars.

16 Teen consumers enjoy getting more and more of these, because the idea of *more is better* makes them happy.

17 What celebrity brands have you bought? What quick-selling goods have you grabbed? What character stickers have you collected?

18 Are you happy with what you have bought, grabbed, and collected?

19 If you are happy with them, that's all right.

20 If you aren't, however, you should try to be a smarter shopper.

21 Here are three shopping tips to live by.

22 TIP 01. STICK TO A LIST.

23 Make a shopping list and carry it around. Run into a store and get what you need.

24 If you can't find anything on the list, walk out empty-handed. You will feel incredibly light.

25 TIP 02. COOL OFF FOR A DAY.

26 When you shop online, don't click "Buy Now." Instead, hit "Add To Cart" and sign out.

27 After 24 hours of cooling off, come back and see if you still want it.

28 TIP 03. FIND OLD TREASURES.

29 Whenever you want to buy something new, go through your closet and see what you have.
Find old treasures and enjoy a new appreciation for them.

---

01 ④   02 ②

03 They like to do what their favorite celebrities do.

04 ④   05 ③

06 *Limited Edition* or *Flash Sale*

07 getting　　08 ⑤　　　09 celebrity

10 옷장에서 찾은 입을 만한 옷　11 ④

12 We should carry it around.

13 ③　　　　14 ④　　　　15 ④

16 Many teens want to look like their heroes.

17 ⑤

18 She wants to buy a pair of new sneakers.

19 ③　　　　20 ③

21 what you have bought, grabbed, and collected

22 ④　　　　23 ④　　　　24 ④

25 Seeing what you have

26 We shouldn't click "Buy Now."

01 유명인들이 사용하는 것을 사용하고 영웅처럼 보이기를 원한다고 하였으므로 유명인 브랜드가 그들을 '멋지고, 행복하며, 인기 있게 만들 것'이라고 생각한다는 것이 적절하다.

02 ① 소민 역시 N-girls가 입고 있는 재킷 하나를 사기를 원한다. ⑤ 많은 십대들이 영웅처럼 보이기를 원한다고 했을 뿐, 영웅이 되기를 원하는 것이 아니다.

03 많은 십대들은 그들이 좋아하는 유명인이 하는 것을 하기를 좋아한다고 하였다.

04 '그들이 충분히 재빠르지 않으면 그것을 얻을 수 없을 것이다'라는 의미가 적절하다.

05 글의 내용상 FOMO가 의미하는 것은 '놓치는 것에 대한 두려움'이 가장 적절하다.

06 빨리 팔리는 상품은 '한정판' 혹은 '반짝 판매'와 같은 표시가 붙은 상품들이다.

07 enjoy는 동명사를 목적어로 취하는 동사이다.

08 답변으로 보아 (A)는 수집품을 완성했다는 의미가 적절하며, (B)는 캐릭터 스티커, 야구 카드 세트를 '포함한다'는 의미이다. 'more is better'라고 하였으므로 more and more가 적절하다. conclude: 결론짓다

09 특히 영화, 음악, 글 혹은 스포츠와 같은 연예 분야에서 유명한 누군가는 '유명인(celebrity)'이다.

10 옷장에서 찾은 입을 만한 옷을 의미한다.

11 목록에 있는 것을 찾을 수 없다면 빈손으로 걸어나오라고 하였다.

12 쇼핑 목록을 작성하고 휴대해야 한다.

13 '~하는 것'이란 의미의 관계대명사 what이 들어가는 것이 적절하다. 관계대명사 what은 앞, 뒤로 불완전한 절이 온다.

14 ④번은 십대들이 좋아하는 유명인들을 의미한다.

15 N-girls는 신상품 재킷을 입고 있다고 하였다.

16 많은 십대들은 그들의 영웅처럼 보이기를 원한다고 하였다.

17 sell like hot cakes: 불티나게 팔리다

18 소민이 사기를 원하는 것은 한 켤레의 새로운 운동화이다.

19 서두르지 않으면 원하는 물건을 살 수 없을 것이라고 생각하는 것은 '놓치는 것에 대한 두려움(FOMO)'에 해당한다.

20 '~을 특징으로 삼는'이라는 의미이므로 현재분사로 쓰는 것이 적절하다.

21 '여러분이 구입하고 손에 넣고 수집한 것'을 의미한다.

22 젊은 소비자들 사이에서 가장 인기 있는 유행 중 하나는 인기 있는 것들을 모으는 것이라고 하였다.

23 '~을 살펴보다'라는 의미를 갖는 것은 go through이다.

24 '장바구니에 추가'를 누르고 로그아웃 하였다가 24시간 후 다시 돌아오라고 하였으므로 sign out이라고 쓰는 것이 적절하다. sign in: (사무실 등에)도착/출발 시 서명하다

25 새로운 물건을 사고 싶을 때마다 사는 것보다는 옷장 안에 가지고 있는 물건을 확인해 보는 것이 더 좋은 생각이라고 하였다.

26 온라인 쇼핑을 할 때 '바로 구입'을 클릭하지 않아야 한다.

서술형 시험대비　　　　　p.142~143

01 We need to think about our shopping habits.

02 They are looking at N-girls wearing a brand-new jacket.

03 Many teens are more than willing to buy what their stars use.

04 Please help me grab a pair. / Help me grab a pair, please.

05 불티나게 팔리는 물건

06 People believe (that) it is the last chance to grab the cool products.

07 It's because the idea of *more is better* makes them happy.

08 The most popular collections include character stickers, baseball card sets, and goods featuring pop stars.

09 Are you happy with what you have bought, grabbed, and collected?

10 what

11 전날 장바구니에 추가한 것

12 You will feel incredibly light.

13 Stick to a list.

01 글을 읽으며 우리의 쇼핑 습관에 대해 생각해 보라고 하였다.

02 두 사람은 신상품 재킷을 입고 있는 N-girls를 보고 있다.

03 많은 십대들은 그들의 스타들이 사용하는 것을 기꺼이 사고자 한다고 하였다.

04 help는 목적격보어로 동사원형이나 to부정사를 취할 수 있다.

따라서 to grab이라고 써도 무방하다.

05 불티나게 팔리는 물건을 의미한다.

06 '반짝 판매' 같은 판매 게시물을 보면 사람들은 그것이 그 멋진 상품들을 손에 넣을 마지막 기회라고 생각한다.

07 십대 소비자들은 '많을수록 좋다'라는 생각이 그들을 행복하게 만들어 주기 때문에 수집품들을 점점 더 많이 가지는 것을 즐긴다고 하였다.

08 가장 인기 있는 수집품으로 캐릭터 스티커, 야구 카드 세트, 팝 스타를 특징으로 삼는 상품 등이 있다고 하였다.

09 '~하는 것'이라고 해석되는 것은 관계대명사 what이다.

10 '~하는 것'이라고 해석되며 불완전한 절을 이끄는 것은 관계대명사 what이다.

11 전날 장바구니에 추가한 물건을 의미한다.

12 목록에 있지 않은 것을 구매하지 않으면 믿을 수 없을 정도로 경쾌한 기분을 느끼게 될 것이라고 하였다.

13 위 글에 따르면 쇼핑 목록을 작성하고 목록에 있는 것만을 사야 하므로 '목록을 고수하세요'라고 조언할 수 있다.

영역별 핵심문제
p.145~149

01 ②
02 (1) celebrity (2) consumer (3) helpful (4) knee
03 ②　　　04 ②　　　05 ⑤　　　06 ④
07 ③　　　08 ③　　　09 ②　　　10 ⑤
11 ⑤　　　12 ②　　　13 ④, ⑤　　　14 ③
15 ①, ④　　　16 it is what I want to read　17 ②
18 ②　　　19 ③　　　20 ③　　　21 ④
22 FOMO stands for Fear of Missing Out.
23 ③　　　24 ③　　　25 ④
26 They include character stickers, baseball card sets, and goods featuring pop stars.
27 (C)–(A)–(B)
28 It's because it has a very small screen.
29 ⑤

01 이륙하다 = take off, 진정하다, 식다 = cool off

02 (1) 그녀는 텔레비전에 나오는 유명인이 되었다. 유명인 = celebrity (2) 기업은 소비자의 권리를 고려해야 한다. 소비자 = consumer (3) 그녀는 내 작업에 대해 도움이 되는 논평을 해 주었다. 도움이 되는 = helpful (4) 나는 넘어져서 무릎을 다쳤다. 무릎 = knee

03 "어떤 사람 또는 무엇인가를 더 큰 집단의 한 부분으로 만들다"는 "포함하다 = include"의 영어 설명이다. ① decorate = 장식하다 ③ match = 어울리다 ④ pet = 만지다 ⑤ product 상품

04 주변을 둘러보아도 되는지 묻는 말에 대하여 허락을 하면서도

너무 멀리 가지는 말도록 경고하는 말(make sure you don't ~)이 들어가야 한다.

05 빈칸 뒤에 이어지는 대화의 "No. I will make an eco bag out of them."을 보면 문장의 빈칸에는 상대의 의도를 묻는 말(Are you thinking of ~?: ~할 작정이니?)이 들어가는 것이 적절하다.

06 문제의 질문은 "소녀는 그 오래된 T-shirts"를 가지고 무엇을 할 것인가?"이다. "I will make an eco bag out of them."을 보면 소녀는 eco bag을 만들려고 하는 것을 알 수 있다.

07 소녀가 방 청소를 하다가 오래된 T-shirts를 발견했고, 소년이 그것으로 무엇을 할 것인지를 물어 보았을 때 소녀는 그것으로 eco bag을 만들 것이라고 대답한다.

08 주어진 문장은 지난주에 새로 산 sneakers에 대하여 신어 보기라도 했는지 묻는 말로 그에 대한 대답 "No. They don't match any of my pants." 앞에 놓이는 것이 적절하다.

09 이어지는 대답 "I see what you mean, but it's now or never."를 보면 서둘러 물건을 구입하려는 것에 대하여 경고하는 내용의 말을 했음을 알 수 있다.

10 Seho가 "it's now or never."(지금 아니면 기회가 없다.)라고 말하는 것으로 보아 지금 아니면 구할 수 없다고 생각하고 있다는 것을 알 수 있다.

11 소녀는 "I'm going to visit the sneaker shop."이라고 했다. 새로운 sneakers를 구입할 것이냐고 묻는 말에 "No, I'm not."이라고 대답했기 때문에 빈칸에서는 sneaker shop에 가는 다른 이유를 말해야 한다.

12 돈을 저축할 필요가 있다는 말을 듣고 (B) 소비를 줄일 작정인지를 묻는다. (A) 그렇다고 대답하고 옷에 돈을 덜 쓰겠다고 한다. (C) 좋지만, 스타일은 포기하지 말라고 조언한다.

13 ④ 선행사 the movie가 있을 때는 관계대명사 that이나 which가 적절하다. ⑤ 문장의 주어가 되는 명사절은 선행사를 포함한 관계대명사 what을 사용하여 "What she said on the phone"이 되어야 한다.

14 ③의 make는 "~을 만들다"의 의미로 쓰인 3형식 동사이고, 나머지는 모두 사역동사로 "make+목적어+목적보어(동사원형)"의 형태를 만들어 "~가 …하게 하다"의 의미가 된다.

15 주어진 보기의 문장과 ①, ④에 사용된 what은 선행사를 포함한 관계대명사 what이고, 나머지는 모두 의문사로 사용된 what이다.

16 선행사 the book과 관계대명사 which를 합해서 선행사를 포함한 관계대명사 what으로 바꾼다.

17 ⓓ 선행사 Everything이 있을 때 관계대명사는 what이 아니라 that이다. ⓔ 선행사가 없는 관계대명사 that은 what으로 바꾸어야 한다.

18 동사 express의 목적어 역할을 할 수 있고 '우리가 마음속에 가진 것'이란 뜻을 표현할 수 있는 관계대명사 what이 알맞다.

19 ⓒ 동사 asked의 목적격보어는 to부정사가 되어야 한다. ⓓ, ⓔ let은 사역동사로 목적격보어 to use는 use, to go는 go가 되어야 한다.

20 ① to call → call ② repeated → repeat ③ cleaning → clean ④ to go → go

21 소민이는 온라인 반짝 판매가 있을 때 운동화를 사기를 원하며 이를 위하여 인호에게 도움을 요청하고 있다. 따라서 충분히 재빠르지 않으면 그것을 얻을 수 없을 것이라고 느끼는 것임을 알 수 있다.

22 FOMO는 '놓치는 것에 대한 두려움'을 의미한다.

23 십대 소비자들은 더욱 더 많이 가지는 것을 즐긴다고 하였으므로 이들이 가진 생각은 '많을수록 좋다'는 것이 자연스럽다.

24 one of the 최상급+복수명사: 가장 ~한 것들 중 하나

25 인호가 완성한 것은 그의 수집품이다.

26 가장 인기 있는 수집품으로 캐릭터 스티커, 야구 카드 세트, 팝스타를 특징으로 삼는 상품 등이 있다고 하였다.

27 (C) 글쓴이가 산 물건에 대해 좋아하는 점으로 시작하여(I'd like to begin with what I like about the product.), (A) 그 다음으로 싫어하는 점을 적고(Now, let me write what I don't like.), 상품에 대한 총평을 남긴 (B) 순서가 가장 적절하다.

28 너무 작은 화면을 가지고 있어서 시간을 읽기가 어렵다고 하였다.

29 스마트 워치가 발걸음을 세어 주어 글쓴이가 충분한 운동을 할 수 있게 도와준다고 하였다.

단원별 예상문제
p.150~153

01 ⑤	02 ③	03 ②	04 ④
05 ②	06 Put on a life jacket before you get in.		
07 ⑤	08 ②	09 ①	10 ①
11 ⑤	12 ④	13 ②	14 ③
15 (A) makes (B) make			
16 ③	17 ⑤	18 ②	19 ③
20 ②			
21 We should go through our closet and see what we have.			
22 cool off for a day			

01 ⑤ "consumer (소비자) - producer (생산자)"는 반의어 관계이고 나머지는 유의어 관계이다. useful 유용한, helpful 유익한, reply 대답하다, answer 대답하다, collect 모으다, gather 모으다 hurt 다치다, injure 다치다

02 (A) A: 옷 사는 데 돈을 덜 써야겠어. B: 잘됐다, 그래도 네 스타일은 포기하지 않도록 해. (B) 좋은 아이디어를 생각해내려면 상상력을 이용해야 한다. 포기하다 = give up, 생각해 내다 = come up with

03 (1) due to = ~ 때문에 (2) give up = 포기하다 (3) carry around = 가지고 다니다 (4) cut down on = 줄이다 (5) cool off = 식히다, 진정시키다

04 "반드시 ~하도록 하라."에 해당하는 경고의 의미는 "make sure you don't ~"이다.

05 주어진 문장은 풀에 들어가기 전에 경고 표지판을 보라는 것으로 "Do you mean the round one over there?" 앞 B에 들어가는 것이 적절하다.

06 입다 = put on, 들어가기 전에 = before you get in

07 "Make sure you don't miss any safety signs."라고 한 것으로 보아, ⑤는 "They must not miss any safety signs."가 되어야 한다.

08 서둘러 물건을 구입하려는 Seho에게 잠시 진정하라는 의미로 "Calm down"(진정해)이라고 이야기한 것이다.

09 "~한 것은 바로 …였다."의 의미를 가지는 강조 구문의 문장이다. it was와 that 사이에 강조하려는 부사구 just a week ago를 쓰고 나머지는 that 뒤에 쓰도록 해야 한다.

10 이 대화에서 Seho는 새로운 sneakers를 사고 싶어 한다. 새로운 신발을 살 가게의 이름은 Sneaker Ground이지만 몇 층에 있는지는 소개되지 않았다.

11 ① going → go ② mails → mail ③ cried → cry ④ to walk → walk

12 ④의 문장은 "make+간접목적어+직접목적어"(~에게 …을 만들어 주다)의 구조이고, 나머지는 모두 사역동사로 쓰여서 "make+목적어+목적격보어(동사원형)"(~가 …하게 하다)의 구조를 가진 5형식이다.

13 ⓐ와 ⓓ는 의문사로 사용된 what이고, 나머지 보기는 모두 관계대명사로 사용된 문장이다.

14 ① to go → go ② to touch → touch[touching] ④ to come → come ⑤ to watch → watching

15 목적격보어로 동사원형이나 형용사를 취할 수 있는 5형식 동사는 make이다.

16 위 글은 사람들의 쇼핑 습관에 관한 글이다.

17 십대들이 그들이 좋아하는 유명인이 사용하는 것을 사는 이유는 그들의 영웅처럼 보이기를 원해서이다.

18 '지켜야 할 세 가지 구매 팁'이라는 의미이므로 전치사 by가 적절하다. live by: ~에 따라서 살다

19 쇼핑 목록에 있는 것을 찾을 수 없다면 빈손으로 걸어 나오라고 하였다.

20 쇼핑 목록은 우리가 정말로 필요한 것만을 구매하도록 돕는다는 것을 알 수 있다.

21 새로운 물건을 사고 싶을 때마다 옷장을 살펴보고 갖고 있는 물건을 확인해 보라고 하였다.

22 바로 구입을 하지 말고 대신 장바구니에 추가한 후 24시간 동안 진정한 이후에 여전히 그것을 원하는지 확인해 보라고 하였다.

서술형 실전문제 p.154~155

01 (i)nclude

02 get

03 Do you mean the round one over there?

04 ⓐ into ⓑ on

05 what she wanted to buy

06 made me feel

07 ③번 ➡ are not fast enough

08 People suffer from FOMO when they see sales signs such as *Limited Edition* and *Flash Sale*.

09 *Limited Edition*, *Flash Sale*

10 It counts his steps, so it helps him get enough exercise.

11 It's because it has a very small screen.

12 He gave only one star to the product.

---

01 주어진 단어는 반의어 관계이다. consumer 소비자 – producer 생산자, include 포함하다 – exclude 제외하다

02 • 동물들이 너무 귀여워요. 우리 더 가까이 가요. • 저는 "하나를 사면 하나를 더 드립니다."라는 문구가 가장 흥미로운 것 같아요. • 그곳에 도착하자마자 꼭 나한테 전화하도록 해. 가까이 가다 = get closer, 얻다 = get, 그곳에 도착하다 = get there

03 "~ 말이니?"의 의미로 상대의 의도를 물어볼 때는 "Do you mean ~?"이라고 한다. 동그란 것 = the round one, 저기 있는 = over there

04 ⓐ (수영장에) 들어가다 = get into, ⓑ 입다, 착용하다 = put on

05 선행사 the hat와 관계대명사 that을 묶어서 선행사를 포함하는 관계대명사 what으로 바꾼다. Kate는 대명사 she로 바꾼다.

06 Kate의 이야기가 Joe를 훨씬 더 기분 좋게 느끼도록 만들어 주었다는 의미로 "Your stories made me feel much better ~" 라고 해야 한다.

07 충분히 빠르지 않으면 그것을 얻을 수 없을 것이라고 느낀다는 표현이 글의 흐름상 자연스럽다.

08 사람들은 '한정판'이나 '반짝 판매'와 같은 판매 게시물을 보면, FOMO(놓치는 것에 대한 두려움)를 겪는다고 하였다.

09 빨리 팔리는 물건은 '한정판' 혹은 '반짝 판매'와 같은 표시가 붙은 것들이다.

---

10 스마트 워치가 발걸음을 세어 주어서 충분한 운동을 하도록 돕는 것이 이 제품에 대해 좋아하는 점이라고 하였다.

11 스마트 워치로 시간을 읽기가 어려운 이유는 그것이 너무 작은 화면을 가지고 있어서이다.

12 글쓴이는 제품에 한 개의 별점만을 주었다.

창의사고력 서술형 문제 p.156

|모범답안|

01 cheese / birds / fish

02 Chatuchak Market / Bangkok, Thailand / goods from every part of Thailand / It is the largest market in Thailand and is visited by about 200,000 visitors each day it is open.

03 what I like about the product. They are very comfortable, so I wear them often / what I don't like about the product. The color of the shoes is white, so they get dirty easily / satisfied / four stars

---

01 (1) cheese (2) birds (3) fish (1) 알크마르 시장에서는, 사람들은 많은 종류의 치즈를 전통적인 방법으로 판매합니다. (2) Ka Faroshi 시장은 다양한 색깔과 크기의 새를 판매합니다. 새들은 사람들에게 굉장히 인기 있습니다. (3) 신선한 생선을 맛보고 생생한 분위기를 느껴 보러 자갈치 시장을 방문해 보세요.

02 짜뚜짝 시장에 가본 적이 있나요? 이 시장은 태국의 방콕에 있습니다. 이 시장에는 15,000개 이상의 점포가 있습니다. 이 시장에서는 태국의 전 지역에서 온 물건들을 판매합니다. 이 시장은 태국에서 가장 큰 시장이고 하루에(주말에만 운영) 약 200,000명이 방문한다고 합니다.

단원별 모의고사 p.157~160

01 ③	02 ④	03 ⑤	
04 (1) (k)nee	(2) (c)elebrity	(3) (b)rand-new	05 ②
06 ③	07 high-end		
08 ④	09 ①	10 ④	11 ②
12 ⑤	13 ③	14 ④	15 ②

16 what you want / what I want

17 ④	18 ④	19 (B)–(A)–(C)	20 ②

21 We should try to be a smarter shopper.

22 ④	23 ⑤

24 Add to Cart, Buy Now

25 go through your closet and see what you have

01 주어진 단어는 반의어 관계이다. include 포함하다, exclude 제외하다, incredible 믿을 수 없는, common 평범한, lively 활발한, gloomy 우울한, slippery 미끄러운, friendly 친절한

02 그녀는 내 작업에 대해 도움이 되는 논평을 해 주었다. helpful(도움이 되는) = useful (유익한) careful 조심스러운, cheerful 활발한, harmful 해로운, wonderful 훌륭한

03 (A) 다치다 hurt (B) 미끄러운 slippery (C) 달리다 run

04 (1) 무릎 : 다리 중간에 있는 구부러지는 관절 (2) 유명한 사람 : 살아 있는 유명한 사람 (3) 신상품의 : 새것이고 아직 사용되지 않은

05 "What are you going to 동사원형 ~?"은 상대의 계획을 묻는 말로 "What are you planning to 동사원형 ~?"이라고 물어볼 수 있다.

06 위 대화에서 소녀가 방을 청소하다가 오래된 T-shirts를 발견하고 그것으로 eco bag을 만들 작정이라고 밝힌다. ① 언제 방을 청소했는지는 알 수 없다. ② 버릴 것이 아니다. ④ eco bag을 가지고 무엇을 할지 언급하지 않았다. ⑤ 알 수 없다.

07 "같은 유형의 다른 상품보다 더 비싸고 품질이 좋은"은 'high-end 고급의"에 해당하는 영어 설명이다.

08 주어진 (가)의 문장은 "just a week ago"를 강조하는 문장으로 it is/was ~ that 강조구문이다.

09 (A) ~할 작정이니? = Are you thinking of ~? (B) 어울리다 = match (C) 선행사를 포함하는 관계대명사 what

10 ① 필요한 것을 다 샀다고 생각하는 것은 Semi이다. ② Sneaker Ground에 가고 싶은 것은 Seho이다. ③ Seho는 일주일 전에 sneakers를 구입했다. ⑤ "It's now or never"는 지금 아니면 기회가 없다는 의미이다.

11 "I'll spend less on clothes."라는 대답을 보면 돈을 덜 쓰고 저축하려는 것(save)을 알 수 있다.

12 소년이 "I'll spend less on clothes."라고 대답한 것을 보면 그 전에는 옷에 돈을 많이 쓰고 있었다고 생각하는 것을 알 수 있다.

13 ③번의 what은 "무엇"이라는 의미로 의문사로 사용되었고 나머지 what은 "~인/한 것"이라는 의미로 선행사를 포함한 관계대명사로 사용되었다.

14 ④번의 had는 사역동사로 사용되어서 목적격보어를 원형 부정사로 써야 한다. had my brother to fix→ had my brother fix

15 첫 번째, 두 번째 문장에는 사역동사 let, make가 쓰였으므로 목적보어 자리에 동사원형이 적절하다. 세 번째 문장은 동명사 주어가 적절하다.

16 "~인/한 것"이라는 의미로 선행사를 포함하는 관계대명사 what을 사용하여 나타낸다.

17 ④ 관계대명사 what이 동사 wear의 목적어 역할을 하는 목적격이기 때문에 동사의 목적어 a shirt는 생략되어야 한다.

18 앞선 문장에서 만족할 경우에 대해서 말하였고 뒤이어 그렇지 않을 경우에 대해 말하고 있으므로 however가 적절하다.

19 (B) 인기 있는 것들을 모으는 것은 젊은 소비자들 사이에서 가장 인기 있는 유행 중 하나임 - (A) 인기 있는 수집품에 해당하는 것들을 열거 - (C) these가 가리키는 것은 (A)에서 언급된 캐릭터 스티커, 야구 카드 세트, 팝 스타를 특징으로 삼는 상품들을 가리킴.

20 동명사 주어는 단수 취급한다. 따라서 is라고 쓰는 것이 적절하다.

21 우리가 구입하고 손에 넣고 수집한 것에 만족하지 못한다면 더 똑똑한 구매자가 되려고 노력해야 한다고 하였다.

22 이어지는 내용으로 보아 하루 동안 진정하라는 조언이 적절하다.

23 위 글은 생활 속에서 지켜야 할 세 가지 구매 팁이다. 따라서 현명한 소비자가 되기 위한 글이라고 볼 수 있다.

24 "바로 구입" 대신에 "장바구니에 추가"를 눌러야 한다.

25 이미 많은 외투를 가지고 있음에도 새로운 것을 사려는 Cindy에게 옷장을 살펴보고 이미 갖고 있는 물건을 확인해 보라고 조언하는 것이 적절하다.

교과서 파헤치기

Lesson **1**

01 대략, 약　　02 어려움　　03 지속되다

04 외로운　　05 무서운　　06 지지하다

07 차례, 순번　　08 눈물, 울음　　09 의견, 생각

10 기분　　11 제공하다, 대접하다

12 (~학년) 학생　　13 스트레스가 많은, 걱정 등을 일으키는

14 주문하다; 주문　　15 가장 적게　　16 이미, 벌써

17 생각, 의견　　18 선물; 현재의, 참석한

19 사생활　　20 일, 직업, 업

21 진가를 알아보다, 고마워하다　　22 시끄러운

23 흥미롭게도　　24 음력의　　25 기쁜

26 괴롭히다, 귀찮게 굴다　　27 대답; 대답하다

28 가격, 물가　　29 의미　　30 자정

31 아마, 도저히　　32 공정한, 공평한

33 (시간, 세월의) 경과, 흐름　　34 허락, 허가

35 ~와 잘 지내다　　36 화내다　　37 ~할 필요가 없다

38 좋아지다　　39 내 생각에는　　40 다시 보다

41 ~을 견디다, 참다　　42 신경을 건드리다

43 ~하는 데 어려움을 겪다

01 already　　02 view / opinion　　03 midnight

04 bother　　05 trade　　06 difficulty

07 fair　　08 appreciate　　09 scary

10 turn　　11 order　　12 last

13 possibly　　14 serve　　15 privacy

16 passing　　17 least　　18 lonely

19 pleased　　20 sometimes　　21 around

22 loud　　23 stressful　　24 interestingly

25 lunar　　26 only　　27 tear

28 price　　29 laughter　　30 support

31 permission　　32 reply　　33 present

34 mood　　35 do without

36 lose one's temper　　37 get together

38 put up with ~　　39 stick by　　40 in my opinion

41 take a second look　　42 end up -ing

43 get along with ~

1 lunar, 음력의　　2 laughter, 웃음　　3 mood, 기분

4 support, 지지하다　　5 difficulty, 어려움

6 privacy, 사생활　　7 last, 지속되다　　8 reply, 대답하다

9 fair, 공정한, 공평한　　10 grandparent, 조부모

11 lonely, 외로운　　12 bother, 괴롭히다　　13 tear, 눈물

14 turn, 차례　　15 appreciate, 진가를 알아보다

16 permission, 허락

Listen & Speak 1 A-1

Have, read / have, story, scary / In my opinion, sad / could

Listen & Speak 1 A-2

Have, seen, movie / have, best / seem to like / How, possibly, view, wonderful

Listen & Speak 1 A-3

Isn't, painting strange / think / after taking, second look, beautiful about / don't, agree with

Listen & Speak 1 B

third graders, important / say that, What should / opinion, make, friends / right, important

Listen & Speak 2 A-1

hear, cream, opened / Sure, have already been / Have, was / great / How, price / high, happy about

Listen & Speak 2 A-2

There, a lot of, here / here, since, ordered / service, slow, happy about / Look at those, over there, being served / Didn't, earlier / fair

Conversation B

go out, eat / food, family, too, loud / How big / seven, grandparents, brothers / big family / don't, at all, privacy / get what, good, have, lonely, only child / what, mean

Real Life Task Step 1

happy, different, asked, whom, More than half, feel, with, number, with, friends, Interestingly, around, asked, alone

Real Life Task Step 2

important, family, life / agree, should, do, have / opinion, try, another / good, have, kind, one another, else, do

31

Listen & Speak 1 A-1

G: Have you read this book?

B: Yes, I have. The story is very scary.

G: Is it? In my opinion, it's a sad story.

B: Well, it could be.

Listen & Speak 1 A-2

B: Have you seen this movie?

G: Yes, I have. It's one of the best movies I've ever seen.

B: You seem to like it a lot. To me, it's just an old movie.

G: How can you possibly say that? In my view, it is just wonderful.

Listen & Speak 1 A-3

B: Isn't this painting strange?

G: Well, I think it's beautiful.

B: Hmm ..., after taking a second look, there is something beautiful about the painting.

G: Hey, you don't have to agree with me.

Listen & Speak 1 B

A: We are now third graders. This year is very important!

B: You can say that again! What should we do to make this year special?

A: In my opinion, we should make more friends.

B: You're right. I think it's also important to read a lot of books.

Listen & Speak 2 A-1

G: Did you hear that a new ice cream store opened last week?

B: Sure. I have already been there.

G: Have you? How was it?

B: The ice cream was great.

G: How was the price?

B: Well, it was very high. I was not happy about it.

Listen & Speak 2 A-2

B: There are a lot of people here.

G: Yes, here are. It's been 30 minutes since we ordered.

B: The service is so slow. I'm not happy about it.

G: Look at those people over there. They are being served now.

B: Didn't we come in earlier?

G: Yes, we did. It's not fair.

Conversation B

Yujin: Did your family go out to eat last weekend?

Seho: Yes, we did. The food was great, but my family is too big and loud.

Yujin: Really? How big is it?

Seho: There are seven of us: my grandparents, my mom, my dad, two brothers, and me.

Yujin: That is a big family!

Seho: Well, I don't like it at all. There's no privacy.

Yujin: I get what you're saying, but to me, it's good to have a big family. I sometimes feel lonely because I'm an only child.

Seho: Yeah ..., I see what you mean

Real Life Task Step 1

W: People often say, "I'm not happy about my family." But we have a different story. We asked 2,000 people, "With whom do you feel happiest?" More than half of them feel happiest when they are with their family. The second-largest number of people are happiest with their friends. Interestingly, around 13% of the people we asked feel happiest when alone.

Real Life Task Step 2

A: It's important to have a happy family to live a happy life.

B: I agree. What should family members do to have a happy family?

A: In my opinion, they should try to help one another.

B: That's a good idea. I think they also have to be kind to one another. What else should they do?

01 may have different meanings

02 readers, How, doing, replies

03 get along, often, whether

04 For, thing, bother, all

05 without, permission, wake up

06 asks, walk, tells, clean

07 getting on my nerves

08 end up, at, worst

09 share, with, who, older

10 When, mood, changing, minute

11 lose, over nothing, watch

12 difficult for, to put

13 turn, be, getting better

14 lose, temper, tries, support

15 better, because, what, like

16 get, feel, toward, other

17 who entered, golden child

18 perfect son, student at

19 Needless, say, such, shining

20 fact, perfect, poor, great

21 eye, whenever, hard, choosing

22 pleased, thanks, for, appreciates

23 difficult, believe, own trade

24 their own difficulties, life

25 At, same, find, meanings

26 would, tell, about, family

27 made, years, grows, passing

01 may have different meanings, different

02 How, doing, Here, their replies

03 ask, whether, get along with, more often than not, not sure whether

04 For one thing, bother

05 comes into, without, permission, shouts at, to wake up

06 asks, to walk, tells me to clean

07 keep getting on my nerves, angry at

08 end up loving, at my worst, to do so

09 share, who is, older than me

10 When, her mood, changing every minute

11 would lose, over nothing, read, watch

12 difficult for me to

13 my turn to be, getting better

14 Whenever, tries to support

15 understand, better than, because, what it feels like

16 get to know, feel greater love, each other

17 who entered, is the golden child

18 a perfect son, perfect student at

19 Needless to say, stressful, such a shining brother

20 poor at, that, am great at

21 no eye for, whenever, hard time choosing clothes

22 pleased, thanks, for, appreciates, fashion sense

23 for me to live with, believe in, own trade

24 their own difficulties, family life

25 At the same time, find special meanings

26 would, tell

27 is made of, tears, laughter, years, grows, passing of time

1 가족이라는 말은 사람들마다 다른 의미를 가질 수 있습니다.

2 우리는 독자들에게 '가족과 어떻게 지내나요?'라고 물었습니다. 여기 그 대답들 중 몇 가지가 있습니다.

3 나는 종종 가족들과 잘 지내는지 나 자신에게 물어보는데, 많은 경우에 잘 지내는지 확신하지 못한다.

4 한 예를 들자면, 가족들은 나를 항상 귀찮게 한다.

5 언니는 일요일 아침에 허락도 없이 내 방에 들어와서 일어나라고 소리친다.

6 그다음에는 엄마가 개를 산책시키라고 하시고, 그러고 나면 아빠가 방을 청소하라고 하신다.

7 가족들은 내가 화가 날 때까지 내 신경을 건드린다.

8 하지만 결국엔 항상 가족들을 사랑하게 되는데, 그들은 내가 가장 어려울 때 함께 있어 주었고, 지금도 내 곁을 지키며, 앞으로도 계속해서 그럴 것이기 때문이다.

9 나는 언니와 방을 함께 쓰는데, 언니는 나보다 두 살이 많다.

10 언니는 십대가 되었을 때, 기분이 매분마다 바뀌기 시작했다.

11 어느 순간 갑자기 아무것도 아닌 일에 화를 내다가 바로 다음 순간 즐겁게 책을 읽거나 영화를 보곤 했다.

12 나는 언니를 견디기 힘들었다.

13 이젠 내가 십대가 될 차례이다. 언니도 아직 십대이지만 점점 나아지고 있다.

14 내가 화를 낼 때마다 언니는 나를 지지해 주려고 노력한다.

15 지금은 나도 십대라는 것이 어떤 느낌인지 알기 때문에 예전보다 언니를 더 잘 이해한다.

16 우리가 서로를 잘 알아 갈수록 우리는 서로에게 더 큰 사랑을 느낀다.

17 우리 형은 올해 대학에 들어갔는데, 누구에게나 사랑받는 아들이다.

18 형은 집에서는 완벽한 아들이고 학교에서는 완벽한 학생이다.

19 말할 필요도 없이, 그렇게 눈부신 형이 있다는 것은 정말 골치 아픈 일이다.

20 하지만 사실 형도 완벽하지 않고, 내가 잘하는 일에는 형편없다.

21 형은 패션을 보는 눈이 없어서, 데이트에 입을 옷을 고르는 걸 어려워할 때마다 내가 항상 그를 도와준다.

22 형이 내 도움을 고마워하고 내 패션 감각을 알아줄 때 기분이 좋다.

23 완벽한 형과 함께 사는 것이 항상 어려운 일은 아니며, "굼벵이도 구르는 재주가 있다."는 것을 나는 믿는다.

24 Kamala, Rachel, 그리고 민수 모두에게 가족생활의 어려움이 있습니다.

25 동시에 그들은 자신들의 가족을 사랑하고 그 안에서 특별한 의미를 찾고 있습니다.

26 여러분은 여러분 가족에 대해 어떤 이야기를 할 건가요?

27 가족은 / 사랑과 눈물 / 웃음과 세월로 만들어집니다. / 가족은 시간의 흐름과 함께 / 점점 더 강해집니다.

1 The word *family* may have different meanings to different people.

2 We asked our readers, "How are you doing with your family?" Here are some of their replies.

3 I often ask myself whether I get along with my family members, and more often than not, I'm not sure whether I really do.

4 For one thing, they bother me all the time.

5 My sister comes into my room without my permission and shouts at me to wake up on Sunday mornings.

6 Next, Mom asks me to walk the dog, and then Dad tells me to clean my room.

7 They keep getting on my nerves until I get angry at them.

8 But I always end up loving them because they have been with me at my worst, still stick by me now, and will continue to do so in the future.

9 I share a room with my sister, who is two years older than me.

10 When she became a teenager, her mood started changing every minute.

11 She would lose her temper over nothing one moment and happily read a book or watch a film the next.

12 It was difficult for me to put up with her.

13 Now it's my turn to be a teenager. My sister is still one, but she is getting better.

14 Whenever I lose my temper, she tries to support me.

15 I also understand her better than before because now I know what it feels like to be a teenager.

16 As we get to know each other better, we feel greater love toward each other.

17 My older brother, who entered university this year, is the golden child.

18 He is a perfect son at home and a perfect student at school.

19 Needless to say, it is really stressful to have such a shining brother.

20 Well, in fact, he is not perfect and is poor at one thing that I am great at.

21 He has no eye for fashion, and I always help him whenever he has a hard time choosing clothes for a date.

22 I feel pleased when he thanks me for my help and appreciates my fashion sense.

23 It is not always difficult for me to live with the perfect brother, and I believe in "every man for his own trade."

24 Kamala, Rachel, and Minsu all have their own difficulties in their family life.

25 At the same time, they love their families and find special meanings in them.

26 What story would you tell us about your family?

27 A family / is made of love and tears, / laughter and years. / It grows stronger with the passing of time.

Listen & Speak 2 B

1. like most about

2. wonderful cook

3. like least about your family

4. have to share, with, not happy about

Real Life Task Step 3

1. important part, life, there are, members should do

2. In our opinion, important for them to have

Before I Read

1. What should, do

2. keep asking, school work, get on my nevers, often lose, temper

3. why I get angry, easily

4. What should, do

5. have, same problem

6. let it go, work

7. get better sooner, later

Listen & Speak 2 B

1. A: What do you like most about your family?

2. B: My father is a wonderful cook.

3. A: Then, what do you like least about your family?

4. B: I have to share a room with my brother. I'm not happy about it.

Real Life Task Step 3

1. Family is a very important part of our happy life, and there are many things family members should do.

2. In our opinion, it is important for them to have a lot of conversations.

3. Next, ...

Before I Read

1. What should I do?

2. Q: When Mom and Dad keep asking me about my school work, they get on my nevers and I often lose my temper.

3. I don't know why I get angry so easily.

4. What should I do?

5. A: Many teenagers have the same problem.

6. Try to just let it go and do your work.

7. Then it will get better sooner or later.

단어 TEST Step 1   p.23

01 (음식을) 제공하다, 시중들다		02 고대의
03 재	04 (우묵한) 그릇, 사발	
05 황제	06 장식	07 제국
08 친선, 호의	09 인기 있는, 유명한	10 신 맛이 나는
11 매운, 향신료를 넣은		12 갓 ~한, 새롭게
13 항아리 모양의	14 역사가, 사학자	15 보호하다
16 왕조	17 상상하다	18 영혼, 정령
19 꽃이 피다	20 조각상	21 결혼, 결혼 생활
22 젓다, 섞다	23 씨앗	24 원래, 최초에
25 마침내, 결국	26 맛있는	27 꽃무늬의
28 (과거의) 이전에, 한때		
29 뻥뻥 소리를 내는 것, 팝콘을 만드는 사람		
30 기원	31 조각	32 발명가
33 기쁜, 만족해하는	34 전기의	35 혼자서
36 ~ 이외에도	37 오래지 않아, 얼마 후	
38 ~에 더하여	39 ~로 만들어지다	40 ~을 생각해 내다
41 ~와 함께 제공되다		42 ~하기 오래전에
43 ~뿐만 아니라 …도		

단어 TEST Step 2   p.24

01 cave	02 dynasty	03 electric
04 origin	05 freshly	06 ancient
07 originally	08 ash	09 seed
10 serve	11 bloom	12 spicy
13 decoration	14 flowery	15 stir
16 bowl	17 spirit	18 emperor
19 slice	20 empire	21 statue
22 goodwill	23 protect	24 marriage
25 noodle	26 inventor	27 sour
28 historian	29 once	30 imagine
31 throw	32 pleased	33 tasty
34 pot-shaped	35 long before	36 be made from
37 come up with	38 by oneself	39 be served with
40 before long	41 by the way	42 in addition to
43 not only ~ but also		

단어 TEST Step 3   p.25

1 flowery, 꽃무늬   2 ancient, 고대의   3 inventor, 발명가

4 ash, 재   5 cave, 동굴   6 arrive, 도착하다

7 pop, 불쑥 나타나다   8 sneakers, 운동화   9 pan, 냄비

10 dynasty, 왕조   11 goodwill, 친선, 호의
12 bowl, (우묵한) 그릇, 사발   13 origin, 기원
14 statue, 조각상   15 seed, 씨앗
16 noodle, 국수 (한 가락)

대화문 TEST Step 1

p.26~27

Listen & Speak 1 A-1

got, phone, haven't you / have / How, like / don't, at all

Listen & Speak 1 A-2

got, sneakers as, present / How cool, How, like them / just love

Listen & Speak 2 A-1

Would, like some / Here, How, like / hot, sweet / glad, like it

Listen & Speak 2 A-2

make, bowl by yourself / looks, wonderful / happy, like

Listen & Speak 2 A-3

How, like, face / pleased, love

Conversation

Would, like, chocolate / Sure, haven't had, ages / How, like / lot, good at / Thanks, glad, By, way, once called / really / enjoyed, emperor, once called, the / surprising, thanks / welcome

Real Life Task Step 1

How, like, What, have, like, cool, Why don't, answer, looking forward to getting

Real Life Task Step 2

What, have, snack / have, apple, like / sounds, like, a lot / glad, like it

Check My Progress 1

got, backpack / present / How nice of / a lot, color / favorite, isn't it

Check My Progress 2

bake, these by yourself / look, wonderful / like to try / do / happy, like it

대화문 TEST Step 2

p.28~29

Listen & Speak 1 A-1

G: You've got a new phone, haven't you?
B: Yes, I have.
G: How do you like it?
B: I don't like it at all.

Listen & Speak 1 A-2

B: I got these sneakers as a birthday present!
G: How cool they look! How do you like them?
B: I just love them.

Listen & Speak 2 A-1

B: Would you like some soup?
G: Yes, I'd love some.
B: Here you go. … How do you like it?
G: It's hot and sweet. I just love it.
B: I'm glad you like it.

Listen & Speak 2 A-2

G: Did you make this bowl by yourself?
B: Yes, I did.
G: It looks just wonderful.
B: Thanks. I'm happy you like it.

Listen & Speak 2 A-3

G: How do you like this face painting?
B: I just love it. Thanks.
G: I'm very pleased you love it.

Conversation

Nara: Would you like some hot chocolate, Junha?
Junha: Sure, I haven't had it for ages! … Mmm.
Nara: How do you like it?
Junha: I like it a lot. You are very good at making hot chocolate.
Nara: Thanks. I'm glad you like it. By the way, did you know that chocolate was once called the "drink of the gods"?
Junha: Was it really?
Nara: Yes, chocolate was first enjoyed by the emperor of the Aztec Empire, and it was once called xoco-latl, "drink of the gods."
Junha: That's surprising! Well, thanks for the gods' drink, Nara.
Nara: You are welcome!

Real Life Task Step 1

W: How do you like the school lunch? What would you like to have for your lunch? We'd like to have your cool ideas on the school lunch menu. Why don't you visit www.mslunch.ms.kr and answer the questions about your school lunch? We're looking forward to getting your answers.

Real Life Task Step 2

A: What do you have on your Monday snack menu?
B: I have ice cream and apple juice. How do you like my menu?
A: That sounds great. I like it a lot.
B: I'm glad you like it.

G: You've got a new backpack, Minsu?

B: Yes, I have. This is my birthday present from my mother.

G: How nice of her! How do you like it?

B: I like it a lot. I like the color.

G: Your favorite color is blue, isn't it?

B: Yes, it is.

Check My Progress 2

G: Did you bake all of these by yourself?

B: Yes, I did.

G: They look just wonderful.

B: Thanks. Would you like to try some cake?

G: Sure.

B: How do you like it?

G: I just love this.

B: Thanks. I'm so happy you like it.

본문 TEST Step 1   p.30~32

01 Don't, love, smell, freshly

02 most popular, historians, enjoyed

03 It, that, originally grown

04 not only, but also

05 seeds, thrown on, over

06 popped, bloomed into

07 to catch, enjoy, flowery

08 used, for decoration, well

09 used, to decorate clothes

10 made, decorations, statues

11 thought, symbol, health, goodwill

12 that, protected, spirits, decorations

13 In addition, around, tasty

14 as well, long before

15 ancient, fortunes, coming, marriage

16 invented, pot-shaped, machines, used

17 ways of, during, century

18 threw, onto, picked out

19 mixed, with fat, cooked

20 thought, wonderful, exciting

21 popular, cooking, over, wooden

22 fanciest, invented, types, seen

23 Finally, electric, was, invented

24 high demand, made by

25 How, like, hot, spicy

26 imagine yourself, ancient, person

27 With, bowl, decorations, fortunes

28 why don't, come, with

본문 TEST Step 2   p.33~34

01 Don't, love, smell, freshly

02 one of, most popular snacks around, that, have enjoyed, more than

03 It was, that, originally grown, that

04 not only, but also, popping corn

05 were thrown on

06 popped, bloomed into

07 to catch, enjoy, flowery

08 used, for decoration

09 used, to decorate clothes

10 made, decorations, statues

11 thought, a symbol of good health, goodwill

12 that, be protected, spirits, decorations made with popped corn

13 In addition to, other, enjoyed, tasty

14 as well as, long before, arrived, West Indies

15 to tell fortunes, coming year, daughters', marriage

16 invented, machines to pop, are, used by

17 It was, that, interesting ways of, during, nineteenth

18 threw, onto, stirred, picked out, corn pieces

19 mixed, with, cooked it

20 wonderful, exciting

21 popular, cooking, over, with, wooden handle

22 was invented by, many types, were seen

23 Finally, was invented

24 Believe, not, in high demand, made by

25 How, like

26 imagine yourself, Native American, inventor

27 With, bowl, can be, pretty decorations, an ancient Chinese, fortunes

28 why don't you, come up with

본문 TEST Step 3   p.35~36

1 펑! 펑! 펑! 당신은 갓 만들어진 팝콘의 냄새를 좋아하지 않나요?

2 그것은 전 세계에서 가장 인기 있는 간식 중 하나이고, 역사가들은 사람들이 5,000년 이상 그것을 즐겨 왔다고 믿고 있습니다.

3 옥수수가 본래 재배된 곳은 중앙아메리카였고, 최초의 팝콘이 발견된 곳은 뉴멕시코의 동굴 안이었습니다.

4 아메리카 원주민들은 옥수수 먹는 것을 좋아했을 뿐만 아니라 옥수수를 튀기는 게임도 즐겼습니다.

5 옥수수 씨는 불 위의 뜨거운 돌들 위로 던져졌습니다.

6 그 다음 그것들은 펑 소리를 내며 튀겨졌고 하얀 꽃 모양으로 피어났습니다.

7 그 게임은 그 꽃 모양의 간식을 잡아서 즐기는 것이었습니다.

8 아메리카 원주민들은 팝콘을 장식을 위해서도 사용했습니다.

9 그들의 십 대 소녀들은 튀겨진 옥수수를 옷을 장식하는 데 사용했습니다.

10 아즈텍족 사람들은 비의 신 조각상을 위해 옥수수 장식품을 만들었습니다.

11 그들은 팝콘을 좋은 건강과 호의의 상징으로 생각했습니다.

12 그들은 튀겨진 옥수수로 만든 장식들을 달면 불쑥 나타나는 정령에 의해 보호받을 것이라고 믿었습니다.

13 아메리카 원주민 외에도, 전 세계의 많은 다른 사람들이 이 맛있는 간식을 즐겼습니다.

14 수마트라인과 인도인뿐 아니라 중국인들도 콜럼버스가 서인도 제도에 도착하기 훨씬 이전부터 팝콘을 만들었습니다.

15 고대 중국에서, 사람들은 다음 해와 그들의 딸들의 장래의 혼사를 점치기 위해 옥수수를 펑 소리를 내며 튀겼습니다.

16 송나라 왕조에서, 중국 사람들은 옥수수를 튀기기 위해 커다란 항아리 모양의 팝콘 튀기는 기계를 발명하였고, 이 기계는 오늘날에도 길거리에서 팝콘 만드는 이들에 의해 사용되고 있습니다.

17 19세기 동안 옥수수를 튀기는 흥미로운 방법들을 시도해 본 것은 바로 미국인들이었습니다.

18 이들 중 일부는 뜨거운 잿더미 위로 옥수수 씨를 던지고, 뒤섞은 다음, 펑 터져 나온 옥수수 알갱이들을 집어냈습니다.

19 다른 이들은 옥수수를 기름이나 버터와 섞고 이를 납작한 냄비에 요리하였습니다.

20 그들은 옥수수를 튀기는 것을 멋지고 재미있다고 생각했습니다.

21 보다 인기 있는 방법은 팝콘을 긴 나무 손잡이가 있는 철사 상자 안에 넣어 덮개가 없는 불에서 요리하는 방법이었습니다.

22 가장 멋진 팝콘 튀기는 기계는 1893년 Charles Cretors에 의해 발명되었는데, 오래지 않아 많은 종류의 흥미로운 팝콘 만드는 기계들이 영화관이나 공원에서 보이게 되었습니다.

23 마침내 가정용 전기 팝콘 기계가 1925년에 발명되었습니다.

24 믿기 힘들겠지만, 팝콘 기계는 그 수요가 많았고, 심지어 학교 동아리에서 중학생들에 의해서도 제작되었습니다.

25 당신은 어떤 팝콘을 좋아하나요? 달콤한, 매운, 향신료를 친 팝콘?

26 다음 번에 팝콘을 즐길 때에는 당신이 아메리카 원주민, 고대 중국인, 혹은 발명가라고 상상해 보세요.

27 한 그릇의 팝콘으로, 당신은 아메리카 원주민이 되어 예쁜 장식을 만들 수도 있고, 또는 고대 중국인이 되어 운세를 점쳐 볼 수도 있습니다.

28 혹은 더 좋게는, 발명가가 되어 당신이 가장 좋아하는 팝콘을 위해 새로운 팝콘 기계를 생각해 내는 것은 어떤가요?

1 Pop! Pop! Pop! Don't you love the smell of freshly made popcorn?

2 It is one of the most popular snacks around the world, and historians believe that people have enjoyed it for more than 5,000 years.

3 It was in Central America that corn was originally grown, and it was in caves in New Mexico that the first popcorn was found.

4 Native Americans not only loved eating corn but also enjoyed the game of popping corn.

5 Corn seeds were thrown on hot stones over a fire.

6 Then they popped and bloomed into white flowers.

7 The game was to catch and enjoy the flowery snacks.

8 Native Americans used popcorn for decoration as well.

9 Their teenage girls used popped corn to decorate clothes.

10 The Aztecs made corn decorations for the statues of the god of rain.

11 They thought popcorn a symbol of good health and goodwill.

12 They believed that they would be protected by popping spirits when they wore decorations made with popped corn.

13 In addition to Native Americans, many other people around the world enjoyed this tasty snack.

14 The Chinese, as well as people in Sumatra and India, made popcorn long before Columbus arrived in the West Indies.

15 In ancient China, people popped corn to tell fortunes for the coming year and their daughters' future marriage.

16 In the Song Dynasty, Chinese people invented large pot-shaped popping machines to pop corn, and these machines are still used by street poppers today.

17 It was Americans that tried interesting ways of popping corn during the nineteenth century.

18 Some threw corn seeds onto hot ashes, stirred, and then picked out the popped corn pieces.

19 Others mixed corn with fat or butter and cooked it in a pan..

20 They thought popping corn wonderful and exciting.

21 A more popular way was cooking popcorn over

an open fire in a wire box with a long wooden handle.

22 The fanciest popcorn popper was invented by Charles Cretors in 1893, and before long many types of interesting poppers were seen in movie theaters and parks.

23 Finally, an electric popcorn popper for the home was invented in 1925.

24 Believe it or not, poppers were in high demand and were even made by middle school students in school clubs.

25 How do you like your popcorn? Sweet, hot, or spicy?

26 Next time you enjoy popcorn, imagine yourself as a Native American, an ancient Chinese person, or an inventor.

27 With a bowl of popcorn, you can be a Native American and make pretty decorations or be an ancient Chinese person and tell fortunes.

28 Or better still, why don't you be an inventor and come up with a new popper for your favorite popcorn?

Real Life Task Step 3

1. On our Monday snack menu, we have ice cream and apple juice.
2. On the Tuesday menu, we have bananas and orange juice.
3. On Wednesday, we enjoy carrot cake and chocolate milk.
4. On Thursday, we have potato chips and milk.
5. And on Friday, we enjoy apple slices and mango juice.

Before I Read

1. Throw corn seeds onto hot ashes.
2. Mix corn with fat and cook it in a pan.
3. Cook corn over an open fire in a wire box.
4. Pop corn in a popcorn popper.

구석구석지문 TEST Step 1   p.41

Write & Speak 2 B

1. How, like
2. just love, How tasty
3. glad, like

Real Life Task Step 3

1. Monday snack menu
2. On, have bananas, orange juice
3. On Wednesday, carrot cake, chocolate milk
4. have potato chips
5. on Friday, enjoy apple slices

Before I Read

1. Throw, onto
2. mix, with fat, cook it
3. Cook, over, in a wire box
4. Pop, a popcorn popper

구석구석지문 TEST Step 2   p.42

Write & Speak 2 B

1. A: How do you like my hamburger?
2. B: I just love it. How tasty!
3. A: Thanks. I'm glad you like.

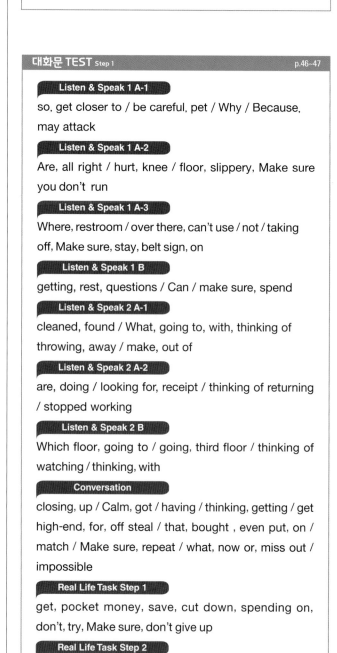

Lesson 3

단어 TEST Step 1   p.43

01 영수증	02 완전히 새로운	03 겪다
04 추천하다	05 반짝 세일	06 움켜쥐다
07 도움이 되는, 유익한		08 공격하다
09 점포	10 다치다	
11 믿을 수 없을 정도로		12 대신에
13 보물	14 맛보다	15 무릎
16 한정판	17 명품의, 고급의	18 생생한, 활발한
19 용돈	20 바닥, 층	21 미끄러운
22 포함하다	23 수집품	24 빈손으로
25 유행	26 특징으로 하는	27 소비자
28 발표	29 유명한 사람	30 훔치다; 도루, 공짜
31 상품	32 전통적인	33 휴게소
34 감상	35 이륙하다	36 들고 다니다
37 ~ 때문에	38 ~을 조심하다	39 줄이다
40 둘러보다	41 기꺼이 ~하려고 하다	
42 ~을 신다, ~을 착용하다		43 로그아웃하다

단어 TEST Step 2   p.44

01 include	02 booth	03 collection
04 consumer	05 floor	06 grab
07 helpful	08 appreciation	09 slippery
10 attack	11 high-end	12 incredibly
13 rest stop	14 instead	15 flash sale
16 suffer	17 limited edition	18 treasure
19 lively	20 celebrity	21 product
22 receipt	23 empty-handed	24 featuring
25 recommend	26 swimsuit	27 presentation
28 return	29 trend	30 steal
31 taste	32 traditional	33 brand-new
34 sale sign	35 make a noise	36 look around
37 take off	38 calm down	39 due to
40 give up	41 stick to	42 cut down
43 carry around		

단어 TEST Step 3   p.45

1 brand-new, 신상품   2 take off, 이륙하다
3 celebrity, 유명한 사람   4 knee, 무릎
5 consumer, 소비자   6 repeat, 반복하다
7 recommend, 추천하다   8 appreciation, 감상
9 treasure, 보물   10 attack, 공격하다

11 return, 반품하다   12 include, 포함하다
13 receipt, 영수증   14 high-end, 고급의
15 slippery, 미끄러운   16 presentation, 발표

대화문 TEST Step 1   p.46~47

Listen & Speak 1 A-1

so, get closer to / be careful, pet / Why / Because, may attack

Listen & Speak 1 A-2

Are, all right / hurt, knee / floor, slippery, Make sure you don't run

Listen & Speak 1 A-3

Where, restroom / over there, can't use / not / taking off, Make sure, stay, belt sign, on

Listen & Speak 1 B

getting, rest, questions / Can / make sure, spend

Listen & Speak 2 A-1

cleaned, found / What, going to, with, thinking of throwing, away / make, out of

Listen & Speak 2 A-2

are, doing / looking for, receipt / thinking of returning / stopped working

Listen & Speak 2 B

Which floor, going to / going, third floor / thinking of watching / thinking, with

Conversation

closing, up / Calm, got / having / thinking, getting / get high-end, for, off steal / that, bought , even put, on / match / Make sure, repeat / what, now or, miss out / impossible

Real Life Task Step 1

get, pocket money, save, cut down, spending on, don't, try, Make sure, don't give up

Real Life Task Step 2

How, like, presentation / helpful / thinking, cutting down, spending / less on clothes / make sure, give

대화문 TEST Step 2   p.48~49

Listen & Speak 1 A-1

G: They are so cute. Let's get closer to them.
M: OK. But be careful, and do not pet them.
G: Why not?
M: Because they may attack you.

Listen & Speak 1 A-2

B: Ouch!

W: Are you all right, Jinsu?

B: No, I'm not. I hurt my knee.

W: The floor is always slippery here. Make sure you don't run.

B: Excuse me. Where is the restroom?

W: It's over there. But you can't use it now.

B: Oh. Why not?

W: We're taking off soon. Make sure you stay in your seat when the seat belt sign is on.

A: Now, we're getting to the rest stop. Any questions?

B: Yes. Can I go to the snack stands?

A: Of course, but make sure you don't spend too much money.

B: OK. Thanks.

G: I cleaned my room and found some old T-shirts.

B: What are you going to do with them? Are you thinking of throwing them away?

G: No. I will make an eco bag out of them.

B: That's a good idea!

B: What are you doing?

G: I'm looking for the receipt for my new watch.

B: Why? Are you thinking of returning it?

G: Yes. It suddenly stopped working.

A: Which floor are you going to?

B: I'm going to the third floor.

A: Are you thinking of watching a movie?

B: No, I'm not. I'm thinking of playing with dogs.

Seho: Oh! It's almost closing time. Hurry up!

Semi(Seho's sister): Calm down, Seho. We've got everything.

Seho: No. I need to visit Sneaker Ground. They're having a sale there.

Semi: What? Are you thinking of getting sneakers?

Seho: Yes. I can get high-end sneakers for 70% off. It's a steal.

Semi: Well, it was just a week ago that you bought blue sneakers there. Have you even put them on?

Seho: No. They don't match any of my pants.

Semi: You see? Make sure you don't repeat the same mistake.

Seho: I see what you mean, but it's now or never. I can't miss out.

Semi: You are impossible.

B: What do you do first when you get your pocket money? I always save 30 percent of my pocket money. How do I do this? I cut down my spending on ice cream and soft drinks. Why don't you give it a try and get RICH? Make sure you don't give up in the middle.

A: How did you like the presentation?

B: It was very helpful. I need to do something to save money.

A: Are you thinking of cutting down your spending?

B: Yes, I am. I'll spend less on clothes.

A: Good for you, but make sure you don't give up your style.

01 makes, shop, what, need

02 on, shopping habits

03 Look at / are wearing, brand-new / looks, cute, to, one / Me, too

04 what, favorite celebrities do

05 than, to buy, use

06 look like, heroes

07 celebrity, make, cool, popular

08 Can, help / What's up / flash sale, help, grab / like crazy

09 like, that, if, enough

10 suffer, when, such as

11 make, believe, chance, grab

12 becomes more like, than

13 What, pick / get it / finally, completes, collection / Good for

14 Collecting, hottest trends, consumers

15 collections include, sets, featuring

16 getting, because, of, makes

17 celebrity, bought, grabbed, collected

18 what, bought, grabbed, collected

19 with them, all right

20 aren't, however, to be   21 are, to live by

22 STICK TO   23 carry, around, into, what

24 anything, empty-handed, incredibly light

25 COOL OFF   26 Instead, Add, sign out

27 cooling off, if, still

28 OLD TREASURES

29 new, through, what, appreciation

01 makes, shop, what you really need

02 on, shopping habits

03 Look at / are wearing, brand-new / looks, cute, to have one, like / too

04 what their favorite celebrities do

05 more than, to buy what, use

06 look like, heroes

07 celebrity brands, make them cool, happy, popular

08 Can, help / What's up / online flash sale, help, grab a pair / like crazy

09 sells like hot cakes, that, be able to, if, not fast enough

10 suffer from, when, such as

11 make, believe, last, chance to grab, cool products

12 becomes more like, than spending

13 a pick / it / finally, completes, collection / for

14 Collecting, is, hottest trends among, consumers

15 most popular collections include, featuring

16 getting, because, of

17 celebrity, have, bought, have, grabbed, have, collected

18 what, have bought, grabbed, collected

19 with them, all right

20 aren't, however, to be, smarter shopper

21 are, to live by   22 STICK TO

23 shopping list, it, Run into, what you need

24 anything on the list, empty-handed, feel incredibly light

25 COOL OFF   26 online, Instead, Add, sign out

27 cooling off, come back, if, still want it

28 OLD TREASURES

29 Whenever, something new, go through, what, old treasures, a new appreciation for them

1 무엇이 여러분을 쇼핑하게 합니까? 여러분은 정말로 필요한 것만을 삽니까?

2 읽어 가며 여러분의 쇼핑 습관에 대해 생각해 보십시오.

3 미나: 저것 좀 봐! / 소민: 왜! N-girls가 신상품 재킷을 입고 있네.
미나: 정말 귀여워 보여. 나도 그것과 꼭 같은 것을 하나 가지고 있어야만 되겠어. / 소민: 나도 그래.

4 많은 십대들은 좋아하는 유명인이 하는 것을 하기 좋아합니다.

5 그들은 스타들이 사용하는 것을 기꺼이 사고자 합니다.

6 그들은 그들의 영웅처럼 보이기를 원합니다.

7 그들은 유명인 브랜드가 그들을 멋지고 행복하며 인기 있게 만들 것이라고 생각합니다.

8 소민: 나 도와줄 수 있어, 인호야? / 인호: 물론이지. 무슨 일이야?
소민: 새로운 운동화의 온라인 반짝 판매가 있을 예정이야. 부탁인데, 내가 한 켤레를 손에 넣도록 도와줘. / 인호: 알겠어. 내가 열심히 클릭할게.

9 한 상품이 불티나게 팔릴 때, 어떤 사람들은 그들이 충분히 재빠르지 않으면 그것을 얻을 수 없을 것이라고 흔히 느낍니다.

10 그들은 '한정판'이나 '반짝 판매'와 같은 판매 게시물을 보면, FOMO(놓치는 것에 대한 두려움)를 겪습니다.

11 게시물들은 그들로 하여금 그것이 그 멋진 상품들을 손에 넣을 마지막 기회라고 믿게 만듭니다.

12 그러면, 빨리 팔리는 물건을 사는 것은 돈을 쓰는 것이라기보다는 게임에서 이기는 것과 같아집니다.

13 인호: 정말 잘 골랐네! / 미나: 너 그거 손에 넣었어, 인호야?
인호: 응, 마침내. 이것이 내 수집품을 완성하네. / 미나: 잘됐네!

14 인기 있는 것들을 모으는 것은 젊은 소비자들 사이에서 가장 인기 있는 유행 중 하나입니다.

15 가장 인기 있는 수집품으로 캐릭터 스티커, 야구 카드 세트, 팝스타를 특징으로 삼는 상품 등이 있습니다.

16 십대 소비자들은 이것들을 점점 더 많이 가지는 것을 즐기는데, '많을수록 좋다'라는 생각이 그들을 행복하게 만들어 주기 때문입니다.

17 어떤 유명인 상표를 구입해 보셨습니까? 어떤 빨리 팔리는 상품을 손에 넣어 보셨습니까? 어떤 캐릭터 스티커를 수집해 보셨습니까?

18 여러분이 구입하고 손에 넣고 수집한 것에 만족하십니까?

19 여러분들이 그것들에 만족한다면, 괜찮습니다.

20 그러나 여러분이 그것들에 만족하지 않는다면, 여러분은 더 똑똑한 구매자가 되려고 노력해야 합니다.

21 여기 생활 속에서 지켜야 할 세 가지 구매 팁이 있습니다.

22 조언 01 목록을 고수하세요.

23 쇼핑 목록을 작성하고 휴대하세요. 상점 안으로 달려가서 필요한 것을 얻으세요.

24 목록에 있는 것을 찾을 수 없다면, 빈손으로 걸어 나오세요. 믿을 수 없을 정도로 경쾌한 기분을 느끼게 될 거예요.

25 조언 02 하루 동안 진정해 보세요.

26 온라인 쇼핑을 할 때 "바로 구입"을 클릭하지 마세요. 대신, "장바구니에 추가"를 누르고 로그아웃 하세요.

27 24시간 동안 진정한 이후에, 돌아와서 여전히 그것을 원하는지 확인해 보세요.

28 조언 03 오래된 보물들을 찾으세요.

29 새로운 물건을 사고 싶을 때마다 옷장을 살펴보고 갖고 있는 물건을 확인해 보세요. 오래된 보물들을 찾고 그것들을 새롭게 감상하며 즐기세요.

1 What makes you shop? Do you buy only what you really need?

2 Read on and think about your shopping habits.

3 Mina: Look at that! / Somin: Wow! N-girls are wearing a brand-new jacket.
Mina: It looks very cute. I have to have one just like it. / Somin: Me, too.

4 Many teens like to do what their favorite celebrities do.

5 They are more than willing to buy what the stars use.

6 They want to look like their heroes.

7 They think celebrity brands will make them cool, happy, and popular.

8 Somin: Can you help me, Inho? / Inho: Sure. What's up?
Somin: There's going to be an online flash sale on new sneakers. Please help me grab a pair. / Inho: Okay, I'll click like crazy.

9 When a product sells like hot cakes, some people often feel that they won't be able to get it if they are not fast enough.

10 They suffer from FOMO, Fear of Missing Out, when they see sales signs such as *Limited Edition* and *Flash Sale*.

11 The signs make them believe that it is the last chance to grab the cool products.

12 Then, getting quick-selling goods becomes more like winning a game than spending money.

13 Inho: What a pick! / Mina: Did you get it, Inho?
Inho: Yeah, finally. This completes my collection. / Mina: Good for you!

14 Collecting popular things is one of the hottest trends among young consumers.

15 The most popular collections include character stickers, baseball card sets, and goods featuring pop stars.

16 Teen consumers enjoy getting more and more of these, because the idea of *more is better* makes them happy.

17 What celebrity brands have you bought? What quick-selling goods have you grabbed? What character stickers have you collected?

18 Are you happy with what you have bought, grabbed, and collected?

19 If you are happy with them, that's all right.

20 If you aren't, however, you should try to be a smarter shopper.

21 Here are three shopping tips to live by.

22 TIP 01. STICK TO A LIST.

23 Make a shopping list and carry it around. Run into a store and get what you need.

24 If you can't find anything on the list, walk out empty-handed. You will feel incredibly light.

25 TIP 02. COOL OFF FOR A DAY.

26 When you shop online, don't click "Buy Now." Instead, hit "Add To Cart" and sign out.

27 After 24 hours of cooling off, come back and see if you still want it.

28 TIP 03. FIND OLD TREASURES.

29 Whenever you want to buy something new, go through your closet and see what you have.
Find old treasures and enjoy a new appreciation for them.

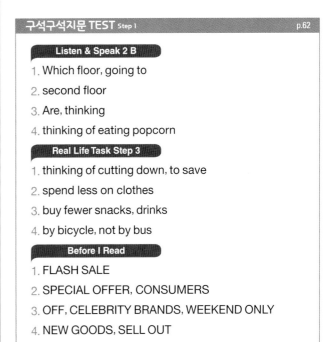

Listen & Speak 2 B

1. Which floor, going to
2. second floor
3. Are, thinking
4. thinking of eating popcorn

Real Life Task Step 3

1. thinking of cutting down, to save
2. spend less on clothes
3. buy fewer snacks, drinks
4. by bicycle, not by bus

Before I Read

1. FLASH SALE
2. SPECIAL OFFER, CONSUMERS
3. OFF, CELEBRITY BRANDS, WEEKEND ONLY
4. NEW GOODS, SELL OUT

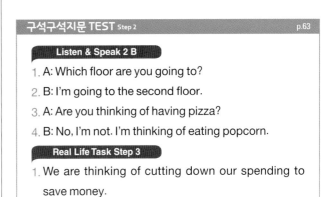

Listen & Speak 2 B

1. A: Which floor are you going to?
2. B: I'm going to the second floor.
3. A: Are you thinking of having pizza?
4. B: No, I'm not. I'm thinking of eating popcorn.

Real Life Task Step 3

1. We are thinking of cutting down our spending to save money.

2. Nara will spend less on clothes.

3. Seho will buy fewer snacks and drinks.

4. Jina will come to school by bicycle, not by bus.

Before I Read

1. FLASH SALE

2. SPECIAL OFFER FOR SMART CONSUMERS.

3. 50% OFF ON CELEBRITY BRANDS FOR THIS WEEKEND ONLY.

4. GRAB THESE NEW GOODS BEFORE THEY SELL OUT.

적중100

영어 기출 문제집

정답 및 해설

능률 | 양현권